GARCIA

Principles of Water Rates, Fees, and Charges

Seventh Edition

American Water Works Association

Manual of Water Supply Practices—M1, Seventh Edition

Principles of Water Rates, Fees, and Charges

Copyright © 1954, 1972, 1983, 1991, 2000, 2012, 2017 American Water Works Association

Disclaimer

Project Manager: Melissa Valentine
Cover Art: Melanie Yamamoto
Production: Glacier Publishing Services, Inc.
Manuals Specialist: Sue Bach

Library of Congress Cataloging-in-Publication Data

Names: Woodcock, Chris, author. | Giardina, Rick, author. | Cristiano, Todd, author.
Title: M1, water rates, fees, and charges / Chris Woodcock, Rick Giardina, Todd Cristiano.
Description: Seventh Edition. | Denver, CO : American Water Works Association, [2017] | Revised edition, 2012. | Includes bibliographical references and index.
Identifiers: LCCN 2016048760 | ISBN 9781625761910 (alk. paper)
Subjects: LCSH: Water-supply--Rates. | Water utilities--Rates.
Classification: LCC HD4456 .W66 2017 | DDC 363.6/10688--dc23 LC record available at https://lccn.loc.gov/2016048760

ISBN-13   978-1-62576-191-0
eISBN-13   978-1-61300-399-2

Printed in the United States of America
American Water Works Association
6666 West Quincy Avenue
Denver, CO 80235-3098
awwa.org

Printed on recycled paper

Contents

Figures

This page intentionally blank.

Tables

This page intentionally blank.

Preface

In 1954, AWWA published the report *Determination of Water Rate Schedules*, which later was issued as the first AWWA manual on water rates. Since then, AWWA Manual M1, *Water Rates*, has been updated several times, most recently in 2012. The fifth edition, titled *Principles of Water Rates, Fees, and Charges*, consolidated several previous publications into what has been referred to as the M1 Super Manual. For a more complete history of AWWA's rate manual publications, see "A Brief History of Water Rates Manuals and Publications—The New England Water Works' Involvement" in the December 2013 edition of the *NEWWA Journal*.

The issues associated with water rates and charges have continued to evolve, and this update of M1, the seventh edition, is a reflection of that evolution. For example, this edition makes current the numeric examples used throughout the manual, consolidates chapters where appropriate, and includes new material reflective of changes in the industry (e.g., chapter III.3, "Emerging Trends"). In the future, the AWWA Rates and Charges Committee will continue to update this manual as new issues and questions arise.

As with the other manuals prepared by the Rates and Charges Committee and AWWA in general, this manual will not prescribe a solution. Rather, it is intended to provide guidance and advice. The examples presented are used only to demonstrate the generally accepted methodologies discussed in this manual. The underlying data and assumptions are not endorsed or recommended either by AWWA or the Rates and Charges Committee for use elsewhere. The purpose of this manual is to describe and present issues associated with developing water rates, fees, and charges; to enumerate the advantages and disadvantages of various alternatives; and to provide information to help users determine water rates, fees, and charges that are most relevant to a particular situation.

This page intentionally blank.

Acknowledgments

The AWWA Management Division Board of Trustees gratefully acknowledges the contributions made by members (past and present) of the Rates and Charges Committee, particularly the Editorial Committee, and others who drafted, edited, and provided the significant and critical commentary essential to developing this manual. The Editorial Committee dedicated countless hours in the final stages of preparation of this edition to ensure the overall technical quality, consistency, and accuracy of the manual.

Editorial Committee

Chris Woodcock, Chair of the M1 Seventh Edition Editorial Committee and Working Group, Woodcock & Associates, Northborough, Mass.

Rick Giardina, Chairman, Rates and Charges Committee, Raftelis Financial Consultants, Denver, Colo.

Todd Cristiano, Vice-Chairman, Hawksley Consulting, a Stantec Company, Denver, Colo.

Paul Matthews, Tualatin Valley Water District, Beaverton, Ore.

Jeffrey Ripp, Wisconsin Public Service Commission, Madison, Wis.

Contributors to the Seventh Edition

Roland Asp, National Fire Sprinkler Association, Linthicum Heights, Md.

Stacey Isaac Berahzer, Environmental Finance Center University of North Carolina at Chapel Hill, Marietta, Ga.

Ann T. Bui, Black & Veatch Corporation, Los Angeles, Calif.

Andrew J. Burnham, Hawksley Consulting, a Stantec Company, Tampa, Fla.

Tom Catlin, Exeter Associates, Columbia, Md.

Kees Corssmit (retired), Geitner Environmental Management, Denver, Colo.

Joe Crea, Raftelis Financial Consultants, Cincinnati, Ohio

Sanjay Gaur, Raftelis Financial Consultants, Pasadena, Calif.

Tom Gould, HDR Engineering, Bellevue, Wash.

Robert Grantham, FCS Group, San Francisco, Calif.

Kerry Heid, Heid Rate & Regulatory Services, Newburgh, Ind.

Cecelia Huynh, Portland Bureau of Water, Portland, Ore.

David Hyder, Hawksley Consulting, a Stantec Company, Bowie, Md.

Jennifer Ivey, Carollo Engineers, Dallas, Texas

Brian Jewett, Black & Veatch, San Marcos, Calif.

Theresa Jurotich, CDM Smith, Seattle, Wash.

Daniel Lanning, Willdan Financial Services/Economists.com, Plano, Texas

Bryan A. Mantz, Public Resources Management Group, Maitland, Fla.

James B. Marshall III, Jackson Thornton Utilities Consultants, Montgomery, Ala.

John Mastracchio, ARCADIS U.S., Clifton Park, N.Y.

Mike Matichich, CH2M, Washington, D.C.

Jason Mumm, Hawksley Consulting, a Stantec Company, Broomfield, Colo.

Robert Ori, Public Resources Management Group, Maitland. Fla.

Kristin Rehg, City of Evanston Utilities Department, Evanston, Ill.

Eric Rothstein, Galardi Rothstein Group, Chicago, Ill.

David F. Russell, Russell Consulting, Newburyport, Mass.

Robert P. Ryall, Willdan Financial Services, Orlando, Fla.

Sean Senescall, Tacoma Public Utilities, Tacoma, Wash.

David G. Shank, San Diego County Water Authority, San Diego, Calif.

June Skillman, Metropolitan Water District of Southern California, Los Angeles, Calif.

Kathryn Sorensen, City of Phoenix, Phoenix, Ariz.

Angie Sanchez Virnoche, FCS GROUP, Redmond, Wash.

John Wright, Raftelis Financial Consultants, Greenwood Village, Colo.

Bill Zieburtz, Hawksley Consulting, a Stantec Company, Atlanta, Ga.

Special thanks goes to *Stephen Kemna* of the Wisconsin Public Service Commission, to *David Fox* of Raftelis Financial Consultants, and to *Christine A. Cramer*, Trilogy Consulting for their assistance in updating this manual.

Introduction

During the last 20 years of the 20th century and now into the second decade of the 21st century, the cost of supplying potable water increased significantly. This rapid increase can be attributed to many factors, including the passage and implementation of the US Safe Drinking Water Act and corollary legislation in other countries, population growth, the need to develop more remote and expensive water supplies, the need to replace aging infrastructure, and rapid economic development in some areas. The amplified costs of meeting water quality requirements and utility plant needs have resulted in increased water rates and charges.

Historically, customers generally paid little attention to their water bills or the rate structure. However, as the rates and charges increased and water bills became a more significant percentage of customers' overall expenses, consumers have become increasingly interested in the rate-setting process. And with the heightened focus on conservation and water-use efficiency, water utilities are also recognizing the effect that rates and charges can have on customer use patterns.

With this recognition, new challenges in customer engagement, revenue stability, and the use of accepted cost-of-service and rate-design approaches become apparent. As the challenges of the industry change, so do the "tools" available, including how customers are charged for service. To this end, the types of rate structures used by utilities and discussed in this manual now include emerging trends in cost-based rate design.

In the past, rates were developed for broad classes of customers with similar usage patterns. With enhanced meter reading capabilities and more powerful billing software, water utilities are more able to tailor rates to individual customer use. The new data and faster computing abilities are enabling the development and implementation of new forms of rates that can better reflect the cost to serve customers and send proper economic signals for the use of our most precious resource.

This seventh edition of AWWA Manual M1 includes an update to the rates charged to retail and wholesale customers outside an "owning city's" boundaries (new section VI), an update to the rates for fire protection service (chapter IV.8), additional treatment of fixed charges and declining revenue (chapter IV.7), an update regarding system development charges (chapter VII.2), new guidance on the growing issue of affordability (chapter V.4), and new chapters on water reuse (chapter V.1) and emerging trends (chapter III.3). The chapter on legal considerations has been removed; readers are referred to AWWA's publication titled *Water Rates, Fees, and the Legal Environment* for more on that matter.

The AWWA Rates and Charges Committee believes that a utility's full revenue requirements should be equitably recovered from customers or classes of customers in proportion to the cost of serving those customers. However, the committee also recognizes that other considerations may, at times, be equally important in determining rates and charges and may better reflect emerging objectives of the utility or the community it serves, including water-use efficiency, revenue stability, and affordability.

The emergence of new rate and pricing policies has brought a continuing evolution in rate structures. In some cases, water rates and charges may have been adopted to achieve certain goals without a full understanding of the impacts or resulting implications. Some rate alternatives, if not properly designed, may even have effects that counteract what was intended.

This manual is intended to help policymakers, managers, and rate analysts consider all relevant factors when evaluating and selecting rates, charges, and pricing policies. It is a comprehensive collection of discussions and guidance on a variety of issues associated with designing and developing water rates and charges.

This manual contains eight sections:

- Section I provides an overview of the rate-setting process and the key steps in completing a cost-of-service analysis.
- Section II discusses the determination of revenue requirements.
- Section III presents the process in which costs are functionalized, allocated, and distributed to classes of customers as well as a discussion of emerging trends.
- Section IV presents various rate structures and how they are developed.
- Section V presents pricing alternatives related to specific customers or groups of customers and a number of rate-design considerations.
- Section VI is a new section devoted to matters associated with rates charged to customers outside a city's or owner's territorial limits, including both retail and wholesale rate considerations.
- Section VII discusses the derivation and implementation of capacity and development charges.
- Section VIII presents various implementation considerations and data requirements.

Section I

Introduction

I.1   Overview of Cost-Based Water Utility Rate-Making

This page intentionally blank.

Chapter **I.1**

Overview of Cost-Based Water Utility Rate-Making

Establishing cost-based rates, fees, and charges is an important component in a well-managed and operated water utility. Cost-based rates provide sufficient funding to allow communities to build, operate, maintain, and reinvest in the water system that provides the community with safe and reliable drinking water and fire protection. Properly and adequately funded water systems also allow for the economic development and sustainability of the local community. The purpose of this manual is to discuss standard practices in financial planning and rate-making that a utility can use to establish cost-based rates, fees, and charges to recover the full costs associated with its water system.

The methods and analyses used to establish cost-based rates, fees, and charges have a long history within the water utility industry. Operators of some of the earliest water systems recognized the need for sufficient funding and rates to properly operate, maintain, and expand their water systems. AWWA appointed the Committee on Water Rates in 1949. As time passed, the utility industry recognized the need for a manual of standard practice. Through the work of this committee, the first AWWA M1 manual, *Water Rates Manual*, was published in 1954. (For a more complete history, see Woodcock 2013.) Many of the same concepts, methodologies, and analyses used in 1954 remain relevant today. As time has passed, AWWA Manual M1 has been updated and expanded to reflect the changing industry and its current financial and rate issues. The development of this seventh edition continues the efforts of many dedicated rate professionals to provide a manual of standard practice for the development and establishment of cost-based water rates, fees, and charges.

As a manual of standard practice, AWWA advocates the use of the generally accepted cost-based principles and methodologies for establishing rates, charges, and fees contained and discussed within this manual. Establishing cost-based and equitable rates is technically challenging and requires, at some level, knowledge and understanding of finance, accounting, budgeting, engineering, system design and operations, customer service, public outreach and communication, and the legal environment as it may relate to setting rates, fees, and charges.

OBJECTIVES OF COST-BASED RATE-MAKING

Water rates developed using the methodologies discussed in this manual, when appropriately applied, are generally considered to be fair and equitable because these rate-setting methodologies result in cost-based rates that generate revenue from each class of customer in proportion to the cost to serve each class of customer. Water rates are considered fair and equitable when each customer class pays the costs allocated to the class and, consequently, cross-class subsidies are avoided.

While recovery of the full revenue requirement in a fair and equitable manner is a key objective of a utility using a cost-of-service rate-making process, it is often not the only objective. The following list contains the typical objectives in establishing cost-based rates (Bonbright, Danielsen, and Kamerschen 1988):

- Effectiveness in yielding total revenue requirements (full cost recovery)
- Revenue stability and predictability
- Stability and predictability of the rates themselves from unexpected or adverse changes
- Promotion of efficient resource use (conservation and efficient use)
- Fairness in the apportionment of total costs of service among the different ratepayers
- Avoidance of undue discrimination (subsidies) within the rates
- Dynamic efficiency in responding to changing supply-and-demand patterns
- Freedom from controversies as to proper interpretation of the rates
- Simple and easy to understand
- Simple to administer
- Legal and defendable

GENERALLY ACCEPTED RATE-SETTING METHODOLOGY

This manual outlines the methodologies and analyses that are used to establish cost-based rates. As displayed in Figure I.1-1, the generally accepted rate-setting methodology includes three categories of technical analysis. The first is the revenue requirement analysis. This analysis examines the utility's operating and capital costs to determine the total revenue requirements and the adequacy of the utility's existing rates. Next, a cost-of-service analysis is used to functionalize, allocate, and equitably distribute the revenue requirements to the various customer classes of service (e.g., residential, commercial) served by the utility. The final technical analysis is the rate-design analysis. It uses the results from the revenue-requirement and cost-of-service analyses to establish cost-based water rates that meet the overall rate-design goals and objectives of the utility.

Sections of this manual have been dedicated to providing detailed discussions of the three types of analysis. Section II of this manual discusses the various technical components of establishing a utility's revenue requirements. Section III discusses the various methodologies that may be used to conduct a cost-of-service analysis. Finally, section IV reviews the various issues and technical considerations in designing water rates.

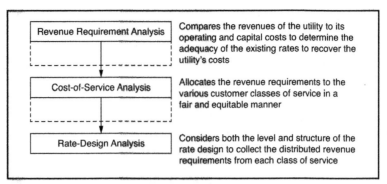

Figure I.1-1 Analytical steps of cost-based rate-making

KEY TECHNICAL ANALYSES OF COST-BASED RATE-MAKING

In establishing cost-based water rates, it is important to understand that a cost-of-service methodology does not prescribe a single approach. Rather, as the first edition of AWWA's Manual M1 noted, "the [M1 manual] is aimed at outlining the basic elements involved in water rates and suggesting alternative rules of procedure for formulating rates, thus permitting the exercise of judgment and preference to meet local conditions and requirements" (AWWA 1954). This manual, like those before it, provides the reader with an understanding of the options that make up the generally accepted methodologies and principles used to establish cost-based rates. From the application of these options within the principles and methodologies, a utility may create cost-based rates that reflect the distinct and unique characteristics of that utility and the values of the community.

Revenue Requirement Analysis

The purpose of the revenue requirement analysis is to determine the adequate and appropriate funding of the utility. Revenue requirements are the summation of the operation, maintenance, and capital costs that a utility must recover during the time period for which the rates will be in place. Two generally accepted approaches for establishing a utility's revenue requirements are discussed in this manual: the cash-needs approach and the utility-basis approach. Section II of the manual provides a detailed discussion and numerical examples about how to establish a utility's revenue requirements using these two approaches, and this section provides a framework for determining how to select between the two approaches.

Cost-of-Service Analysis

The purpose of the cost-of-service analysis is to equitably distribute the revenue requirements between the various customer classes of service served by the utility. The cost-of-service analysis determines what cost differences, if any, exist between serving the various customer classes. The two generally accepted methodologies for conducting the cost-of-service analysis are called the base-extra capacity method and the commodity-demand method. The functionalization, allocation, and distribution process of the base-extra capacity and commodity-demand methodologies are generally considered fair and equitable because both approaches result in the revenue requirements being distributed to each class in proportion to each class's contribution to the system cost components. Discussions of both cost-of-service methodologies, along with numerical examples to illustrate their differences, are provided in section III of this manual.

Rate-Design Analysis

The final technical analysis is the rate-design analysis. This analysis determines how to recover the appropriate level of costs from each customer class of service. There are different rate structures that may be used to collect the appropriate level of revenues from each customer class of service. Section IV of this manual covers the selection and development of rate designs in detail.

OTHER WATER RATE ISSUES AND CONSIDERATIONS

In addition to the topics previously discussed, this manual also contains guidance on a variety of other water rate and cost recovery issues, capacity and development charges, and water rate implementation issues. These topics are discussed in sections V through VIII.

Section V provides an overview of many distinct situations and pricing considerations that utilities may need to address. It is not unusual for a utility to face situations where a customer or group of customers has unique characteristics and circumstances. These situations include reuse rates and charges, standby rates, drought and surcharge rates, low-income affordability rates, negotiated contract and economic development rates, indexed rates, price elasticity, marginal cost pricing, and miscellaneous and special charges. Regardless of the distinctive situation and pricing considerations, the cost-based principles and methodologies as discussed within this manual should be adapted for the cost analysis to provide proper support for the rates.

Section VI is devoted to the development of rates for customers outside a municipality that owns the system. It has been expanded to include an overview of setting rates for outside customers, with chapters on wholesale (or bulk) charges and retail sales.

In recent years, the cost of system expansion and customer growth has had a significant financial impact on utilities. The development of cost-based connection fees, system development charges, or dedicated capacity charges are the topics reviewed in section VII.

Finally, while cost-of-service principles for rate-making and related fees and charges rely on significant amounts of financial analysis, engineering analysis, and policy decisions, it is necessary to engage the public. These topics, along with the data needs for developing cost-based rates, are discussed in section VIII of the manual.

REFERENCES

AWWA. 1954. Manual M1. *Water Rates Manual,* 1st ed. Denver, Colo.: AWWA. p. 1.

Bonbright, J.C., A.L. Danielsen, and D.R. Kamerschen. 1988. *Principles of Public Utility Rates,* 2nd ed. Arlington, Va.: Public Utilities Reports. pp. 383–384.

Woodcock, C.P.N. 2013. A Brief History of Water Rates Manuals and Publications. *Journal of the New England Water Works Association,* December.

Section II

Revenue Requirements

This page intentionally blank.

Chapter **II.1**

General Concepts for Establishing Revenue Requirements

The development of a utility's revenue requirements is the first analytical step of the comprehensive rate-setting process. The determination and establishment of a utility's revenue requirements is the basis for setting the overall level of the utility's rates, while providing the utility with adequate and sustainable funding levels for both operating and capital costs. The revenue requirement analysis provides the utility with an understanding of the size and timing of needed rate adjustments to existing rate levels and perhaps the rate structure.

In providing adequate water service to its customers, every water utility must receive sufficient total revenue to ensure proper operation and maintenance (O&M), development and sustainability of the system, and preservation of the utility's financial integrity. The total revenue requirements for most utilities are largely financed from revenues derived from selling water to their customers. Other revenue not derived from the sale of water may come from a variety of sources such as rentals, provision of various services to other utilities or entities, and system development charges or impact fees.

ADEQUACY OF REVENUES

The overall adequacy of water revenues can be measured by comparing projected annual revenue requirements to be met from rates with projected revenues under existing or authorized rates.

Length of Projections

Revenue projections can be made for any length of time, depending on the purpose of the projection. For budgetary purposes, utilities may project only one year ahead. From a strategic financial planning or revenue-adequacy standpoint, projections beyond 10 years tend to be quite speculative and are of questionable value. Accordingly, a projection period of about five years is generally considered adequate for near-term financial planning purposes. This time frame provides a reasonable forecast of anticipated future revenue needs, thereby assisting management, policymakers, and the public to foresee potential revenue shortfalls under existing rates and to avoid surprises when future changes in rate levels are requested or announced. Additionally, many utilities have capital improvement plans that use a comparable five-year time frame. When a utility adequately plans ahead, the projections in a five-year planning horizon are typically sufficient to satisfy investors, bond-rating agencies, and other interested parties. These projections are indicative of the security of potential investment in the utility system. The other advantage of projecting revenue requirements over a five-year planning horizon is that it may allow the utility to better anticipate any major changes in rates, and take action immediately to help mitigate or lessen those projected changes in rate levels.

Regardless of the projection period used, the utility should review its projections at least annually to incorporate changed conditions. A financial projection model should be considered a living document subject to change as conditions change. The projection period used in this chapter is assumed to be the utility's next five fiscal years. However, the principles discussed apply to any projection period appropriate for the particular circumstances. In making projections for more than one year, measures of revenue adequacy (i.e., indicated annual deficiencies) do not necessarily imply that an immediate rate change sufficient to cover deficiencies for the entire projection period (e.g., five-year period) is required or recommended. Rate changes for only a portion of the projection period may be appropriate. At the same time, implementation of smooth rate transitions is generally preferable to large one-time rate adjustments.

Other Adequacy Studies

The adequacy of water revenues is measured and studied to aid the process of rate-making for future service. Studies can be made for other purposes, including

- input for overall financial planning and budgeting;
- support for (and often part of) documentation for issuance of debt securities to be financed from utility revenues; and
- measurement or evaluation of the adequacy of revenues in the past or future as a part of contractual, litigation, rate-proceeding, bond covenant compliance, or other requirements.

Rate-making and planning require projections of future revenue needs. The issuance of debt securities and contractual, litigation, or rate-proceeding requirements may necessitate both evaluation of past performance and projections of future adequacy.

APPROACHES TO PROJECTING REVENUE REQUIREMENTS

The two generally accepted and practiced approaches to projecting total revenue requirements of a water utility are the cash-needs approach and the utility-basis approach. Each has a proper place in utility practice, and each, when properly used, can provide for sound utility financial strategies. A broad overview of the elements of revenue requirements to be considered under each of these two accepted approaches is presented in the following section. These approaches are discussed further in section VI, with regard to consideration

Table II.1-1 Normalization factors

Factors Affecting Revenues	Factors Affecting Revenue Requirements
Number of customers served	Number of customers served
Customers' water-use trends	Customers' water-use trends
Rate changes	Non-recurring sales
Non-recurring sales	Weather
Weather	Conservation
Conservation	Use restrictions
Use restrictions	Inflation
Price elasticity	Interest rates
Wholesale contractual terms	Wholesale contractual terms
	Capital finance needs
	Changes to tax laws
	Other changes in operating and economic conditions

of retail and wholesale rates applicable to customers located outside the jurisdictional boundaries of the owner utility.

General Techniques

Utilities should realize that it is acceptable to measure total revenue requirements using one approach and, subsequently, allocate those costs among customer classes using another approach (e.g., use a cash-needs approach for revenue requirements and then convert it to a utility basis for purposes of the cost-of-service analysis). Historical data must be normalized or adjusted to reflect conditions that may not continue into the future. Such factors include, but are not limited to, those listed in Table II.1-1. Each of these factors as well as other appropriate factors must be considered when projecting revenues and revenue requirements.

Actual performance will generally vary from projected performance. The projections are intended to forecast, as nearly as practicable, the future levels of revenue and revenue requirements so that the utility may make adequate, but not excessive, adjustments in rate and other revenue sources in a timely manner.

TEST YEAR

An important starting point for establishing a utility's revenue requirements is determining the test year or test period to be reviewed. The test year may represent a specific 12-month period of time or it may be an annualization of a rate-design period of more or less than one year.

Test-year periods are usually of three general types: historical, projected (future), or pro forma. A historical test-year period is defined as a prior 12-month period for which actual costs and data are available. The advantage of the historical test year is the use of actual costs and data. The disadvantage is that the costs and data may actually lag behind the utility's current costs. In contrast to a historical test year, a projected test period is a future time period in which all of the costs and data are projected, except perhaps fixed costs such as existing debt-service schedules. The advantage of a projected test year is that the rates to be developed for the test year will likely match up to the utility's budget or anticipated costs. The disadvantage of this approach is that it may be difficult to project costs, and it lacks the certainty of a historical test year. Finally, a pro forma test year is a combination of the historical and projected test year. A pro forma test period begins with historical data and costs and then adjusts only for those "known and measurable" costs or changes. An example of a known and measurable change would be a labor agreement that specifies a certain percentage adjustment to labor rates. Simple inflation is not considered a known and measurable change in costs. The disadvantage of the pro forma test year is that it may not fully capture changes in costs, but the advantage is that it has adjusted for only those costs that can clearly be documented as needing adjustment in the test year.

Generally, government-owned utilities are free to set their own policies regarding test-year periods. However, investor-owned utilities and those government-owned utilities that are under the jurisdiction of utility commissions are subject to particular legislative and regulatory practices that must be followed. These practices vary from jurisdiction to jurisdiction.

Methods of Accumulating Costs

Once the test year or time period for establishing the revenue requirements has been determined, the next decision is the method that will be used to accumulate costs within the revenue requirement analysis. The two generally accepted methods of accumulating costs for the revenue requirements are the *cash-needs approach* and the *utility-basis approach*. Each of these methods and the component costs contained within each method is discussed in more detail in the following sections.

Cash-Needs Approach

The objective of the cash-needs approach for developing revenue requirements is to provide revenues sufficient to recover total cash requirements for a given time period. Generally, the cash-needs approach is used by government-owned utilities (except in those jurisdictions where regulation requires the use of the utility-basis approach). In this manual, the term *cash needs*, as it applies to measuring revenue requirements of a utility, should not be confused with accounting terminology of the *cash-basis* accounting method of revenue and expense recognition. From a rate-making perspective, *cash needs* refers to the total revenues required by the utility to meet its annual cash expenditures, whereas the accounting term *cash basis* refers to revenues being recognized as earned when cash is received and expenses charged when cash is disbursed. The cash-needs approach to measuring revenue requirements of a utility may be evaluated on the cash, accrual, or modified accrual basis of accounting.

Generally, revenue requirement studies using the cash-needs approach are more straightforward to calculate than revenue requirement studies using the utility-basis approach. Many utilities budget in a format that may be very similar to the cash-needs approach.

Revenue requirement components. Basic revenue requirement components of the cash-needs approach include O&M expenses, taxes or transfer payments, debt-service payments, contributions to specified reserves, and the cost of capital expenditures that are not debt financed or contributed (i.e., capital improvements funded directly from rate revenues). Depreciation expense is not included within the cash-needs revenue requirement.

Operation and maintenance expenses. Depending on the test year selected, the O&M expense component can be projected based on actual expenditures and adjusted to reflect anticipated changes in expenditures during the projected test-year period. Adjustments to historical O&M expenses are determined by incorporating known and measurable changes to recorded expenses, and by using well-considered estimates of future expenses.

Generally O&M expenses include salaries and wages, fringe benefits, purchased power, purchased water, other purchased services, rent, chemicals, other materials and supplies, small equipment that does not extend the useful life of major facilities, and general overhead expenses. For a government-owned utility, other elements of O&M expense might also include the costs of support services rendered by the municipality to the utility, such as the use of computer facilities, assistance in collecting water bills, procurement activities, human resources administration, fleet management, and other support services.

Taxes or transfer payments. A utility may be required to pay certain taxes as part of their normal operations (e.g., a state utility tax on gross revenues). A utility may have several tax payments for their locality. In contrast to a tax payment, a transfer payment may be for items such as a payment in lieu of taxes (PILOT). AWWA's policy statement on Financing, Accounting, and Rates states that "Water and wastewater utility funds should not be diverted to uses unrelated to water and wastewater utility services. Reasonable taxes, payments in lieu of taxes, and/or payments for services rendered to the water utility by a local government or other divisions of the owning entity may be included in the utility's revenue requirements after taking into account the contribution for fire protection and other services furnished by the utility to the local government or to other divisions of the owning entity" (AWWA 2015). Accordingly, payments made to a municipality's general fund should reimburse the general fund for the necessary cost of goods and/or services required by the water utility to provide water service. Transfers from the water fund to a municipal general fund, in addition to those specifically identified above, may be applicable to unique local situations and should be considered in conjunction with legal requirements and in conformance with the previously referenced AWWA policy statement.

Debt-service payments and specified reserves. The debt-service component of the cash-needs approach usually consists of principal and interest payments on bonds or other outstanding debt instruments. It may also include debt-service reserve requirements as established by the indenture or covenant. Other reserves are often required to provide for operating working capital, emergency repairs and replacements, as well as for routine replacements and extensions. In addition to debt service and payments to reserve fund accounts, many utilities are required to provide net revenues sufficient to cover the bonded debt, particularly if revenue bonds are involved. Typically, debt-service coverage requirements specify that revenues be sufficient to meet O&M expenses and taxes and, at a minimum, to equal or exceed a stated percentage of the annual debt-service payments. Coverage requirements are a test of the adequacy of utility revenues and do not necessarily represent a specific cash requirement, unless debt-service coverage is the controlling factor in terms of the overall annual revenue needs of the utility, which may be the case in a particular year. The coverage requirements are intended to provide a measure of security for bondholders. As such, coverage requirements must also be considered in determining the total annual revenue needed to comply with the utility's debt covenant agreements.

Rate-funded capital expenditures. This component of the cash-needs approach is not all capital expenditures, but rather, only that portion of the capital expenditures to be paid during the test year from current rate revenues. Capital expenditures may be classified into three broad categories: normal annual (routine) replacement of existing facilities, normal annual extensions and improvements, and major capital replacements and improvements. A utility should periodically review and update its needs in each of these areas to recognize changing conditions. Projections for such needs are essential in developing overall revenue requirement projections. These projections of total capital needs should be accompanied by estimates of contributions received from developers or customers, government grants, and other nonutility sources.

Government-owned utilities commonly use current revenues to finance

- normal annual replacements,
- extensions, and

- improvements (such as meters, services, vehicles, smaller mains, valves, hydrants, and similar items that occur regularly each year).

Major capital projects are typically financed with a combination of long-term debt and equity or cash generated from annual utility revenues. Capital costs are distributed over the term of the bonds by repaying the debt over several years and using equity. An advantage of using long-term debt to fund major capital expenditures is that it results in a better matching of customers' charges with the use of the facilities so that existing customers will not be paying 100 percent of the initial cost of facilities that will be used for many years. Debt-service coverage compliance may result in the generation of annual revenues that may be available for funding of a portion of major capital improvements from annual revenues.

Utility-Basis Approach

The utility-basis approach to measuring revenue requirements is typically mandated for investor-owned water utilities. It is mandated or permitted for government-owned utilities in jurisdictions where the utility is regulated by a utility commission or other similar regulatory body.

The utility-basis approach for determining revenue requirements consists of O&M expenses, taxes or transfer payments, depreciation expense, and a "fair" return on rate base investment. While the utility-basis approach is in some ways similar to the cash-needs approach, where these two methods diverge is in how capital infrastructure is funded within the rates. The cash-needs approach uses debt-service and capital expenditures funded from rates. In contrast, the utility-basis approach uses depreciation expense and a return on rate base.

Municipal or government-owned utilities may also use the utility-basis approach for purposes of cost allocation. It is considered an appropriate method for calculating the costs of service applicable to all classes of customers, but it is particularly applicable to those customers located outside the geographical limits of a government-owned utility. When a government-owned utility provides service to customers outside its geographical limits or corporate boundary, the situation is similar to the relationship of an investor-owned utility to its customers because the owner (political subdivision) provides services to nonowner customers (customers outside its geographical limits). In this situation, the government-owned utility, like an investor-owned utility, is entitled to earn a reasonable return from nonowner customers based on the value of its plant investment required to serve those customers. Some jurisdictions have laws or guidelines to regulate the rates that government-owned utilities charge customers located outside their limits. Section VI discusses the considerations in using the utility-basis approach for determining rates for outside-city retail and wholesale customers.

Utility-Basis Projections for Government-Owned Utilities

For a government-owned utility, the total level of annual revenue required may be similar under either the cash-needs approach or the utility-basis approach. The O&M expense component of total revenue requirements is usually the same under both approaches. Under the utility-basis approach, the annual requirement for capital-related costs consists of two components: depreciation expense and return on rate base. Using the cash-needs approach, capital infrastructure-related costs are recovered through total debt service (principal and interest), cash financed capital additions and extensions, and debt-service coverage considerations.

Depreciation expense. Depreciation is a real part of the cost of operating a utility, whether government owned or investor owned. Depreciation is the loss in value of facilities not restored by current maintenance that occurs to the property because of wear and tear, decay, inadequacy, and obsolescence. The annual depreciation expense component of revenue requirements allows the utility to recover its capital investment over the anticipated useful life of the depreciable assets. Therefore, it is fair that this expense be borne by the customers benefiting from the use of an asset during its useful life.

Depreciation expense should be based on the depreciable plant investment that is in service during the period for which rates are being established. Because depreciation expense is a noncash requirement, the inclusion of depreciation expense in calculating revenue requirements provides the utility with funds that are available for use as a source of capital for replacing, improving, and expanding systems or for repaying debt.

Return on rate base. The return component is intended to pay the annual interest cost of debt capital and provide a fair rate of return for the total equity capital employed to finance facilities used to provide water service. Although the annual interest costs can be readily ascertained, the cost of equity capital is more difficult to determine. The return to the equity owner should be in keeping with the return in other enterprises having corresponding risks. Moreover, the return should be sufficient to ensure confidence in the financial integrity of the enterprise so as to maintain its credit and to attract and hold capital. More discussion of the considerations in establishing a fair rate for return for service to customers located outside the political boundaries of the owner utility system is provided in section VI of this manual.

The utility basis of determining revenue requirements usually necessitates establishing a *rate base* (defined as the value of the assets on which the utility is entitled to earn a return) and setting a fair rate of return on the rate base. The rate base is primarily composed of the depreciated value of the utility's property devoted to serving the public. In addition, the utility may be permitted to include an allowance in the rate base for working capital and, in limited instances, construction work in progress. On the other hand, grants and contributions (such as government grants, developer-donated facilities, and other nonutility supplied funds) are generally deducted from the utility's rate base.

As previously mentioned, another element of utility-basis revenue requirements for a government-owned utility may be payments for services to the general fund of the municipality or PILOT to other government entities.

Utility-Basis Projections for Investor-Owned Utilities

The total annual revenue requirements of an investor-owned utility include O&M expenses, depreciation expense, income taxes, other taxes, and return on rate base. The O&M expenses, depreciation expense, and return on rate base for an investor-owned utility involve the same considerations discussed for a government-owned utility using the utility-basis approach.

Federal, state, provincial, or local income taxes must be paid by an investor-owned utility and, therefore, are properly included in determining total revenue requirements. Other taxes, such as property taxes, gross receipts taxes, and payroll taxes, must also be recognized.

Each utility commission and regulatory body has its own rules, regulations, and policies for determining total revenue requirements. In preparing for any rate matter within a specific jurisdiction, the utility must determine the procedures and policies of the regulatory body and follow those policies in determining its revenue requirements.

Revenue Requirements for Government-Owned Utilities

Government-owned utilities typically select a projected test year in recognition of budgetary requirements, bond indentures, and rates being designed for a *future* period. The test year may simply correspond to an upcoming fiscal year or represent the annualization of the period for which rates are intended to be effective. For example, if projected revenue requirements and revenues indicate that an overall 18 percent increase in revenues would meet the revenue requirements over a 36-month period, the utility may wish to use a test year that averages the revenue requirements and revenues for the 36-month period or separate the test-year period into three separate 12-month test-year periods to phase the rates in over that time. The selection of the test-year period in this instance would be dependent on the timing and magnitude of annual increases required.

When selecting a test year for a government-owned utility, legislative or debt-indenture requirements may need to be considered. Certain government-owned utilities are required by their ordinance or governing documents to establish rates and charges that are adequate to provide for specific revenue requirements and coverages for certain projected test periods. These revenue requirements and coverages generally require projections based on historical data to develop a future test year in evaluating the adequacy of revenues under proposed rates and charges.

Debt-related agreements may include provisions that could influence the selection of the test year. The specified debt-service coverage tests and conditions for the issuance of additional bonds must often be considered when selecting a test year. Some debt indentures specify that rates be enacted for each upcoming fiscal year or for a specific period in the future.

Revenue Requirements for Investor-Owned Utilities

Most investor-owned utilities must follow the established practices and requirements of the applicable utility commission or regulatory agency when selecting a test year. Many regulations require the use of a historical test year, which may be adjusted for known or reasonably anticipated changes (i.e., a pro forma test year). Some regulatory agencies allow a current test year that includes a combination of historical and projected data while others may accept a future test year.

A comparison of example test-year revenue requirements for a government-owned utility on both the cash-needs and utility-basis approaches is shown in Table II.1-2. A parallel statement of the revenue requirements for a similarly sized investor-owned utility is also included.

As shown in Table II.1-2, the O&M expense component of the total test-year revenue requirement is the same for the investor-owned utility as for the government-owned utility using either the cash-needs or the utility-basis approach. Using the utility-basis approach, the annual depreciation expense component of total revenue requirements, shown on line 5 in Table II.1-2, is $1,242,000. This is determined by applying a proper schedule of depreciation rates to the total depreciable plant investment in service. In the example, the depreciation value is calculated by multiplying the composite depreciation rate, about 1.85 percent, by the total depreciable plant investment ($67,185,000—from Table II.5-2, line 1; year 2 is the test year used in this example). Under the utility-basis approach, the annual depreciation expense allowance is the same for either an investor-owned or a government-owned utility.

For a government-owned utility to meet the total cash-revenue requirements under the utility-basis approach, the level of return to be derived from rates in the example is required to be $2,545,000 ($2,623,000 – $78,000), as shown on lines 8 and 9 of Table II.1-2. Assuming a rate base of $48,558,000 (year 2 from Table II.5-2, line 9), the overall rate of

Table II.1-2 Summary of test-year revenue requirements (in $1,000)

Line No.	Item	Government-Owned Utility		Investor-Owned Utility
		Cash-Needs Approach	Utility-Basis Approach	Utility-Basis Approach
1	O&M Expenses	$6,837	$6,837	$6,837
2	Debt Service	2,580		
3	Debt-Service Reserve	180		
4	Capital Improvements	1,141		
5	Depreciation Expense		1,242	1,242
6	Other Taxes			1,080
7	Income Taxes			1,150
8	Return (Operating Income)		2,623	3,325
9	Other Operating Revenues	(78)	(78)	(78)
10	Nonoperating Revenues	(159)		
11	Net Balance From Operations	123		
12	Total Revenue Requirements From Rates	$10,624	$10,624	$13,556

return for the hypothetical government-owned utility is about 5.2 percent. In any particular government-owned utility, the magnitude of existing debt service and the policy regarding the amount of revenue financing of capital improvements will influence the required level of return. This may result in an indicated need for an overall rate of return markedly different from the example shown later in chapter II.5.

For the same example utility on an investor-owned basis, income taxes and other taxes must be considered when determining annual revenue requirements. The element of other taxes, shown on line 6 of Table II.1-2, amounts to $1,080,000 and could include business, occupational, gross receipts, and other types of taxes.

The income-tax element of the investor-owned utility's cost of service is based on the application of a composite tax-rate allowance for both federal and state income taxes to total taxable income. In this example, taxable income equals total revenue less O&M expense, depreciation expense, other taxes, and interest expense. Income tax is shown on line 7 to be $1,150,000.

The rate base for the investor-owned utility is less than that for the government-owned utility by the amount of accumulated deferred income taxes.

An overall rate of return of 8 percent on the rate base of $41,460,000 was assumed, resulting in a requirement for return (operating income) of $3,325,000 as noted on Table II.6-5 (year 2, lines 16 and 15, respectively). The higher return for the investor-owned utility assumed in Table II.1-2 results from the weighted cost of debt and equity capital. This return would be expected to be greater than the resulting overall 5.2 percent rate of return shown for the government-owned utility. The rate of return for the government-owned utility in this example is adequate only to provide for cash needs beyond O&M expense and capital requirements covered by depreciation expense.

Where a government-owned utility is serving customers outside its jurisdiction who are considered to be nonowners, the applicable rates of return may properly reflect a differential between owners and nonowners. For a government-owned utility providing service to nonowners, developing an appropriate rate of return may reflect embedded interest cost and return on system equity. Once established, the rate of return assigned to system owners would be developed to recognize residual cash needs to meet the utility's cash-based revenue requirements. Consideration of **differential rates of return** is addressed subsequently in section VI of this manual.

From the example shown in Table II.1-2, it is apparent that the overall revenue requirement to be obtained from water rates varies with the type of ownership and other system requirements. In the example, the overall level of revenue requirements varies from $10,624,000 for the government-owned utility paying no income taxes, financed with tax-free bonds, and in which the customers have made the equity investment for which no return is required, to $13,556,000 for an investor-owned utility paying all taxes, with no tax-free financing available, and having to pay a fair and reasonable return to equity investors who provided a portion of the investment requirements.

REFERENCE

AWWA. 2015. AWWA Statements of Policy on Public Water Supply Matters. In *AWWA Officers and Committee Directory*. (Revised June 7, 2015.) Denver, Colo.: AWWA. www.awwa.org/about-us/policy-statements.aspx (accessed May 20, 2016).

Chapter **II.2**

Revenues

Revenues are the lifeblood of a water utility. Without adequate revenues, the quality of service will deteriorate from the lack of proper maintenance and system improvements, and the utility will not be financially or operationally sustainable.

SOURCES OF REVENUE

Two basic sources of revenue are available to a water utility: operating revenues and non-operating revenues. *Operating revenues* include sales of water to general customers and other services that are usually provided under standard rate schedules or by contractual arrangements. *Nonoperating revenues* can include tax revenues, gains or losses from the sale of property, rental of nonoperating property, interest income, and other items not usually directly related to the provision of water service.

Additionally, in some government-owned utilities, transfers from the government entity's general fund are used as a revenue source to fund such items as debt service, various capital outlays, and, in some cases, operation and maintenance (O&M) expenses. With the exception of dedicated funds, utilities that use such transfers are not considered to be adequately financed, self-sustaining enterprises.

Revenue Classifications

Table II.2-1 shows typical revenue classifications. As noted in the table, sales to general retail customers may be subdivided into unmetered (if applicable) and metered sales, and each category is usually further subdivided into customer classes such as residential, commercial, and industrial. Additional subdivisions or alternative classifications may include such categories as governmental, apartments, and single-family and multifamily dwellings. Some utilities use the customer's meter size to classify retail customers (e.g., small, medium, and large meters).

Where applicable to government-owned utilities, each of these general water service classes is considered separately in determining whether it is inside or outside the jurisdictional limits of the owning agency.

Sales for resale generally consist of deliveries to customer groups, such as suburban cities or water districts, on a wholesale basis through master meters. Other special sales

Table II.2-1 Typical revenue classifications

Operating Revenues	Nonoperating Revenues	Contributions to Capital
General Water Service	Merchandising and contract services (jobbing)	Developer and customer contributions
Unmetered sales		
Metered sales	Rents from nonoperating property	Grants
Sales for resale (wholesale)	Interest and dividend income	System development charges
Other special sales	Gains or losses from disposition of property	
Private fire protection service		
Public fire protection service	Tax revenues	
Other	Transfers from other government funds	
Miscellaneous service revenues	Allowance for funds used during construction	
Forfeited discounts		
Rents from water property	Other nonoperating revenues	
Other water revenues		

may include irrigation, air conditioning, standby, off-peak, interruptible, and individual contract service where special rates may apply.

Private fire protection service revenues include charges for sprinkler-service connections, standpipes, private fire hydrants, and other fire protection facilities located on the customers' premises. Public fire protection service revenues generally include charges for service provided through public fire hydrants or user charges (see chapter IV.8, "Rates for Fire Protection Service").

Miscellaneous service revenues include any revenues resulting from other services regularly provided by the utility. This includes, among other elements, revenues from charges for connecting or disconnecting service, special meter readings, temporary hydrant use, new account charges, and collection-related charges.

Forfeited discounts include revenues from discounts foregone as a result of untimely payment of water bills. They can also include penalties assessed for late payment of water bills.

Rents from water property include rental income from the lease or rental of operating property and equipment.

Other water revenues may include providing billing services for other outside utilities or providing other services such as laboratory testing, and other such services generally established as the cost of providing such services.

Nonoperating revenues is the income that is derived from sources that are not generally related to the ongoing day-to-day operating activities of the utility. Rents from nonoperating property include rental income from utility property not used for operating purposes (such as the rental of buildings on land purchased to acquire water rights). If the utility has investments that earn interest or dividends, such income should be reported in the interest and dividend income account.

If a utility sells or otherwise disposes of an item of utility property, the net proceeds are reported as gains or losses from sale or disposition of utility property. The net gain or loss is measured by the net selling price less the net book cost (book cost less accumulated depreciation) of the property sold.

Tax revenues usually consist of ad valorem or other taxes assessed for the benefit of the water utility. Transfers from other government funds are often considered to be similar to grants and are usually treated the same; these transfers would not include payments for water service.

Allowance for funds used during construction (AFUDC) is an accounting entry designed to permit the utility to recover the costs associated with financing ongoing, long-term construction activities. Typically, AFUDC cannot be included in the current-period revenue requirement but instead is added to the cost of the construction and capitalized.

Other nonoperating revenues is an all-encompassing term for items of nonoperating revenues that do not warrant a separate, individual accounting. Nonoperating revenues are considered to be "below-the-line" items; that is, they are not necessarily treated as available to meet the O&M or debt-service revenue requirements of the utility.

Developer and customer contributions consist of cash or property donated for plant construction. These contributions may include such items as the investment in the distribution system associated with a new subdivision, the cost of tapping into the water main, and the cost of a customer's service connection, meter, and meter installation.

It is common for utilities to impose connection charges, system development charges (SDCs), or other such charges (section VII) on developers or property owners to pay for capital improvements required to serve growth and new or expanded development. These charges transfer the cost burden related to growth to new customers and help mitigate the cost of growth to existing customers. SDCs are accounted for as capital contributions and are reported separately in the Statement of Revenues and Expenses and in the Statement of Net Assets in accordance with Governmental Accounting Standards Board Statement No. 34 requirements. To the extent that this income is included in the utility's financial tests, such as for calculating debt-service coverage, the utility should refer to its specific bond covenants. However, it is suggested that such tests or ratios should be computed both with and without the inclusion of these revenue sources. Because such growth-related revenues are subject to potential significant annual variation, it may be necessary to adjust water service rate levels upward to accommodate for the potential reduction or loss in SDC revenues to maintain necessary debt-service coverage levels, if such revenues had been counted for in meeting the minimum debt-service coverage requirement. In the case of investor-owned utilities, such fees and charges have usually been treated as contributions in aid of construction on the utility's books and not as a revenue item.

Grants are usually considered to be contributions made by the granting agency, such as the federal government.

CASH VERSUS ACCRUAL REVENUES

Cash receipts are sometimes used as a basis for setting and adjusting water rates. However, most investor-owned water utilities and many government-owned utilities maintain their accounting records on an accrual basis. The accrual method of accounting provides a better matching of revenues and expenses and a more accurate assessment of the profitability of the utility than cash-basis accounting.

Some government-owned water utilities operate on a cash basis of accounting because of bond indenture or other requirements. Recognizing that cash revenues often lag accrued revenues, government-owned utilities must account for this lag in cash receipts and provide resources for it, particularly if they operate strictly on a cash basis of accounting. As noted in chapter II.1, accounting terminology should not be confused with rate-making terminology. The cash-needs approach to measuring the revenue requirements of a utility and setting rates may be, and often is, used whether the utility's accounting records follow the cash, accrual, or modified-accrual basis of accounting.

UNBILLED REVENUES

All water meters are not typically read and billed at the same time, because most water utilities cycle their billing process throughout the month. Under any cycle-billing system, there are unbilled revenues at the end of each accounting period, representing the water sales from the last billing of each customer to the end of the accounting period. Thus, earned revenues do not typically equal the billed revenues for any accounting period. The difference between the unbilled revenues at the end and at the beginning of an accounting period is the accrued amount to be applied to the billed revenues to determine the earned revenues for the accounting period.

If there is no growth in the number of customers, no rate change during the accounting period, and customer usage is stable, there will be little difference between earned revenues and billed revenues. However, if customer growth is significant or if a rate change takes effect during the period, the unbilled revenues at the end of the accounting period will differ from those at the beginning. Therefore, this accrued amount may be large, and earned revenues may be significantly different from billed revenues.

Some utilities bill service charges or minimum charges in advance. In such cases, some billed, but unearned, revenues could exist at the end of each accounting period. Therefore, if the unearned revenues at the end of the accounting period exceed the unearned revenues at the beginning of the accounting period, a negative revenue accrual would result.

For rate-making purposes, the accrued amount must be excluded from base revenues because rate changes and customer growth are annualized and added to the billed revenues. Thus, if the accrual adjustment is not excluded, base revenues would be adjusted twice for rate changes and growth.

PROJECTING REVENUE

In projecting revenue that may be available to the utility from the sources listed in Table II.2-1, the utility must first develop adequate historical data as a basis for projecting future revenues.

Historical Data

The amount of revenue that may be derived from water rates under any particular rate schedule can be appropriately projected based on historical data regarding customer billing. The amount and detail of needed data vary, depending on the local situation. The most accurate projections result from separately summarizing and analyzing billing data for each customer classification.

For metered accounts, the utility may need to compile the number of bills rendered by customer class and meter size, and the water sales by rate block. This compilation usually includes adjustments for credits, additional billings, partial bills, final bills, and changes in the number of customers served. The compilation should include a verification procedure, such as a comparison with billed revenues. The verification procedure should also include confirmation of the days billed. A change in the billing cycle or in the makeup of the billing routes could result in test-year billings for more or less than 365 days. To properly analyze billed revenues, the utility must have billings for 365 days.

Flat-rate revenues and fire-service revenues can be annualized by establishing the average number of billing units for each rate level during the historical base year. Growth projections can be added if applicable.

In many situations, particularly for smaller utilities, detailed billing data are not available. In such cases, the utility must estimate a satisfactory basis for projection of anticipated revenues.

Projection Considerations

Reasonable projections of each revenue category listed in Table II.2-1 must be considered and made as appropriate. As previously noted, it is often necessary to normalize or adjust historical data to reflect abnormal conditions that may have caused unusual variations. Some of the most common areas for adjustment are discussed in the following sections.

Growth in number of customers. Growth in the number of customers served can be projected by recognizing historical growth patterns, growth restrictions and changes in economic conditions, and by awareness of proposed developments in the service area. Historical customer class average water use and/or revenues per customer are normally adequate to project revenues in growth situations. However, if the current rates have not been in effect for a sufficient period to establish valid average revenue per customer, historical average revenues need to be adjusted to reflect rate changes. Also, it is often necessary to perform special analyses of projected future revenues from existing or new industrial or other large-use customers.

The number of customers served at any particular point in time, such as historical year end, needs to be annualized so that projections ultimately reflect a full year's service. Often the trend in the average of beginning and end-of-year number of customers of record provides a satisfactory method of projection. A factor that would require adjustments includes the effects of past annexation of new customers, an occurrence not likely to be repeated with regularity. Another factor that would necessitate an adjustment would be the effects of a major area-wide economic downturn or upturn that is not typical of a long-term trend.

Non-recurring sales. Sales not expected to continue in the future should be eliminated from projections. This would include a large-volume water user going off the system, abnormally high sales caused by an incorrect meter reading if not credited during the base year, leakage of customers' plumbing, and temporary purchases. Sufficient data must be accumulated to calculate the volume of non-recurring sales and an appropriate adjustment made to revenue projections.

Weather normalization. In many areas, weather conditions can greatly affect water sales. Thus, the utility should consider adjusting past sales when weather conditions have been abnormal. It is useful to follow a procedure that correlates average water use per customer over a period of years with temperature, rainfall, and other climatic conditions. These data are used together with normal climatic data to project water sales under normal weather conditions. Normal climatic conditions may be established using long-term averages as reported by the National Weather Service for the service area.

Care should be exercised when attempting to normalize water sales for weather. Other variables that affected the historical data may have more effect on the results than the weather normalization itself and, therefore, should be reflected in the revenue study.

Conservation. Revenue projections may need to be adjusted to reflect conservation measures installed in the past or to reflect conservation measures to be used in the future. These projections can be difficult to adjust. Past conservation measures may permanently reduce water sales, so comparing water sales before the conservation measures were installed could overstate future projections. The effects of future conservation measures can be difficult to quantify and support. However, a diligent attempt should be made to estimate the effect of conservation efforts on revenues; otherwise, actual revenues may differ significantly from projections.

Price elasticity. Most water use is considered to be relatively insensitive to changes in the price of water (price inelastic). However, uses such as outdoor lawn watering and industrial sales may be somewhat more sensitive to the price of water. Many utilities have experienced water-use reductions due to, at least in some measure, increases in the price of water. Major rate increases have, at times, reduced industrial water sales. The addition

Table II.2-2 Number of customers and water consumption

Line No.	Customer Class	Number of Customers (average)					
		Historical Year	Projected Years				
			1	2	3	4	5
1	Residential	15,180	15,330	15,480	15,630	15,780	15,930
2	Commercial	1,200	1,210	1,220	1,230	1,240	1,250
3	Industrial	35	35	35	35	35	35
4	Wholesale	4	4	4	4	4	4
5	Private Fire	150	150	150	150	150	150
6	Public Fire	1	1	1	1	1	1
7	Total	16,570	16,730	16,890	17,050	17,210	17,370

Line No.	Customer Class	Water Consumption (1,000 gallons)					
		Historical Year	Projected Years				
			1	2	3	4	5
1	Residential	950,000	958,000	968,000	977,000	986,000	996,000
2	Commercial	465,000	469,000	473,000	477,000	481,000	484,000
3	Industrial	1,095,000	1,095,000	1,095,000	1,095,000	1,095,000	1,095,000
4	Wholesale	230,000	230,000	230,000	230,000	230,000	230,000
5	Private Fire	N/A*	N/A	N/A	N/A	N/A	N/A
6	Public Fire	N/A	N/A	N/A	N/A	N/A	N/A
7	Total	2,740,000	2,752,000	2,766,000	2,779,000	2,792,000	2,805,000

*N/A = not available

of billings for other utility services based on water usage, such as wastewater services, can also affect water use.

Water utilities are investigating, and many have implemented, pricing techniques intended to modify water demand. Some regulatory agencies are also considering this method to promote water conservation. Extreme care should be used in projecting revenues that reflect these pricing techniques because generalized water price-elasticity information may not apply to specific circumstances. See chapter V.7 for a more comprehensive discussion of this topic.

EXAMPLE

Tables II.2-2 and II.2-3 illustrate an example projection of utility revenues. These tables, and additional tables presented in chapters II.3, II.4, and II.5, are intended to assist the reader in recognizing customer base, water use, revenues, O&M expenses, capital structure, and associated capital costs as part of the projection process. The information and methodology used in developing these tables apply equally to government-owned and investor-owned water utilities. The adequacy of projected five-year revenues according to existing rates is presented in a flow-of-funds analysis for the government-owned utility and an operating income statement for the investor-owned utility.

Revenue sources typically available to utilities have been discussed in this chapter. Included in the tables are water sales revenue from residential, commercial, industrial, and wholesale customer classes; revenue from charges for private and public fire protection; other miscellaneous operating revenues; and nonoperating income. Table II.2-2 summarizes a projection of the average number of customers served and the associated

Table II.2-3 Water sales and miscellaneous revenues

Line No.	Customer Class	Historical Year	Projected Revenues				
			1	2	3	4	5
1	Residential	$4,980,000	$5,031,000	$5,082,000	$5,130,000	$5,178,000	$5,229,000
2	Commercial	1,500,000	1,521,000	1,533,000	1,545,000	1,557,000	1,569,000
3	Industrial	1,860,000	1,860,000	1,860,000	1,860,000	1,860,000	1,860,000
4	Wholesale	360,000	360,000	360,000	360,000	360,000	360,000
5	Private Fire	120,000	120,000	120,000	120,000	120,000	120,000
6	Public Fire	810,000	810,000	810,000	810,000	810,000	810,000
7	Subtotal	9,630,000	9,702,000	9,765,000	9,825,000	9,885,000	9,948,000
8	Other Operating Revenues	60,000	75,000	78,000	81,000	84,000	87,000
9	Nonoperating Income	165,000	150,000	159,000	168,000	177,000	186,000
10	Total	$9,855,000	$9,927,000	$10,002,000	$10,074,000	$10,146,000	$10,221,000

water use by customer class for each of the years in the example study period. As noted, the projections for the number of customers and water use are equally applicable to both government-owned and investor-owned utilities.

The number of customers and water use by customer class for the most recent historical year are presented in Table II.2-2 to serve as a reference point for the reader. As previously discussed, a review of historic changes in customer growth, use per customer, and variance in usage patterns caused by weather and other factors is necessary for sound projections. In Table II.2-2, these underlying factors are assumed to have been recognized in preparing the forecast. It may be noted that not all classes are expected to experience growth.

Table II.2-3 shows projected revenues under existing rates for a government-owned utility. In projecting revenues under existing rates, service charges or minimum bill charges and fire protection charges are applied to the projected number of customers/ bills, and average unit revenues applicable to water usage (volume charges) are applied to the projected water use (both number of customers and water usage as previously developed in Table II.2-2). A similar procedure would be followed in projecting revenues under existing rates for an investor-owned utility.

Projected revenues from miscellaneous operating and nonoperating sources are based on historical average revenue levels from these sources. In some instances, such as revenue from forfeited discounts or late payment penalties, projected revenues from these sources may be directly related to projected water sales revenues. Other miscellaneous revenue sources, such as charges for connecting and disconnecting service, may vary directly with the projected number of customers or the growth in number of customers. Such relationships should be determined based on an analysis of the applicable revenue accounts.

This page intentionally blank.

Chapter **II.3**

Operation and Maintenance Expenses

For any utility to be self-sufficient, the utility must recover its full revenue requirements on a continuing basis. Chapter II.1 provided an overview of revenue requirements and how they are determined under both a cash-needs approach and a utility-basis approach. As noted in chapter II.1, O&M expenses include a major part of revenue requirements. In this chapter, O&M expenses for both government-owned and investor-owned utilities are discussed. Specific items include

- classifying O&M expenses by functional cost category;
- identifying non-recurring O&M expenses;
- identifying capitalized O&M expenses;
- identifying special considerations for government-owned utilities, including interdepartmental O&M expenses and payments to the general fund; and
- estimating O&M expenses.

O&M expenses are the prudent and necessary costs to operate and maintain source of supply, treatment, pumping, transmission and distribution facilities; as well as the cost of customer service, and administrative and general expenses. O&M expenses are typically measured and reported for a period of one year corresponding to the fiscal time period of the entity being reported.

In this chapter, O&M expenses exclude depreciation expense and expenditures that would significantly extend the lives of the facilities beyond those first contemplated, as well as taxes. A review and discussion of these items are covered in chapters II.4 and II.5.

CLASSIFYING O&M EXPENSES

To properly account for O&M expenses, it is necessary to develop a common accounting method for classifying expenses consistently from year to year. Specifically, O&M expenses should be classified in a manner to achieve the following goals:

- Permit proper monitoring and reporting of each O&M expense item.
- Separate capital expenditures from O&M expenses.
- Provide appropriate information to utility managers for operating the utility in a cost-effective manner.
- Provide historical data in a format that facilitates projections.
- Support cost-of-service and rate-making calculations.
- Enhance comparability or benchmarking of expenses among water utilities.

Chart of Accounts

The most effective way to classify and track O&M expenses on a consistent basis is through a detailed chart or system of accounts. For an O&M expense to be appropriately classified, the chart of accounts is used to properly code the expense item; that is, as a water utility completes each financial transaction, a record of that transaction is tracked into the appropriate account within the chart of accounts. Typically, the larger and more complex the utility, the greater the need for a more detailed chart of accounts.

The National Association of Regulatory Utility Commissioners has recommended a "Uniform System of Accounts," which is widely used by regulated utilities and can be modified for government-owned utilities. Other charts of accounts that meet the goals previously set forth are also used.

IDENTIFYING NON-RECURRING O&M EXPENSES

Some O&M expenses do not have the characteristics of ongoing annual expenses. These expenses are not incurred repeatedly from year to year but rather occur infrequently. A good example of a non-recurring O&M expense is the cost of painting a water storage tank. Tank painting does not create a new asset but provides maintenance to an existing asset. This expense is an O&M expense even though it might only be incurred once every 10 years.

Amortization

Many utilities amortize infrequently occurring O&M expense over the expected period between expenditures to minimize major fluctuations in annual expenses. Non-recurring O&M expenses that might be amortized include certain maintenance activities (such as tank painting), regulatory expenses, and planning studies. For example, a utility that has one tank might paint that tank every 10 years. In this case, the cost of painting the tank would be amortized over 10 years, and the annual expense would be one-tenth of the total cost.

Scheduling

If possible, groups of non-recurring O&M expenses should be scheduled in such a way that approximately the same expense is incurred annually. For example, a utility may have 10 storage tanks, and one tank is painted each year. By the time the tenth tank is painted in the tenth year, it is time to repaint the first tank, and so on. In this case, the cost of tank painting would be expensed annually rather than amortized over a 10-year period.

IDENTIFYING CAPITALIZED O&M EXPENSES

From a revenue requirement standpoint, it is important to recognize that some expenditures that might normally be considered O&M expenses must be capitalized. An example of such an expenditure would be salaries and wages of employees who devote time to a project that is a capital investment. Such salaries, wages, and accompanying overhead (e.g., related payroll taxes, workers' compensation, materials and supplies, and transportation expenses) are capitalized as a part of the cost of the project. When capitalized, such expenditures are not included as O&M expenses but are accounted for and depreciated in the same manner as other capitalized costs associated with the project.

IDENTIFYING SPECIAL CONSIDERATIONS FOR GOVERNMENT-OWNED UTILITIES

The accounting system and related chart of accounts should be structured to provide each utility manager with information to track expenses by organizational unit. Government-owned utilities may also adopt the chart of accounts used by the local government accounting system. In some cases, an appropriate chart of accounts may be mandated by state or other governing law. In these situations, specific "object" expense accounts are applied across the organizational units of the local government. An example of how O&M items might be grouped in a government environment is

- personal services,
- contractual services,
- commodities,
- administration, and
- interdepartmental expenses.

Each category could contain numerous expenses to provide further detail.

Many utilities adopt more than one chart of accounts for O&M expenses. One chart might provide for effective rate setting and utility comparability (i.e., more functional in nature; source of supply, treatment, pumping), and another might provide for cost accountability by organizational unit, which permits consistency with state and local government-mandated accounting systems. As long as the utility meets the goals of classification of expenses described at the beginning of this chapter, any one or more expense accounting systems may be satisfactory. However, for cost allocation purposes, a more functional set of O&M accounts (e.g., source of supply, treatment) can facilitate a more equitable allocation and distribution of costs.

Interdepartmental O&M Expenses

Many government-owned water utilities are a part of a city or county government. In such cases, these local governments may provide support services to the utility department. Support services might include planning, purchasing, personnel, accounting, legal, fleet management, and data processing.

To recognize all O&M expenses, it is important to identify interdepartmental O&M expenses incurred on behalf of the water department by other city or county departments. Otherwise, the total expense of providing water service is not identified and, therefore, comparisons with other water utilities are less meaningful. In addition, the utility may not be recovering the total cost of service from its customers. To address this issue, many local governments have developed systems that allocate interdepartmental support expenses to various departments. In such cases, it is relatively simple to properly allocate interdepartmental expenses to the water utility. If no system exists, the allocation factors can usually be estimated using some logical basis. For example, the ratio of personnel within the water department to total city personnel might be used to allocate city personnel expense to the water department.

Payments to General Fund

Other cash revenue requirements that may require financing from water system revenues might include payment to the general fund for such items as payment in lieu of taxes, gross receipts taxes, or a dividend payment. These additional requirements depend on each local situation and should be considered when applicable. Reference is made to the AWWA policy on such payments and is discussed in chapter II.1 of this manual.

ESTIMATING O&M EXPENSES

In projecting future O&M expenses, factors that will affect future expenses must be adequately analyzed. Recent experience regarding O&M expenses, as recorded by the utility, serve as an important base for projections. Trends in such expenses should be recognized, but normalization of past experience is important in the analysis.

Expense projections should recognize such factors as changes in the number of customers served, changes in water demand, inflation, and changes in operating conditions or maintenance needs that may be expected within a projection period.

EXAMPLE

Table II.3-1 shows a projection of O&M expenses for an example water utility. The projections are assumed to apply equally for a government-owned or investor-owned utility. The expenses for the most recent historical year provide a reference point for the reader.

The functional cost categories of O&M expenses, as shown in Table II.3-1, reflect those that may be included in a chart of accounts. The various expenses within each functional cost category are identified and grouped for the application of appropriate price and quantity variables to each line item. For example, in addition to recognizing changes in unit costs caused by inflationary trends, purchased power and chemical expenses would also increase in proportion to variations in projected water sales volumes. Customer accounting expenses may increase in proportion to increases in the number of customers served and inflation.

It should be noted that on line 4, water treatment chemicals, the expenditure for chemicals in projected year 1 is less than the amount in the historical year. This may be attributed to a change in treatment process or an abnormally high chemical cost incurred in the historical year because of the quality of the raw water. The large increases in projected year 3 for pumping purchased power (line 2), water treatment chemicals (line 4), other (line 5), and administrative and general employee benefits (line 15) are the result of an assumed major water treatment plant expansion coming on line and associated O&M expenses. Such adjustments in projecting O&M expenses are often necessary to present a valid depiction of future expenditures.

Table II.3-1 O&M expenses*

Line No.	O&M Expense Category	Historical Year	Projected Years				
			1	2	3	4	5
1	Source of Supply	$249,000	$258,000	$270,000	$279,000	$291,000	$303,000
	Pumping						
2	Purchased Power	684,000	729,000	777,000	1,125,000	1,197,000	1,275,000
3	Other	534,000	555,000	579,000	600,000	624,000	651,000
	Water Treatment						
4	Chemicals	378,000	348,000	363,000	606,000	633,000	663,000
5	Other	435,000	453,000	471,000	849,000	882,000	918,000
	Transmission & Distribution						
6	Storage	72,000	75,000	78,000	81,000	84,000	87,000
7	Transmission Mains	144,000	150,000	156,000	162,000	168,000	175,200
8	Distribution Mains	216,000	225,000	234,000	243,000	252,000	262,800
9	Meters & Services	429,000	447,000	465,000	483,000	501,000	522,000
10	Hydrants	36,000	36,000	39,000	39,000	42,000	45,000
11	Other	201,000	210,000	216,000	225,000	234,000	246,000
	Customer Accounting						
12	Meter Reading & Collection	672,000	705,000	741,000	777,000	816,000	858,000
13	Uncollectable Accounts	126,000	129,000	132,000	135,000	138,000	141,000
	Administrative & General						
14	Salaries	537,000	558,000	582,000	603,000	627,000	654,000
15	Employee Benefits	492,000	513,000	531,000	672,000	699,000	726,000
16	Insurance	324,000	390,000	405,000	423,000	438,000	456,000
17	Other	738,000	768,000	798,000	828,000	864,000	897,000
18	Total O&M Expense	$6,267,000	$6,549,000	$6,837,000	$8,130,000	$8,490,000	$8,880,000

*Information applies to both government-owned and investor-owned utilities.

This page intentionally blank.

Chapter **II.4**

Taxes

Investor-owned water utilities are responsible for paying taxes to local, state, and federal authorities. These taxes may include property and franchise taxes paid to local authorities; gross receipts, income, capital stock, and franchise taxes paid to state authorities; and income taxes and payroll taxes paid to the federal government. Although municipally owned water utilities are generally not subject to taxation by the local, state, or federal governments, municipal water utilities sometimes make payments in lieu of property taxes to the local municipalities that own them.

This manual makes no attempt to fully cover the subject of taxation for utilities. This chapter is intended to alert the reader to the complexities of utility taxes and the need for specific tax expertise in considering tax obligations when determining the utility's need for adequate revenues.

LOCAL TAXES

The most common form of local tax is the property tax, but franchise taxes may also be levied. A franchise tax may be a flat fee or based on the utility's gross or net revenues. Property taxes are based on the assessed value of utility property located within the jurisdiction of the taxing authority. Therefore, the water utility must maintain property records in a manner that enables the tax authority to determine the book value of utility plant investment (which is subject to taxation) within individual local taxing jurisdictions. Where multiple municipalities or taxing districts are involved, separate investment records must be maintained. Each local taxing authority will also have its own individual tax rates, making it complicated to calculate total property tax.

Although, municipally owned utilities are not normally subject to taxation by local, state, or federal authorities, they may be subject to local taxes for property that is owned outside the owning community (such as watershed land). In some cases, however, a municipal water utility may make payments in lieu of taxes to the municipality that owns the utility. Such payments may be calculated as though the utility is privately owned and subject to property or franchise taxes or may be established at some lesser amount. For municipal utilities regulated by a state regulatory commission, the amount and appropriateness of any payments in lieu of property taxes can be an issue in rate cases. Some commissions only allow payments for actual services received.

STATE TAXES

Various states use different methods of assessing taxes, such as gross receipts taxes, franchise taxes, capital stock taxes, and income taxes on investor-owned utilities. The gross receipts tax is usually a fixed percentage of all revenues with no allowance for deductions. Therefore, if the gross receipts tax is 1 percent of revenues and revenues are $10,000,000, the gross receipts tax would be 1 percent of $10,000,000, or $100,000. Any revenue increase, whether because of growth or a rate increase, will result in a higher overall tax payment.

Generally, state income taxes are levied on revenues net of expenses and are usually a fixed percentage of taxable income. However, some jurisdictions have graduated income tax rates. Deductions from revenues permitted in calculating state income taxes may be different from those allowed for federal income taxes. For example, accelerated depreciation used in calculating federal income taxes may not be permitted as deductions when calculating state income taxes. Because each jurisdiction has a different approach to income taxes, the utility must verify the particular rules of the jurisdiction where revenues are taxed for details on allowable deductions.

FEDERAL TAXES

Investor-owned utilities are responsible for paying federal income taxes to the federal government. Federal taxable income is calculated by deducting operation and maintenance (O&M) expenses, tax depreciation expense (which is usually calculated at a higher rate than regulatory depreciation expense), interest expense, various administrative expenses, and state and local taxes from revenues.

It should be noted that tax laws and regulations are subject to change. This manual does not attempt to discuss all current tax matters and only illustrates the issues addressed. However, it should be recognized that taxable income may differ from book income as a result of several items in addition to differences between tax and book depreciation. The following items are not intended to be all-inclusive or to provide tax advice but are presented to alert the user to some of the potential differences.

- The utility must add the estimated unbilled revenues due at the end of the tax year and subtract the estimated unbilled revenues for the previous year. The difference, whether positive or negative, is included in taxable revenues.

- Uniform capitalization rules require capitalization of construction-period interest, sales and use tax, payroll taxes on construction, and property taxes, thereby increasing the tax liability.

- Bad-debt expense must reflect actual uncollectibles for the tax year rather than reflecting the accrual made under the reserve method for determining bad-debt expense.

Tax Depreciation

Depreciation is permitted as a deduction from revenues for federal income tax purposes. There are several different tax depreciation methods that affect water utilities. These methods reflect accelerated rates of depreciation when compared to rates prescribed by regulatory commissions or book accounting purposes.

Asset depreciation range system. The class life asset depreciation range (CLADR or ADR) system is an elective system of depreciation for assets placed in service after 1970 and before 1981. This system classifies costs by industry and type of asset, and permits depreciable lives, which are up to 20 percent shorter than the tax guideline class life. The

ADR system permits significant increases in depreciation amounts to be recognized in computing taxes.

Accelerated cost recovery system. The accelerated cost recovery system (ACRS) is a mandatory system, with few exceptions, of tax depreciation for assets placed in service after Dec. 31, 1980, and before Jan. 1, 1987. Using ACRS, the cost of eligible depreciable property is recovered over a specified period depending on the class of property. In determining the recovery allowances, the statutory percentage is applied to the unadjusted basis of the property. A great proportion of water utility property may be written off over 15 years.

Modified accelerated cost recovery system. Effective Jan. 1, 1987, the Tax Reform Act of 1986 (TRA-86) modified the former ACRS (modified ACRS or MACRS) by prescribing depreciation methods for each MACRS class instead of providing statutory depreciation tables. Under MACRS, the method of depreciation was increased from 150 percent declining balance to 200 percent declining balance for property with 3-, 5-, 7-, and 10-year recovery periods. The 150 percent declining balance method still applies to property with 15- and 20-year recovery periods. Investment in office buildings and other nonresidential property is recovered over a period of 39 years using the straight-line depreciation methodology.

Investment Tax Credit

The TRA-86 repealed the investment tax credit (ITC) for all property placed in service after Dec. 31, 1985, and for all qualified progress expenditures made on or after Jan. 1, 1986. Therefore, the only ITC generated in years subsequent to 1985 is the ITC earned with respect to qualified ITC transitional property.

TAX ISSUES IN RATE CASES

Federal income taxes embedded in customer rates can be broken down into two parts: current taxes and the total provision. Current taxes refer to actual taxes payable and are calculated by applying the appropriate tax rate to taxable income. As previously discussed, taxable income is derived by deducting O&M expenses, tax depreciation, interest expense, and any other allowable deductions from revenues.

The total provision adjusts current tax for any tax deferrals reflected in the cost of service. Deferrals serve to normalize the utility's total income taxes to reflect differences in the treatment of items for book and regulatory purposes. Deferrals can be either positive or negative.

Deferred Taxes

Deferred taxes are tax liabilities from a current tax period that are postponed to a future tax period. Such liabilities normally result when expenses used to compute current taxable net income are different from expenses used to compute current book net income. However, over a sufficient time period, the totals of both deductions are the same. Differences result when tax laws treat expenses differently than either rate-making or generally accepted accounting principles. A timing difference then results in the reporting and recording of taxes for an accounting period.

For rate-making purposes, most utility commissions now recognize a level of taxes in the revenue requirement that does not fluctuate with variations between the level of tax deductions and the corresponding level of book expenses occurring in a particular test year. Rather, most commissions spread tax deductions over the average service life of a unit of property. Such rate-making treatment is now required if a taxpayer wants to use the ACRS or MACRS tax depreciation. This type of rate-making treatment produces cash flow for a water utility, because taxes are reflected in the rate-making revenue requirement that are greater than those taxes owed the federal government. A positive cash flow exists as long as the taxes that are deferred exceed the sum of the amortizations of all the deferred taxes from prior years' transactions.

Although such timing differences can result from many variances between tax and book expenses, it is a common practice to record only significant tax-timing differences or those changes that present the greatest potential liability. The most significant and most commonly discussed tax-timing difference, which occurs on an annual and recurring basis, is the change that results from using accelerated depreciation for tax purposes and straight-line depreciation for book purposes. Table II.4-1 shows an example of this process using ACRS and the 34 percent tax rate that applies to companies with less than $10 million of taxable income. Another common timing difference results when large maintenance expenses, such as tank painting, must be claimed as tax deductions in the year the expense is incurred, but the expense is amortized over several years for book and rate-making purposes. Similar examples include premature retirement of plant facilities or other accounting treatments for extraordinary expenses.

Normalization Process

For rate-making purposes, deferred taxes are accounted for by a process called normalization. When tax normalization is used, the difference between rate-making taxes and actual tax expense due to the excess of tax or book depreciation (or other book-tax timing differences) is recorded as accumulated deferred income taxes. The balance of accumulated deferred income taxes is then deducted from the rate base on which an investor-owned utility is allowed to earn a return.

Using normalization stabilizes revenue requirements to reflect the spreading of any tax benefits associated with using accelerated tax depreciation rates over the life of the applicable property. This allows all customers who use the property to share the tax benefits. If normalization is not used, revenue requirements would be lower in the early years of an asset's life. This is because tax depreciation rates are greater than straight-line book depreciation rates, which creates a lower taxable income for that accounting period. Revenue requirements would then be higher in the later years of the property's life, when the situation is reversed.

Flow Through

Until ACRS rates for tax depreciation became effective for property installed after 1980, state commissions either normalized the effects of tax depreciation (as previously discussed) or immediately passed on to ratepayers the effects of the tax reductions that resulted from using accelerated depreciation. If the tax benefits were immediately passed on to ratepayers, the practice was known as flow through. Flow-through rate-making occurs when the higher tax depreciation amounts, which occur in the early life of property additions, are used to compute tax liabilities for rate-making purposes. In later years, when such tax deductions become less than book depreciation amounts, tax liabilities and revenue requirements need to be greater to support the same level of utility plant.

One of the arguments raised to support flow-through treatment is that as time goes on there will be further plant additions and other large tax depreciation amounts to deduct for rate-making purposes. Also, in a viable growing utility, one tax deduction for a new plant will offset the loss of a deduction for an older plant. Thus, all ratepayers will share tax benefits, even though those tax benefits may not coincide with the property in place to serve those particular customers.

Current law mandates that normalization be authorized for rate-making purposes for plants installed after 1980 in order for a taxpayer to claim ACRS and MACRS rates

Table II.4-1 Tax versus book depreciation

Year (1)*	Depreciation Expense		Excess Tax Depreciation, $ (4) = (2) − (3)	Deferred Taxes, $ (5) = (3) × 34%	Accumulated Deferred Taxes, $
	Tax, $ (2)	Book, $ (3)			
1	50,000	20,000	30,000	10,200	10,200
2	100,000	40,000	60,000	20,400	30,600
3	90,000	40,000	50,000	17,000	47,600
4	80,000	40,000	40,000	13,600	61,200
5	70,000	40,000	30,000	10,200	71,400
6	70,000	40,000	30,000	10,200	81,600
7	60,000	40,000	20,000	6,800	88,400
8	60,000	40,000	20,000	6,800	95,200
9	60,000	40,000	20,000	6,800	102,000
10	60,000	40,000	20,000	6,800	108,800
11	60,000	40,000	20,000	6,800	115,600
12	60,000	40,000	20,000	6,800	122,400
13	60,000	40,000	20,000	6,800	129,200
14	60,000	40,000	20,000	6,800	136,000
15	60,000	40,000	20,000	6,800	142,800
16	0	40,000	(40,000)†	(13,600)	129,200
17	0	40,000	(40,000)	(13,600)	115,600
18	0	40,000	(40,000)	(13,600)	102,000
19	0	40,000	(40,000)	(13,600)	88,400
20	0	40,000	(40,000)	(13,600)	74,800
21	0	40,000	(40,000)	(13,600)	61,200
22	0	40,000	(40,000)	(13,600)	47,600
23	0	40,000	(40,000)	(13,600)	34,000
24	0	40,000	(40,000)	(13,600)	20,400
25	0	40,000	(40,000)	(13,600)	6,800
26	0	20,000	(20,000)	(6,800)	0
Total	1,000,000	1,000,000	0	0	

NOTES:
   Basis: $1,000,000
   Tax life: 15 years, 150% declining balance
   Book life: 25 years, straight line
*Numbers in parentheses represent the column numbers.
†Numbers in parentheses represent negative numbers or credits.

when computing the tax depreciation deduction. However, the law permits flow-through rate-making for other tax benefits.

Interest Synchronization

Most state commissions calculate the level of interest to be used in determining taxable net income for rate-making purposes using a method called interest synchronization. This methodology is based on the premise that, for rate-making purposes, the revenue requirements reflect the recovery of a certain level of interest expense. It is this interest expense that should be used as the tax deduction rather than the interest expense the company actually incurs. In other words, the level of interest expense that the customers are required to pay is the level of interest expense that should be used as a deduction from revenues before calculating the tax liability customers are required to pay.

Synchronized interest expense will differ from interest expense reflected in the records when

1. the appropriate rate base for establishing revenue requirements differs from the total amount of debt and equity used to determine the cost of capital,
2. an imputed or theoretical capital structure is substituted for the actual capital structure, or
3. interest rates are adjusted for issuance expenses or other items.

Consolidated Tax Returns

Current tax law permits a taxpaying corporation with several different affiliated corporate identities to file a consolidated tax return. A consolidated tax return is advantageous if one or more of the participating corporations incurs a loss in the tax-accounting period.

Consolidated tax returns raise several issues, including how to allocate consolidated income tax liability and the regulatory treatment accorded to the so-called tax savings when the pool of taxpayers operates in multiple jurisdictions.

The water utility has several options for handling the tax benefit. The first option is to reimburse the company sustaining the taxable loss for the "negative tax" it contributed to the pool. In effect, this option leaves the companies with taxable income in an unchanged tax position and provides the loss-sustaining company with cash. Another approach is to reallocate taxes to the group that has taxable income.

This brings up the second issue regarding interjurisdictional allocation of tax benefits. What is the appropriate regulatory treatment of a regulated operating company participating in the consolidated tax return? The question is whether or not to reimburse the loss-sustaining companies for their "negative income tax" contributed to the consolidation if a regulatory commission in another state jurisdiction adopts a portion of that benefit for the ratepayers of its own state. Most state commissions do not impute an effective tax rate under this scenario. However, some state commissions do.

Inclusion of Taxes Within the Revenue Requirements and Rates

In developing a utility's revenue requirements, care needs to be taken in understanding how and where the taxes are included on the customer's bill. Simply stated, when the tax is included as a part of the rate charged to customers, the revenue requirements should include those taxes. If the utility bills the tax on the customer's bill after the "rate portion" of the bill has been determined, the revenue requirements should exclude those taxes to avoid double-charging of the taxes (once in the revenue requirement and rate design, and then again on the customer's bill as a separate and calculated line item). Alternatively, a utility may separately calculate the tax on a customer's bill and include the payment of the tax in determining the revenue requirements to be recovered through rates. If this is done, the utility should also include a corresponding tax revenue offset to make the entire transaction equal from a revenue and tax expense perspective.

Chapter **II.5**

Capital-Related Costs

Under both the cash-needs approach and the utility-basis approach to determining revenue requirements for a water utility, there are capital infrastructure-related costs to be met in addition to the operation and maintenance (O&M) expenses.

For utilities using the cash-needs approach, capital-related costs include debt-service payments (both principal and interest) on existing and proposed future debt, contributions to specific reserves, and the cost of capital expenditures that are not debt financed or contributed. Required debt-service coverage may also affect total revenue needs. Depreciation expense is not included as an element of capital cost in the cash-needs approach.

For utilities using the utility-basis approach, the capital-related costs include depreciation expense and return on rate base. The return on rate base provides for payment of interest on debt and a return on the equity provided by investors. Many of the factors that are related to the utility-basis approach apply to investor-owned utilities, regulated government-owned utilities, and nonregulated governmental utilities that serve customers outside of the city and/or wholesale customers.

CASH-NEEDS APPROACH

Utilities that determine revenue requirements using the cash-needs approach do so in conjunction with the annual budgetary process. This is the case whether the utility operates as a part of a general municipal government or as a separate enterprise. The budget sets out the use of funds to pay for capital-related costs, such as principal and interest payments on debt, contributions to specific reserves, and the portion of capital replacement and improvements that is cash funded. Under this approach, revenue requirements do not include depreciation expense or a return on rate base. However, they are often subject to fiscal covenants and targets, such as minimum financial ratios. Projections of revenue requirements should recognize receipts of contributions from developers or customers, government grants, and other nonutility sources that may offset capital needs.

It is common practice for utilities to finance a portion of its capital improvement program from annual revenues (sometimes referred to as pay-as-you-go, or PAYGO, capital funding). Often, normal annual replacements, extensions, and improvements (such as meters, services, vehicles, smaller mains, and similar items that occur on a regular basis each year) are funded in this way. Also, utilities may use current revenue to fund a portion of major capital replacements and improvements. However, major capital projects are typically debt financed, because the repayment of the debt over several years reduces fluctuations in annual revenue requirements, diminishes spikes in rates, and more closely matches capital costs to the useful life of the facility. Thus, if capital projects are financed with long-term debt, existing customers will not be required to pay 100 percent of the initial cost of facilities to be used by future customers. Compliance with debt-service coverage covenants may provide for cash funding of a portion of the annual capital improvement needs.

Debt-Service Component

The debt-service component of the cash-needs revenue requirement includes principal and interest payments associated with bonds, loans, and other debt instruments. It may also include debt-service reserve requirements as established by the bond indenture authorizing the debt. Other reserves may be required to provide for emergencies, unexpected major repairs and replacements, and routine replacements and extensions, but these are often not included in the debt-service component of the revenue requirement.

In the example financial projection for the government-owned utility presented in this manual (see Tables II.6-1, II.6-2, and II.6-3), the annual revenue requirement in any given year for normal annual replacements, extensions, and improvements is assumed to be approximately 2 percent of the prior year's gross plant investment, which in projected year 1 amounts to $1,118,400 (Table II.5-1, line 21 of the historical year times 2 percent).* In addition to paying for such normal annual improvements from system revenues, it is assumed (for purposes of the example) that the debt-service reserve associated with a new bond issue to finance the treatment plant improvements will be equal to one year's debt service, and this reserve requirement will be funded from annual revenues over a five-year period. Another possible option for funding the debt-service reserve would be with proceeds from the bond issue. For an assumed bond issue amount of $9,000,000, the annual debt-service payment is assumed to be $900,000 (or approximately a 6.5 percent interest rate amortized equally over 20 years), and therefore, the total debt-service reserve requirement amounts to $900,000 in the example. The annual debt-service reserve funding requirement would amount to $180,000 each year over the five-year funding period. It is assumed that the bonds are issued in the middle of projection year 1, with one-half year's debt-service reserve payment incurred in that year. Therefore, the annual debt service associated with the existing revenue bonds amounts to $1,680,000. The debt service on the proposed new $9,000,000 bond issue is assumed to be $900,000 annually over a 20-year period, with one-half year's debt-service payment accrued in projected year 1. Thus, the total debt service for the example utility in projected year 1 amounts to $2,130,000.

Many utilities are required by the rate covenants of their debt indenture to generate net revenues in excess of annual debt service, particularly if revenue bonds are used. Debt-service coverage requirements vary, but they typically specify that net revenues, after meeting O&M expenses, must exceed the annual debt-service payments by a stated percentage, generally in the range of 25 to 50 percent. A coverage requirement of 50 percent has been used for the example utility; the coverage requirement may be stated as a percentage (150 percent) or a ratio (1.50 times) as applied to the annual debt-service payment in a given year. Debt-service coverage requirements are a test of the adequacy of

---

* The use of a percentage of gross plant is one approach that may be used to determine an appropriate level of normal annual replacements. In this example, the use of 2 percent assumes an overall weighted average of a 50-year useful life for the system assets. A formal asset management program provides the best financial and planning tool for determining the needed level of normal annual replacement funding.

Table II.5-1 Total (gross) plant in service—Year end*

Line No.	Plant Account	Historical Year	Projected Years 1	2	3	4	5
	Intangible						
1	Organization	$18,000	$18,000	$18,000	$18,000	$18,000	$18,000
	Source of Supply						
2	Land	1,269,000	1,269,000	1,269,000	1,269,000	1,269,000	1,269,000
3	Reservoir	1,647,000	1,647,000	1,872,000	1,872,000	1,947,000	1,947,000
	Pumping						
4	Land	69,000	69,000	69,000	69,000	69,000	69,000
5	Structures	1,521,000	1,521,000	1,521,000	1,521,000	1,746,000	1,746,000
6	Electrical Pumping Equipment	1,590,000	1,620,000	1,680,000	1,680,000	1,725,000	1,785,000
7	Other Pumping Equipment	672,000	672,000	672,000	717,000	717,000	777,000
	Water Treatment						
8	Structures	702,000	702,000	1,752,000	1,752,000	1,752,000	1,827,000
9	Water Treatment Plant	5,148,000	5,343,000	13,293,000	13,368,000	13,488,000	13,578,000
	Transmission & Distribution						
10	Land	105,000	105,000	105,000	105,000	105,000	105,000
11	Structures	195,000	195,000	195,000	195,000	195,000	195,000
12	Distribution Storage	4,437,000	4,437,000	4,527,000	4,572,000	4,572,000	4,587,000
13	Transmission Mains	9,734,000	10,004,400	10,226,400	10,466,400	10,676,400	10,934,400
14	Distribution Mains	14,602,000	15,006,600	15,339,600	15,699,600	16,014,600	16,401,600
15	Services	7,506,000	7,641,000	7,761,000	7,866,000	7,926,000	8,016,000
16	Meters	3,309,000	3,369,000	3,414,000	3,444,000	3,519,000	3,564,000
17	Hydrants	1,899,000	1,929,000	1,944,000	1,974,000	2,019,000	2,049,000
	General						
18	Land	12,000	12,000	12,000	12,000	12,000	12,000
19	Structures	753,000	753,000	783,000	873,000	873,000	873,000
20	Other Pumping Equipment	732,000	732,000	732,000	867,000	867,000	942,000
21	Total Plant in Service	$55,920,000	$57,045,000	$67,185,000	$68,340,000	$69,510,000	$70,695,000

*Information applies to both government-owned and investor-owned utilities.

utility revenues to repay outstanding debt and do not necessarily represent a specific cash requirement or funding obligation, unless the requirement becomes the controlling factor in terms of revenue needs in a particular year. The debt-service coverage requirements are a legal (contractual) requirement and are intended to provide a measure of security for bondholders and must be considered in determining the total annual revenue needed. Amounts collected to meet the coverage requirements are typically used to cash-fund capital projects, or add to financial reserves and/or cash balances, depending on the requirements of the bond indenture and the utility's cash management objectives.

Financing Constraints

Financing constraints may limit the amount or type of capital financing available to a utility and may be set forth in the local government's ordinance or charter. These limits may include debt caps or debt-to-equity-ratio minimums.

The capital financing plan and resulting annual revenue requirements will be affected by the financial constraints if any of the stipulated ratios or coverages have not been met. For example, assume a utility with a bond covenant requiring a debt-service coverage ratio of 1.25× or 125 percent has financial requirements as follows:

Annual Operations:		
1.	Gross Revenue	$9,777,000
2.	Less: O&M Expenses and Taxes	6,549,000
3.	Net Revenue Available for Debt Service	$3,228,000
4.	Less: Annual Debt Service	2,130,000
5.	Net Available	$1,098,000
6.	Plus: Nonoperating Income	150,000
7.	Balance Available for Capital Projects	$1,248,000
Capital Project Financing:		
1.	Current Capital Project Costs	$10,125,000
2.	Available From Annual Operations	1,248,000
3.	Borrowings	9,000,000
4.	Total Available for Capital Costs	$10,248,0000

The annual debt-service coverage for this example utility would be measured as net revenue available for debt service divided by annual debt service, or $3,228,000 ÷ $2,130,000 = 1.52. This meets the minimum 1.25 debt-service coverage requirement established in the bond covenant. In the financial planning process, it is generally common practice to establish a projected debt-service coverage target or goal at a greater level than the required minimum coverage level. This conservative planning provides for some variance in either revenues (being lower than projected) or expenses (being higher than projected) and helps to provide more certainty that the minimum debt-service coverage level will be met.

In the previous example, if the a debt-service coverage target was set at 1.75 for financial planning purposes, gross revenue would need to be adjusted upward (e.g., a revenue/rate increase) by $500,000 (the difference between the required dollar amount of coverage at 1.75× and the actual net revenue available for debt service ([$2,130,000 × 1.75] – $3,228,000 = $500,000) to a total of $10,277,000 ($9,777,000 + $500,000). Under these conditions, the utility could use the additional revenues to cash-fund (PAYGO) more capital investment and reduce the amount of debt borrowing.

In summary, for utilities using the cash-needs approach, the revenue requirements include O&M expense, debt service, and the cash needs associated with the portion of capital costs funded on a PAYGO basis. In addition, the financial constraints that apply to a specific utility may affect the proportion and amount of the revenue sources and/or the allowable revenue requirement.

UTILITY-BASIS APPROACH

Under the utility-basis approach to determining revenue requirements, the revenue requirements include O&M expense, depreciation expense, and a return on rate base. The depreciation expense and return on rate base portions of the revenue requirement are intended to provide for the recovery of and return on the utility's invested capital in providing service. The capital cost components of the revenue requirement are discussed in the following sections.

Depreciation Expense

Depreciation is the loss-in-service value not restored by current maintenance and is incurred in connection with the consumption or prospective retirement of the plant in the course of service.

Utilities that use the utility-basis approach include depreciation of tangible property (that is used and useful) in the revenue requirements as a means to recover capital invested in the utility system over time. Depreciation expense allows for the systematic amortization and recovery of the original cost of the investment to place an asset in service, less the estimated net-salvage value, over the estimated average service life of that asset. Depreciation expense is typically recovered on a straight-line basis, that is, on an equal annual basis over the average service life of the asset. The straight-line approach is intended to assess this cost of doing business equally each year to customers who benefit from the use of the asset during its entire life.

Although the concept of depreciation is simple, considerable statistical work may be required to determine the average service life to be used in establishing depreciation rates. A detailed explanation of statistical studies is beyond the scope of this manual, but readers can obtain an explanation from literature on the subject.

Using the straight-line depreciation method, the annual depreciation cost is determined as follows:

$$\text{Annual Cost (\$)} = \frac{(\text{Total Asset Value} - \text{Net Salvage Value})}{\text{Estimated Service Life}}$$

where net salvage equals salvage realized less the cost of removal.

The summary of such calculations for each depreciable plant account, when applied to the original cost of the account item, results in the total depreciation expense for the year. Some utilities use a composite rate that applies to all depreciable plant assets. Another method sometimes used for computing annual depreciation expense is the remaining-life method wherein the unrecovered balance in the account less net salvage is recovered over the average remaining service life.

The handling of the depreciation expense associated with contributed assets is an issue that can arise using the utility-basis approach. The inclusion or exclusion of depreciation expenses on contributed assets by a regulatory commission is primarily driven by the regulatory commission's viewpoint of the role of depreciation expense in the rate-making process. The decision to include the depreciation expense may also be driven by the entity contributing the assets (ratepayers, developers, other governmental agencies).

Rate Base (Plant Investment)

Rate base is the value of property on which a public utility is allowed to earn a specific rate of return, in accordance with the rules set by a regulatory agency or contractual agreement. In general, rate base consists of the value of the property as used by the utility to provide service and typically consists primarily of plant in service less accumulated depreciation; plus construction work in progress (CWIP) or an allowance for funds used during construction (AFUDC), inventory, and working capital; less contributed capital (CIAC, or contributions in aid of construction), customer advances, and deferred taxes. Determining the rate base, or net plant investment, to which the rate of return should be applied (i.e., the rate base) involves several considerations. Individual regulatory agencies have specific requirements concerning the items allowed in the rate base. Considerations related to plant in service include the use of historical costs or current value and the *used and useful* standard, which is described below.

There are varying viewpoints regarding the inclusion of CWIP in the rate base. CWIP is, by definition, not used and useful. However, there may be specific situations or conditions that may warrant inclusion of CWIP in the rate base. Including CWIP in the rate base is subject to considerations such as the allowance of interest during construction, estimated date in service, the nature of the construction, and the materiality of the expenditure.

Determining working capital needs requires estimates (sometimes in total or in great detail) of the lag between paying expenses and receiving revenue. This determination is sometimes simplified by using a typical working capital amount, such as one-eighth (45 days) to one quarter (90 days) of O&M expenses as a reasonable surrogate for a more formal lead-lag study.

Deferred-tax determinations are affected by changing corporate federal income tax rates.

The determination and valuation of rate-base components and associated issues have been addressed in numerous commission and court cases. Thus, determining the rate base requires knowledge of applicable legal precedents and practices in the utility's regulatory jurisdiction.

More detailed discussions of the various components of rate base are provided in the following sections. The discussions do not attempt to enumerate the various rules of practice used by individual commissions to establish a rate base; instead, the sections review those principles and practices that are generally accepted by many courts and commissions.

Plant in service. In accordance with most, if not all, accounting systems, the original cost of plant in service is recorded on the utility's books. The original cost may be different from the price the current owner paid for the property, but it is the cost of the plant when it was first dedicated to public service. Any difference between the price paid by the current owner and the original cost is classified as an acquisition adjustment, which may or may not be included in the rate base. Nearly all regulatory commissions use an original cost basis for valuing plant in service to be included in the rate base.

The primary issue related to including the plant in the rate base is whether the plant is used and useful in providing utility service. The used-and-useful standard implies that the facility is built and provides service to customers but also includes an examination of the utility's prudence in deciding to construct or purchase the plant (e.g., excess capacity). The original cost of a used-and-useful plant, prudently constructed or purchased, is typically the largest element of the rate base.

Accumulated depreciation. The deduction of accumulated depreciation from the original cost of plant results in the net book value of plant available to serve current and future customers. From the viewpoint of depreciation as capital recovery, accrued depreciation represents the accumulation of the return of capital to the utility. The accumulated provision for depreciation (also called the book depreciation reserve) is available from the books and records of the utility.

Past depreciation practices, especially the methods used to calculate annual depreciation, should be reviewed for consistency with regulatory practice before the book reserve is used. Also, the basis for recording large acquisitions should be reviewed for consistency. Adjustments should be made if appropriate.

Construction work in progress. Where it is permitted, the inclusion of CWIP in the rate base recognizes the utility's capital investment in infrastructure currently being constructed. Although the plant is not yet used and useful in providing service, it is expected to be in the near future and, therefore, may be considered a benefit or potential benefit to the current ratepayer. Regulators often require work to be completed within a specified time period, evidence that funds were borrowed to finance the construction, and proof of improved quality of service before CWIP can be included in the rate base. The most conservative rate-making perspective regarding CWIP is to exclude it from the rate base. However, specific and unique circumstances may provide a rational basis for inclusion of CWIP in the rate base.

The inclusion of CWIP in the rate base raises equity questions, especially for long-term construction projects that will not be placed in service in the near term. Should current ratepayers provide a return on plant that does not provide service to them? Questions such as this one, in addition to considerable customer dissatisfaction associated with the inclusion of CWIP in the rate base (especially in the electric industry), have resulted in some state laws being passed that prevent or severely restrict the inclusion of CWIP in the rate base. Even where not prohibited by law, many regulatory commissions limit the inclusion of CWIP in the rate base to circumstances where the utility can demonstrate financial need.

An alternative to including CWIP in the rate base is capitalization of financing costs related to the project as part of the original cost of plant. For lengthy construction projects, interest during construction or an AFUDC can become a substantial amount. This amount will increase the rate base and depreciation base throughout the life of the facility. The capitalization of financing costs may cause cash-flow problems for the utility until the project is completed and entered onto the books.

Working capital. The primary elements of working capital include materials and supplies, and cash working capital. Other elements may include prepayments, unamortized balance of non-annual O&M expenses, and a minimum bank balance.

The allowance for materials and supplies in the rate base permits the utility to earn a return on the prudent investment in inventory of parts and supplies required to maintain service. A common method of determining the materials and supplies allowance is a 13-month average of the balance as recorded on the books.

The allowance for cash working capital in the rate base permits the utility to earn a return on the capital required to fund operating costs in advance of the receipt of revenue. Normally, there is a lag between the payment of costs and the receipt of revenues. However, depending on the frequency of billing and other factors, the utility may receive revenue in advance of having to pay expenses. A detailed lead-lag study can be performed to determine a weighted average period of time between cost and revenue. The working capital requirement is the average daily amount of costs times the average days between the receipt of revenue and the payment of expenses determined by the lead-lag study. For smaller utilities, the one-eighth-of-O&M method is frequently used. This method simply takes one-eighth (45 days) of the level of O&M expenses to estimate the needed level of working capital.

Contributions and advances. CIAC (i.e., capital or plant supplied by customers, developers, or public authorities) are excluded from the rate base. In many systems of accounts, nonrefundable contributions are credited against the utility plant in service, and all subsequent rate-base determinations use the amount of plant net of the contributed plant. Customer advances are also normally deducted from the rate base until they are refunded. Un-refunded advances are transferred to contributions where they continue to be deducted from the rate base.

Other non-investor capital. Deductions from the rate base for accumulated investment tax credits, where applicable, and deferred taxes represent the elimination of capital provided by ratepayers to pay taxes that are either forgiven or delayed to a later date by the government as an incentive to modernize plant facilities. The accumulation of deferred taxes results from the annual differences between normalized income taxes, which are based on depreciation expense consistent with the rate-making allowance, and income taxes based on depreciation expense consistent with the methods and class lives prescribed by the Internal Revenue Service. To the extent unamortized investment tax credits exist, normal practice is to deduct the amortization from income tax expense.

Other rate-base adjustments. The previous discussion of the components of rate base is not all-inclusive. Items such as unamortized acquisition adjustments, prepayments, and minimum bank balances are sometimes recognized. Other possible rate-base components, such as the unamortized balance of an extraordinary expense, are not discussed but may deserve consideration.

Table II.5-1 shows the total gross plant in service for the example utility at of the end of the most recent historical year and the projected year-end balances for each year in the five-year study period. The projected additions to total plant in service recognize the capital improvement program of the utility and include both major bond-financed improvements and normal annual additions financed from system revenues and CIAC. The major $9,000,000 water treatment plant addition is included in projected year 2 of Table II.5-1.* Other additions recognize the total additions financed from annual revenues and net of allowances for anticipated retirements. The total plant in service provides the largest element of the rate base as previously indicated in this chapter.

Table II.5-2 (line 1) uses the total plant in service from Table II.5-1 (line 21) to determine the annual rate base for both a government-owned and an investor-owned utility. Although there are potentially many differences in rate base between the two types of utilities, in the development of rate base for example purposes, the major difference is the deduction of accumulated deferred income taxes for the investor-owned utility. The deductions of accumulated depreciation (line 2), CIAC (line 7), and customer advances for construction (line 8), and the additions of materials and supplies (line 4), cash working capital (line 5), and CWIP (line 6) to utility plant in service are generally similar for both government-owned and investor-owned utilities in determining the rate base. Although future projections of annual rate base may not be a general practice for investor-owned utilities, it provides a useful planning function in evaluating the adequacy of revenues under existing rates and the potential need for future rate adjustments, which will be discussed in chapter II.6.

It should be noted that including CWIP in the rate base, as shown in this example, is not accepted by all jurisdictions. Some jurisdictions specifically prohibit such inclusion for investor-owned utilities. In other jurisdictions, regulatory commissions, by practice, exclude CWIP from rate base because it requires current customers to pay a return on plant intended to benefit future customers.

RATE OF RETURN

In general in a competitive market environment, the need to earn income as a source of, and a return on, capital provides business with the incentive to increase sales and revenues, if adequate capacity exists, and to minimize costs. Participants' ability to compete for this income determines how these resources are allocated to these participants. Those economic activities demonstrating the greatest expected income relative to the perceived risks will generally attract the available resources.

In a competitive economy, risks and income vary over time as some industries or companies become more, or less, profitable. These changes in actual results and expected future performance cause resources to shift among industries and companies. This competitive market structure generally provides an efficient allocation of resources.

---

* This addition is included in the Structures (line 8) and Water Treatment Plant (line 9) categories.

Table II.5-2 Test-year rate base (in $1,000)

Line No.	Rate Base Component	Projected Years				
		1	2	3	4	5
1	Utility Plant in Service	$57,045	$67,185	$68,340	$69,510	$70,695
2	Less: Accumulated Depreciation	(15,090)	(16,332)	(17,688)	(19,068)	(20,469)
3	Net Plant in Service	41,955	50,853	50,652	50,442	50,226
	Plus:					
4	Materials and Supplies	840	873	909	945	984
5	Cash Working Capital	819	855	1,017	1,062	1,110
6	Construction Work in Progress	3,300	312	324	336	348
	Less:					
7	Contributions in Aid of Construction	(2,850)	(3,000)	(3,150)	(3,300)	(3,450)
8	Customer Advances for Construction	(1,230)	(1,335)	(1,440)	(1,545)	(1,650)
9	Test-Year Rate Base (Government-Owned)	42,834	48,558	48,312	47,940	47,568
10	Less: Accumulated Deferred Income Taxes	(5,856)	(7,098)	(7,071)	(7,041)	(7,011)
11	Test-Year Rate Base (Investor-Owned)	$36,978	$41,460	$41,241	$40,899	$40,557

General Principles

Whether the utility is government owned or investor owned, the return component is intended to recover the annual interest cost of debt capital and provide a "fair" rate of return for the equity capital employed to finance facilities used to provide water service. The return to the equity owner should be commensurate with the return in other enterprises competing for equity capital and having comparable risks. The return should be adequate to enable the utility to maintain its credit and to attract new capital. Further details on risk factors may be found in section VI.

CAPITAL STRUCTURE

For a utility to compete successfully in the capital markets, courts and regulatory commissions have determined that it should be allowed a return based on its cost of capital. The cost of capital represents the weighted cost of the various classes of capital (generally debt and common stock) used by the water utility. The following example reflects how the total cost of capital for a utility is determined. The resulting 8 percent weighted cost of capital is used to determine the required level of revenue for the investor-owned utility discussed in chapter II.6.

Component	Total Cost	Percentage of Total	Component Cost Rate, %	Weighted Cost, %
Long-Term Debt	$20,000,000	50.0	6.0	3.0
Common Equity	20,000,000	50.0	10.0	5.0
Total Cost of Capital	$40,000,000	100.0		8.0

Mathematically, the weighted cost of capital analysis is quite simple, but numerous issues can affect the total rate of return. The actual capital structure of the utility is most often used to determine the proportions (weighting) of the debt and equity components. However, the relative components (capital structure) of debt and equity can change over time. Sometimes the actual capital structure of a water utility may have excessive amounts of debt or equity. In such cases, an alternative capital structure is used to determine a fair rate of return. If the water utility is a subsidiary of another company (holding company), the parent company's capital structure may be deemed to provide the appropriate weighting of the costs of capital. In other situations, regulatory agencies have imputed a hypothetical capital structure based on an examination of similar companies or industries.

Based on the previous example, if the amount of common equity in the capital structure is reduced, the total rate of return is reduced. However, if the amount of debt is increased, the water utility's debt-interest requirements are increased, creating additional financial risk for the utility. If the additional financial risks increase, the relative costs of capital could actually increase. Also, bond indenture coverage requirements may limit the amount of debt capital. Good financial management practice results in a balance between debt and equity capital that minimizes the total cost of capital.

Cost Rates for Capital Components

Determination of the cost of long-term debt is usually based on the actual cost of any debt capital outstanding or to be issued in the near future. Occasionally, the cost of recent debt issues of similar companies is used to indicate investors' expectations regarding debt costs, especially in the case of proposed issues. In addition to the interest rate stated on the bond, other costs, such as premiums and discounts, should be considered in determining the cost of debt.

The most difficult issue in determining the cost of capital relates to the cost of common equity. Unlike debt, there is no fixed interest rate. The issue is how to determine a return on equity capital sufficiently high to enable the utility to maintain its credit and to attract capital but not so high as to be excessive.

Many factors motivate potential investors to purchase a given stock. These factors include dividends paid, earnings, current book value, growth in book value, and stock appreciation. Analysts may not agree on the relative role of past, current, and expected earnings, dividends, and prices, and they may also disagree over what time periods should be used to compute earnings, dividends, and prices. As such, there is no single method for determining a fair or reasonable rate of return. However, there are two landmark cases that established the principles commonly relied on for determining a fair rate of return for regulated utilities. The first such case is the *Bluefield Water Works* case decided by the US Supreme Court in 1923. In its decision in this case, the Court stated the following:

> The return should be reasonable, sufficient to assure confidence in the financial soundness of the utility and should be adequate, under efficient and economical management, to maintain and support its credit and enable it to raise the money necessary for the proper discharge of its public duties. (*Bluefield Water Works and Improvement Co. v. Public Service Commission of West Virginia*, 262 US 679 (1923).)

The principles were further addressed by the US Supreme Court in the *Hope Natural Gas* case. There, the Court elaborated on the reasonableness issue by stating the following:

> It is important that there be enough revenue not only for operating expenses but also for the capital costs of the business. These include service on the debt

and dividends on the stock. (*Federal Power Commission v. Hope Natural Gas Co.*, 320 US 391 (1944).)

The most common method for determining the return on equity for regulated investor-owned utilities is the discounted cash-flow (DCF) method. Other methods, such as the capital asset pricing model (CAPM), are sometimes used as a check on the results of the DCF method. Chapter VI.1, "Overview of Outside Customer Rates," presents approaches that should be considered for municipally owned utilities.

In summary, for utilities using the utility-basis approach, the revenue requirements include O&M expense, annual depreciation expense, and a return on rate base. The annual depreciation expense component allows the utility to recover its original capital investment (a return of capital), and the return on rate base provides the opportunity for the utility to earn a reasonable rate of return on invested capital. The return should be adequate to enable the utility to maintain its credit and to attract new capital.

This page intentionally blank.

Examples of Revenue Requirements

The previous chapters have described the various elements that comprise the revenues and revenue requirements of government-owned and investor-owned utilities. They have also covered some of the considerations involved in projecting these elements for a future study period. This information will now be used to consolidate the various projections into a flow-of-funds schedule for the government-owned utility and an operating income statement for the investor-owned utility. These schedules can then be used to measure the adequacy of revenues under existing rates to meet projected revenue requirements over the study period.

GOVERNMENT-OWNED UTILITIES

For government-owned utilities, the initial measure of whether revenues under existing rates are adequate is made to determine whether such revenues are sufficient to meet the utility's cash requirements over the study period. Table II.6-1 shows a flow of funds under existing rates for the government-owned utility. Operating revenue (lines 1, 2, and 3) and nonoperating revenue (line 10) were developed previously in Table II.2-3, while O&M expenses (line 4) were projected in Table II.3-1. The revenue requirement for total debt service (lines 7, 8, and 9) and other obligations (lines 11, 12, and 13) were discussed in chapter II.5.

Line 14 of Table II.6-1 shows that the revenues under existing rates for the government-owned utility are just adequate to meet projected revenue requirements in projected year 1 (and achieve the required debt-service coverage ratio of 1.50×). However, beginning in projected year 2, annual revenue requirements exceed annual revenues by increasing amounts each year. The percent deficiencies in annual water service revenue are indicated on line 17. Lines 19, 20, and 21 of Table II.6-1 show the cumulative water service revenue under existing rates, cumulative net balance, and cumulative percent deficiency beginning with projected year 2. The cumulative percent deficiency indicates the overall percentage increase in revenues that must be implemented at the beginning of projected

Table II.6-1 Flow of funds—Existing rates* (in $1,000)

Line No.	Item	Projected Years				
		1	2	3	4	5
	Operating Revenues					
1	Water Service	$9,702	$9,765	$9,825	$9,885	$9,948
2	Other Operating Revenue	75	78	81	84	87
3	Total Operating Revenue	9,777	9,843	9,906	9,969	10,035
4	O&M Expense	(6,549)	(6,837)	(8,130)	(8,490)	(8,880)
5	Taxes Other Than Income					
6	Net Operating Revenue	3,228	3,006	1,776	1,479	1,155
	Debt Service					
7	Outstanding Bonds	(1,680)	(1,680)	(1,680)	(1,680)	(1,680)
8	Proposed Bonds	(450)	(900)	(900)	(900)	(900)
9	Total Debt Service	(2,130)	(2,580)	(2,580)	(2,580)	(2,580)
10	Nonoperating Revenue	150	159	168	177	186
	Other Obligations					
11	Capital Improvements	(1,118)	(1,141)	(1,344)	(1,367)	(1,390)
12	Debt-Service Reserve	(90)	(180)	(180)	(180)	(180)
13	Total Other Obligations	(1,208)	(1,321)	(1,524)	(1,547)	(1,570)
14	Net Balance From Operations (line 6 + 9 + 10 + 13)	40	(736)	(2,160)	(2,471)	(2,809)
15	Beginning of Year Balance		40	(696)	(2,856)	(5,327)
16	End of Year Balance	$40	($696)	($2,856)	($5,327)	($8,136)
17	% Deficiency–Water Service Revenues (line 14 / line 1)		7.5%	22.0%	25.0%	28.2%
18	Debt-Service Coverage (line 6 / line 9)	1.52	1.17	0.69	0.57	0.45
19	Cumulative Water Service Revenue (Year 2 Forward)		$9,765	$19,590	$29,475	$39,423
20	Cumulative Net Balance		(696)	(2,856)	(5,327)	(8,136)
21	Cumulative % Deficiency (line 20 / line 19)		7.1%	14.6%	18.1%	20.6%

* Information is for a government-owned utility with cash basis.

year 2 to overcome the indicated deficiency in revenues under existing rates for an initial period of years. A one-year increase would amount to 7.1 percent; a two-year increase, 14.6 percent; and so on. The data from Table II.6-1 enable the utility to evaluate its antici-pated financial condition and plan for future rate adjustments.

Table II.6-2 shows a flow of funds under increased rates for the government-owned utility. Many rate increase options are available to meet the indicated deficiencies shown in Table II.6-1. For illustrative purposes, the alternative presented in Table II.6-2 provides for an initial one-year revenue increase in projected year 2 of 8.8 percent, followed by an increase of 11.5 percent in projected year 3 and a 5.0 percent in year 4, which is adequate to meet the revenue requirements for the remainder of the five-year study period.

In addition to meeting annual cash revenue requirements, the net operating revenue shown on line 10 of Table II.6-2 provides coverage on the annual debt service of at least 1.50 times, as shown on line 21. Also, as cautioned in chapter II.5, for financial planning

Table II.6-2 Flow of funds—Increased rates* (in $1,000)

Line No.	Item	Projected Years 1	2	3	4	5
	Operating Revenues					
1	Water Service—Existing Rates	$9,702	$9,765	$9,825	$9,885	$9,948
2	Year 2—Revenue Increase 8.8%		859	865	870	875
3	Year 3—Revenue Increase 11.5%			1,229	1,237	1,245
4	Year 4—Revenue Increase 5.0%				600	603
5	**Total Water Service Revenue**	9,702	10,624	11,919	12,591	12,672
6	Other Operating Revenue	75	78	81	84	87
7	**Total Operating Revenue**	9,777	10,702	12,000	12,675	12,759
8	O&M Expense	(6,549)	(6,837)	(8,130)	(8,490)	(8,880)
9	Taxes Other Than Income					
10	**Net Operating Revenue**	3,228	3,865	3,870	4,185	3,879
	Debt Service					
11	Outstanding Bonds	(1,680)	(1,680)	(1,680)	(1,680)	(1,680)
12	Proposed Bonds	(450)	(900)	(900)	(900)	(900)
13	**Total Debt Service**	(2,130)	(2,580)	(2,580)	(2,580)	(2,580)
14	Nonoperating Revenue	150	159	168	177	186
	Other Obligations					
15	Capital Improvements	(1,118)	(1,141)	(1,344)	(1,367)	(1,390)
16	Debt-Service Reserve	(90)	(180)	(180)	(180)	(180)
17	**Total Other Obligations**	(1,208)	(1,321)	(1,524)	(1,547)	(1,570)
18	Net Balance From Operations (line 10 + 13 + 14 + 17)	40	123	(66)	235	(86)
19	Beginning of Year Balance		40	163	97	333
20	End of Year Balance	$40	$163	$97	$333	$247
21	Debt-Service Coverage (line 10 / line 13)	1.52	1.50	1.50	1.62	1.50
22	Cumulative Water Service Revenue (Year 2 Forward)		$9,765	$19,590	$9,885	$19,833
23	Cumulative Net Balance		163	97	170	84
24	Cumulative % Surplus (line 23 / line 22)		1.7%	0.5%	1.7%	0.4%

* Information is for a government-owned utility with cash basis.

purposes, it is advisable to set the debt-service coverage target at a level higher than the required minimum level. Accordingly, the example utility may wish to consider a higher revenue adjustment in year 2, even though cash revenue requirements and minimum required and target coverage levels are all expected to be achieved.

Table II.6-3 contains an example of the cash-needs revenues desired from rates—the user charge revenue requirements. User charge revenue requirements include O&M expenses, debt service, and other expenditures, as noted on lines 6 and 7 of Table II.6-3. Net revenue requirements are obtained by deducting or adding the total nonrate or nonoperating revenues listed on line 11 of the table. Nonrate revenues can consist of items listed in Table II.2-1. Additionally, in arriving at the net revenue requirements to be recovered

Table II.6-3 Calculation of cash-basis user charge revenue requirements* (in $1,000)

Line No.	Item	Projected Years				
		1	2	3	4	5
	O&M Expense	$6,549	$6,837	$8,130	$8,490	$8,880
1	Taxes Other Than Income					
2	Debt Service					
3	Outstanding Bonds	1,680	1,680	1,680	1,680	1,680
4	Proposed Bonds	450	900	900	900	900
5	Total Debt Service	2,130	2,580	2,580	2,580	2,580
	Other Obligations					
6	Cash Paid Capital Improvements	1,118	1,141	1,344	1,367	1,390
7	Debt-Service Reserve	90	180	180	180	180
8	Total Other Obligations	1,208	1,321	1,524	1,547	1,570
	Nonrate Revenue					
9	Other Operating Revenue	(75)	(78)	(81)	(84)	(87)
10	Nonoperating Revenue	(150)	(159)	(168)	(177)	(186)
11	Total Nonrate Revenues	(225)	(237)	(249)	(261)	(273)
12	Net Balance From Operations	40	123	(66)	235	(86)
13	Total User Charge Revenue Requirements	$9,702	$10,624	$11,919	$12,591	$12,672

*Information is for a government-owned utility with cash basis.

by rates, the change in the fund balance should also be considered—line 12 on Table II.6-3. For the example utility, the net revenue requirements to be met from rates for the test year (year 2 of the projected period) total $10,624,000 and are used in subsequent chapters of this manual for illustrating the allocation and distribution of costs (section III) and rate design (section IV).

INVESTOR-OWNED UTILITIES

For the investor-owned utility, projected revenues are shown under existing rates (Table II.6-4) and with rate increases (Table II.6-5) needed to meet annual revenue requirements. Annual revenue requirements include a target rate of return, or weighted cost of capital of 8.0 percent, as discussed in chapter II.5. Lines 1 and 2 of Table II.6-4 for the investor-owned utility were developed in a similar manner as previously described in chapter II.2 related to the development of revenues for the government-owned utility shown in Table II.2-3. The differences in water service revenue between the government-owned utility and the investor-owned utility are indicative of the additional revenue requirements for the investor-owned utility associated with such items as taxes, rate of return, and so forth, and the treatment of nonoperating revenues for rate-setting purposes.

Line 4 of Table II.6-4, O&M expense, was previously projected in Table II.3-1. Depreciation expense as shown in Table II.6-4, line 5, was determined in the development of the accumulated depreciation numbers presented in Table II.5-2. The level of taxes other than income tax (line 6) and federal and state income taxes (line 8) were deemed as fairly typical for the hypothetical utility example in this manual.

Table II.6-4 Operating income statement—Existing rates* ($1,000)

Line No.	Item	1	2	3	4	5
	Operating Revenues					
1	Water Service—Existing Rates	$12,948	$13,035	$13,119	$13,197	$13,284
2	Other Operating Revenue	75	78	81	84	87
3	**Total Operating Revenue**	13,023	13,113	13,200	13,281	13,371
	Operating Expenses					
4	O&M Expense	(6,549)	(6,837)	(8,130)	(8,490)	(8,880)
5	Depreciation	(1,140)	(1,242)	(1,356)	(1,380)	(1,401)
6	Taxes Other Than Income	(915)	(1,080)	(1,095)	(1,116)	(1,140)
7	**Subtotal Operating Income Before Income Taxes**	4,419	3,954	2,619	2,295	1,950
8	Federal and State Income Taxes	(1,288)	(942)	(408)	(278)	(140)
9	**Operating Income**	3,131	3,012	2,211	2,017	1,810
10	Rate Base	$36,978	$41,460	$41,241	$40,899	$40,557
11	Rate of Return % (line 9 / line 10)	8.5%	7.3%	5.4%	4.9%	4.5%

*Information is for an investor-owned utility with utility basis.

Table II.6-5 Operating income statement—Increased rates* (in $1,000)

Line No.	Item	1	2	3	4	5
	Operating Revenues					
1	Water Service—Existing Rates	$12,948	$13,035	$13,119	$13,197	$13,284
2	Year 1—Revenue Increase 0.0%					
3	Year 2—Revenue Increase 4.0%		521	525	528	531
4	Year 3—Revenue Increase 9.5%			1,296	1,304	1,312
5	Year 4—Revenue Increase 1.8%				271	272
6	Year 5—Revenue Increase 1.6%					246
7	**Total Water Service Revenue**	12,948	13,556	14,940	15,299	15,647
8	Other Operating Revenue	75	78	81	84	87
9	**Total Operating Revenue**	13,023	13,634	15,021	15,383	15,734
	Operating Expenses					
10	O&M Expense	(6,549)	(6,837)	(8,130)	(8,490)	(8,880)
11	Depreciation	(1,140)	(1,242)	(1,356)	(1,380)	(1,401)
12	Taxes Other Than Income	(915)	(1,080)	(1,095)	(1,116)	(1,140)
13	**Subtotal Operating Income Before Income Taxes**	4,419	4,475	4,440	4,397	4,313
14	Federal and State Income Taxes	(1,288)	(1,150)	(1,136)	(1,119)	(1,085)
15	**Operating Income**	3,131	3,325	3,304	3,278	3,228
16	Rate Base	$36,978	$41,460	$41,241	$40,899	$40,557
17	Rate of Return % (line 14 / line 15)	8.5%	8.0%	8.0%	8.0%	8.0%

*Information is for an investor-owned utility with utility basis.

As noted on Table II.6-5, which reflects a series of rate increases, the resulting operating income (line 15) divided by rate base (line 16), which was developed in Table II.5-2, results in the anticipated rate of return shown on line 16 of Table II.6-5. Annual rate increases presented in Table II.6-5 were designed to meet the desired overall rate of return of 8.0 percent, because the revenues under existing rates are inadequate to meet this targeted rate of return beginning in projected year 2, as shown on Line 11 of Table II.6-4.

Section III
Cost Allocation

This page intentionally blank.

Allocating Revenue Requirements to Cost Components

The total annual cost to provide water service to customers is the utility's annual revenue requirement, as discussed in chapters II.1 through II.6 of this manual. One of the key financial objectives for a utility is to maintain a revenue stream from its general water service rate structure, along with other miscellaneous operating revenues and nonoperating income that meet the total annual cost of service. Another basic tenet followed in the development of the general water service rate structure is that it recovers the cost of providing service to the various classes of customers of the utility in an equitable manner. This chapter and next one discuss an approach or process to identify the customer class cost-of-service responsibility, which is generally recognized and accepted by government-owned utilities as well as by both state regulatory commissions and courts of law. The customer class cost-of-service information resulting from this process will serve as a useful tool to the utility in providing equitability in its rate structure.

The cost-of-service process includes the following steps:

1. Identify annual revenue requirements by function or activity (including source of supply, pumping, treatment, etc.).

2. Allocate these functional costs to appropriate cost components (including those related to annual usage, peak demands, customer meters and bills, and direct fire protection).

3. Develop units of service by customer class for each cost component.

4. Develop unit costs of service by dividing the total costs for each cost component by the respective total system units of service.

5. Distribute costs to customer classes based on the unit costs of service and each class's units of service for each cost component.

The first two steps of this cost allocation process are discussed in this chapter, while the last three steps are explored in chapter III.2.

It should be noted that for the remainder of this manual, the example cost-of-service allocations and rate designs are predicated on a government-owned utility, using projected year 2 in various tables, and the utility basis for revenue requirements, with the units of service (metered consumption and number of customers from Table II.2-2), plant investment/rate base (from Table II.5-1 and Table II.5-2), and revenue requirements (from Table II.6-4) developed in previous chapters and tables in this manual.

ASSIGNING REVENUE REQUIREMENTS TO FUNCTIONAL COSTS

The first step in the process begins with the projection or determination of the annual revenue requirements. The total annual cost of service should be identified in as much detail as possible by "utility function." Utility function refers to the type of operational activity with which a particular cost is identified. This could include source of supply, raw water pumping, treatment, treated water pumping, distribution storage, distribution mains, transmission mains, fire hydrants, customer service lines, meters, customer service activities (meter reading, billing, and collection), engineering, planning, and various general overhead and management functions (legal, human resources, accounting, etc.). For operation and maintenance (O&M) expense, these "functional" costs can be further separated into the categories of labor/payroll, power and other purchased services, chemicals and other materials and supplies, and equipment. Such expenses are similar for both government-owned and investor-owned utilities.

The total annual capital expenditures and associated overhead costs should be captured for each utility function and recorded and maintained in the utility's fixed asset accounting records. Because annual capital expenses for different functions can vary considerably from year to year, capital costs are typically allocated based on past investments as an indicator of the trend for ongoing investments. Accordingly, the allocation of the accumulative book value of fixed assets by function is the principal tool used in the cost allocation process for capital-related annual revenue requirements. In the cash basis of revenue requirements, the sum of the annual debt service, debt-service reserves, and annual capital costs not financed through debt would be allocated to the cost components in the same proportion or ratios as the allocation of the utility's fixed assets. For the utility basis of revenue requirements, the net book value (used in the determination of the rate base) and annual depreciation expenses can be allocated directly to the cost components. The revenue requirement related to return on investment would be allocated in proportion to the net book value or rate base.* Chapters II.2 and II.4 describe the detailed accounting records for these cost activities that should be maintained to provide adequate information for the cost-of-service allocation process as well as for other utility planning purposes.

Taxes are another revenue requirement for an investor-owned utility and can include both state and federal income taxes and, if applicable, other types of taxes, such as property taxes or franchise fees paid to state and local authorities. Although government-owned utilities are generally not subject to taxation, they are sometimes subject to property taxes or payment in lieu of taxes (PILOT) that are included in the calculation of revenue

---

* In some studies, the gross (un-depreciated) value is used. The net (depreciated) value minimizes the value of older assets and maximizes the value of new assets. Given that capital replacement expenditure would typically be for older (more fully depreciated) assets, the use of the net asset value may reduce the weight given to older assets. Accordingly, the gross value (un-depreciated asset value) is viewed by some as a better way to allocate the cash-based capital costs. Others believe that the full replacement value should be used for allocation purposes because older assets that may get replaced were typically purchased at lower costs than what would be needed for replacement.

requirements under both the cash-needs and utility-basis approach. The nature of the basis for the tax (or PILOT), as applicable to the investor-owned utility or government-owned utility, would determine how it is assigned to functional categories. If the tax is based on assessed property value, it may be appropriate to assign it to the various functions in proportion to the utility's fixed assets, or, if the property has a distinct purpose (e.g., water supply land), it may be allocated directly to the appropriate function. If the tax is based on the total income of the utility (i.e., income taxes), it may be appropriate to assign it to the various functions in proportion to the sum of the overall resulting allocation of both O&M expenses and capital-related costs. The allocation of applicable taxes is often best undertaken following the assignment of the functionalized costs to appropriate cost components, which is discussed in the following section.

ALLOCATING FUNCTIONALIZED COSTS TO COST COMPONENTS

The costs incurred in a water utility are generally responsive to the specific service requirements or cost drivers imposed on the system by its customers. Each of the various water utility facilities are designed and sized to meet one or more of these cost drivers, and the capital costs incurred in the construction/installation of these facilities as well as the O&M expenses incurred in running the system are, in turn, linked to these service requirements. The principal service requirements that drive costs include the annual volume of water consumed, the peak water demands incurred, the number of customers in the system, and the fire services required to maintain adequate fire protection. Accordingly, these service requirements are the basis for the selection of the cost categories, or *cost components*, used in the second step in the cost-of-service allocation process. The manner in which the total annual cost of service is assigned or allocated to each of these cost components is discussed in the remainder of this chapter.

Each class of customers of the water utility has a specific level of service or cost responsibility associated with each of these cost components. The discussion of these class responsibilities and the resulting distribution of the annual cost of service to each class is the subject of chapter III.2.

In allocating the annual costs of service to cost components, the specific cost components vary, depending on the basis of allocation used. The two most widely used methods of allocating costs are the base-extra capacity method and the commodity-demand method. In their respective ways, both methods of cost allocation recognize that the cost of serving customers depends not only on the total volume of water used but also on the rate of use, or peak-demand requirements. In addition, both methodologies recognize customer-related costs as a valid cost function, as well as direct fire service–related costs. Other methods of cost allocation, involving incremental, marginal, or special-use service, apply only in special situations. Legal constraints might limit the application of these other methods.

The overall cost allocation process under either the base-extra capacity or the commodity-demand method includes

- allocation of costs to the cost components of base, extra capacity, customer and fire protection costs (in the base-extra capacity method), or to commodity, demand, customer, and fire protection costs (in the commodity-demand method); and

- distribution of costs allocated to the various cost components to classes of customers according to the respective responsibility of the customer classes for each of the component costs.

The allocation of costs to cost components by the base-extra capacity method and the commodity-demand method are discussed and illustrated in the remainder of this chapter.

Base-Extra Capacity Method

Using the base-extra capacity method, costs are usually separated into four primary cost components: base costs, extra capacity costs, customer costs, and direct fire protection costs. In detailed rate studies, some of these elements may be broken down further into two or more subcomponents.

Base costs are expenses that tend to vary with the total quantity of water used plus those O&M expenses and capital costs associated with service to customers under average load conditions, without the elements of cost incurred to meet water-use variations and resulting peaks in demand. Base costs include a portion of O&M expenses of supply, treatment, pumping, and distribution facilities. Base costs also include capital costs related to water plant investment associated with serving customers to the extent required for a constant, or average, annual rate of use.

Extra capacity costs are expenses associated with meeting peak-demand rate-of-use requirements in excess of average (base) use and include O&M expenses and capital costs for system capacity beyond that required for average rate of use. These costs may be subdivided into costs necessary to meet maximum-day extra demand, maximum-hour demand in excess of maximum-day demand, or other extra demand criteria (such as the maximum five-day demand) that may be appropriate for a particular utility.

Customer costs comprise those expenses associated with serving customers, irrespective of the amount or rate of water use. They include, but are not limited to, meter reading, billing, customer accounting, customer service, and collecting expense, as well as maintenance and capital costs related to meters and services. In detailed studies, the costs for meter reading and billing and for customer accounting and collecting may be considered one subcomponent; maintenance and capital costs related to customer meters and services may be considered another subcomponent.

Direct fire protection costs are those expenses that apply solely to the fire protection function. Usually, such costs are simply those directly related to public fire hydrants and related branch mains and valves. Private fire protection direct costs may also be included in this cost category but accounted for separately from the direct public fire costs. It should be noted that the costs allocated to the direct fire protection cost component are usually only a small part of the total cost of fire protection. As more fully described and illustrated in chapters III.2 and IV.8, a significant portion of extra capacity costs can be allocated to fire protection in distributing costs to customer classes.

In the base-extra capacity method, costs must be carefully separated between base costs and extra capacity costs. The appropriate allocation factors between base and extra capacity vary among systems and should be determined on the basis of the actual operating history or design criteria for each system. For purposes of this manual, the example uses system demands with annual average day use of 7.5 million gallons per day (mgd) and a maximum-day use of 11.55 mgd. Accordingly, facilities designed to meet maximum-day requirements, such as a treatment plant, may be allocated 65 percent (7.5 mgd/11.55 mgd) to the base cost component and 35 percent [(11.55 mgd – 7.5 mgd) / (11.55 mgd)] to the maximum-day extra capacity cost component. In the example, the system is assumed to have maximum-hour requirements of 16.65 mgd. Therefore, facilities designed to meet maximum-hour requirements may appropriately be allocated to the base, maximum-day extra capacity, and maximum-hour (in excess of maximum-day) extra capacity cost components. The base cost component would be allocated 45 percent (7.5 mgd/16.65 mgd); the maximum-day extra capacity cost component would be allocated approximately 25 percent [(11.55 mgd – 7.5 mgd) / (16.65 mgd)]; and the maximum-hour extra capacity component would be allocated approximately 30 percent [(16.65 mgd – 11.55 mgd) / (16.65 mgd)]. In each case, it is the incremental or extra demand that is used for each cost component.

As previously discussed, total costs of service using the utility-basis approach for revenue requirements are represented by three principal elements: O&M expense, depreciation expense, and return on investment. In some instances, PILOT may also be included as an element in cost of service. O&M expense and depreciation expense are annual amounts, which have been previously identified by utility function, that can be allocated directly to cost components. For a government-owned utility, the cash-based capital costs can be allocated to cost components based on the allocation of the net book value of assets. (It is noted that the development of rate base by utility function for the example utility used in this manual was previously developed for year 2 in Tables II.5-1 and II.5-2.) This serves as a basis for subsequent distribution of responsibility for return to the various customer classes. As discussed earlier, if PILOT is a revenue requirement, it may be allocated similarly to rate base or based on the functional use of property.

Table III.1-1 presents an example of the allocation of rate base to cost components under the base-extra capacity cost allocation method. The various elements of rate base shown in Table III.1-1 are valued at the net book value (original cost less accrued depreciation) of the water system, based on the accounting records of the utility as projected for the test period. In the example presented in Table III.1-1, investment in source of supply, land, land rights, and impounded reservoir structures are allocated 100 percent to the base cost component. Such an allocation recognizes the fact that such facilities are often sized principally to meet annual supply requirements in total, whether or not daily needs vary.

In some cases, reservoirs may function to provide not only total annual supply requirements but also fluctuations in use on a seasonal or daily basis. Utilities can evaluate each particular local situation to determine if some portion of the impounded reservoir-related costs should be allocated to the extra-capacity cost function. The source of supply for many utilities may also include well supply or a river intake. In these instances, a portion of the rate base for source of supply may be allocated to maximum-day or maximum-hour extra capacity, depending on the basis of design or usage characteristics associated with the well supply. It is important to note that the examples presented in this manual are for demonstration purposes only, and each utility needs to conduct appropriate analyses regarding its own situation.

As a continuation of the example demands presented previously, raw and treated water pumping and treatment facilities in Table III.1-1 are allocated 65 percent to base and 35 percent to the maximum-day extra-capacity cost components because these facilities are designed to meet maximum-day demands. It is noted that if the example were to separately identify reservoir intake facilities or raw water transmission mains, these facilities would also be allocated 65 percent to base and 35 percent to the maximum-day extra-capacity cost components. Treated water transmission mains are allocated 65 percent to base and 35 percent to maximum-day in recognition that mains are primarily designed to meet base and maximum-day loads. Treated water distribution mains are allocated 45 percent to base, 25 percent to maximum-day extra capacity, and 30 percent to maximum-hour extra capacity in recognition that distribution mains provide both maximum-day and maximum-hour service.

If a utility has wholesale service customers, depending on the nature of the service to such customers (i.e., number, size, and location of connections; contractual terms; and other considerations), the costs associated with distribution mains of the water system may be allocable to only retail customers. For purposes of the example presented in this manual, it is assumed that distribution mains are used by all customers. Distribution storage–related facilities, such as elevated storage tanks, serve principally to assist utilities in meeting maximum-hour extra capacity requirements and, therefore, in this example, are allocated 90 percent to the maximum-hour extra-capacity cost component. Recognizing that distribution storage provides some element of system reliability, the base cost component is assigned 10 percent of such facilities. The percentage factor used to allocate distribution

Table III.1-1 Allocation of rate base—Base-extra capacity method (test year)

Line No.	Rate Base Component	Total	Base	Extra Capacity Maximum Day	Extra Capacity Maximum Hour*	Customer Meters & Services	Direct Fire Protection Service
	Intangible						
1	Organization	$18,000	$9,000	$3,000	$3,000	$3,000	$0
	Source of Supply						
2	Land	1,269,000	1,269,000				
3	Reservoir	1,221,000	1,221,000				
	Pumping						
4	Land	69,000	44,850	24,150			
5	Structures	1,107,000	719,550	387,450			
6	Electrical Pumping Equipment	1,128,000	733,200	394,800			
7	Other Pumping Equipment	471,000	306,150	164,850			
	Water Treatment						
8	Structures	1,278,000	830,700	447,300			
9	Water Treatment Plant	11,496,000	7,472,400	4,023,600			
	Transmission & Distribution						
10	Land	105,000	10,500		94,500		
11	Structures	144,000	14,400		129,600		
12	Distribution Storage	3,060,000	306,000		2,754,000		
13	Transmission Mains	7,010,000	4,556,500	2,453,500			
14	Distribution Mains	10,516,000	4,732,200	2,629,000	3,154,800		
15	Services	6,792,000				6,792,000	
16	Meters	2,988,000				2,988,000	
17	Hydrants	1,212,000					1,212,000
	General						
18	Land	12,000	6,858	3,249	1,893		
19	Structures	570,000	253,959	120,294	70,112	111,786	13,849
20	Other Pumping Equipment	387,000	172,425	81,673	47,602	75,897	9,403
21	Net Plant in Service	50,853,000	22,658,692	10,732,866	6,255,508	9,970,682	1,235,252
	Plus:						
22	Materials & Supplies	873,000	388,959	184,240	107,382	171,208	21,211
23	Cash Working Capital	855,000	380,939	180,441	105,168	167,678	20,773
24	Construction Work in Progress	312,000	143,520	78,000	90,480		
	Less:						
25	Contributions and Advances	(4,335,000)				(4,335,000)	
26	Test-Year Rate Base	$48,558,000	$23,572,110	$11,175,548	$6,558,537	$5,974,569	$1,277,236

*Maximum-hour demand in excess of maximum-day demand.

storage largely depends on engineering considerations as well as the operating and design characteristics of the reservoirs in each particular system. Meters and services are allocated to the customer meters and services cost component. Fire hydrants are allocated to the direct fire service cost component.

Table III.1-2 Allocation of depreciation expense—Base-extra capacity method (test year)

Line No.	Item	Total	Base	Extra Capacity Maximum Day	Maximum Hour*	Customer Meters & Services	Direct Fire Protection Service
	Source of Supply	$35,400	$35,400	$0	$0	$0	$0
1	Reservoir						
	Pumping						
2	Structures	28,800	18,720	10,080			
3	Electrical Pumping Equipment	31,800	20,670	11,130			
4	Other Pumping Equipment	12,600	8,190	4,410			
	Water Treatment						
5	Structures	33,000	21,450	11,550			
6	Water Treatment Plant	251,400	163,000	88,400			
	Transmission & Distribution						
7	Structures	3,600	3,240		360		
8	Distribution Storage	85,500	8,550		76,950		
9	Transmission Mains	193,300	125,645	67,655			
10	Distribution Mains	290,000	130,500	72,500	87,000		
11	Services	146,700				146,700	
12	Meters	64,500				64,500	
13	Hydrants	36,900					36,900
	General						
14	Structures	14,700	6,549	3,102	1,808	2,883	357
15	Other Pumping Equipment	13,800	6,148	2,912	1,697	2,706	335
16	Total Depreciation Expense	$1,242,000	$548,063	$271,740	$167,816	$216,789	$37,592

*Maximum-hour demand in excess of maximum-day demand.

The value of office buildings, furniture and equipment, vehicles, and other general plant resources is allocated to cost components on the basis of the resulting allocation of other plant facilities. Construction work in progress (CWIP) is allocated to cost components on the same basis as similar elements of plant in service. In the example, it is assumed that all CWIP is associated with transmission and distribution mains. In many water utility systems, the accounting records will show contributions in aid of construction (CIAC) that are ordinarily deducted from the rate base before applying rate-of-return percentages. CIAC should be deducted from plant value according to the purposes for which the contributions were made. The example illustrated in Table III.1-1 assumes that all contributions in this instance are related to customer meters and services. The results of the allocation of rate base to the various cost components, as illustrated in Table III.1-1, provide a basis for subsequent distribution of capital costs to these components and then to the customer classes, as further explained in chapter III.2.

Table III.1-2 illustrates the allocation of annual depreciation expense to cost components under the base-extra capacity method. The categories of items of depreciation expense are allocated to cost components in the same manner described in the allocation of rate base.

Table III.1-3 Allocation of O&M expense and nonrate revenue—Base-extra capacity method (test year)

Line No.	Item	Total	Base	Extra Capacity Maximum Day	Extra Capacity Maximum Hour*	Customer Costs Meters & Services	Customer Costs Billing & Collection	Direct Fire Protection Service
1	**Source of Supply**	$270,000	$270,000	$0	$0	$0	$0	$0
	Pumping							
2	Purchased Power	777,000	699,300	77,700				
3	Other	579,000	376,000	202,650				
	Water Treatment							
4	Chemicals	363,000	363,000					
5	Other	471,000	306,150	164,850				
	Transmission & Distribution							
6	Storage	78,000	7,800		70,200			
7	Transmission Mains	156,000	101,400	54,600				
8	Distribution Mains	234,000	105,300	58,500	70,200			
9	Meters & Services	465,000				465,000		
10	Hydrants	39,000						39,000
11	Other	216,000	41,040	21,600	41,040	103,680		8,640
	Customer Accounting							
12	Meter Reading & Collection	741,000					741,000	
13	Uncollectable Accounts	132,000	62,040	18,480	7,920	18,480	23,760	1,320
	Administrative & General							
14	Salaries	582,000	218,630	89,629	32,596	101,073	131,645	8,428
15	Employee Benefits	531,000	199,471	81,775	29,740	92,216	120,109	7,689
16	Insurance	405,000	152,139	62,371	22,683	70,334	91,608	5,865
17	Other	798,000	299,770	122,893	44,694	138,584	180,502	11,556
18	Total O&M Expenses	6,837,000	3,202,390	955,048	319,072	989,367	1,288,624	82,498
19	Nonrate Revenue	($78,000)	($29,000)	($12,000)	($4,000)	($14,000)	($18,000)	($1,000)

*Maximum-hour demand in excess of maximum-day demand.

Table III.1-3 presents an example of the allocation of O&M expense to cost components under the base-extra capacity method. In general, O&M expense for each facility is allocated to cost components in a manner similar to that for rate base.

Expenses that generally vary directly with water usage are assigned to the base cost component. Chemical costs are typically an example of such an expense and are therefore allocated to the base cost component. Assuming that the energy portion of the example utility's power cost comprises 71 percent of the power bill and the demand charge represents 29 percent, the maximum-day extra capacity portion of the power cost would amount to approximately 10 percent of the total (29% × 35% extra capacity), with the balance of power costs, or 90 percent, being allocated to base cost. The extent to which power costs are allocated to the extra-capacity cost component depends on the variations in electric demands incurred in pumping and the energy/demand electric rate structure that applies to pumping.

Expenses other than power, chemical, and customer-related costs can be allocated to cost components on the basis of operating considerations or the design capacity requirements of each facility. Such expenses, if designed to meet maximum-day requirements, are allocated 65 percent to base cost and 35 percent to maximum-day extra capacity cost. Expenses related to facilities designed to meet maximum-hour requirements are allocable 45 percent to base cost, 25 percent to maximum-day extra capacity cost, and 30 percent to maximum-hour extra capacity cost. Expenses related to distribution storage are allocated in the same manner as for rate base—that is, 10 percent to base cost and 90 percent to maximum-hour extra capacity costs.

Expenses for meters and services are allocated directly to the customer meters and service cost component while expenses for customer billing and collection are allocated directly to the customer billing and collection cost component. In the example, administration and general expense associated with salaries, employee benefits, insurance, and other administration and general expenses are allocated on the basis of the allocation of all other expenses, exclusive of power and chemical costs. In some more detailed studies, salary costs and associated benefits can be directly assigned to specific functions and allocated based on the allocation of other items within that function.

Commodity-Demand Method

In the commodity-demand method, costs of service are separated into four primary cost components: commodity costs, demand costs, customer costs, and direct fire protection costs. In detailed rate studies, some of these elements may also be broken down further into two or more subcomponents.

Commodity costs are costs that tend to vary with the quantity of water produced. They usually include costs of chemicals, a large part of power costs, and other elements that increase or decrease almost directly with the amount of water supplied. Costs related to impounded reservoir source of supply or other costs that vary with average daily demands, such as raw water transfer pumping costs, may also be considered as commodity costs. Purchased water costs, if bought on a unit volume basis, would also be considered as commodity costs. However, recognition of recent practices to include a demand charge in addition to commodity charge in purchased water agreements may dictate that demand portions of purchased water costs be allocated to demand components.

Demand costs are associated with providing facilities to meet the peak rates of use, or demands, placed on the system by the customers. They include capital-related costs on plant designed to meet peak requirements, plus the associated O&M expenses. This cost component may be broken down into costs associated with meeting specific demands, such as maximum-day and maximum-hour demands, or other periods of time that may be appropriate to the utility that has to meet these demands. In the commodity-demand method, costs must be carefully separated between commodity costs and demand costs. The appropriate allocation factors between commodity and demand costs usually vary among systems and should be determined on the basis of the design criteria for each system.

The definition of *customer costs* for this method is the same as for the base-extra capacity method. Direct fire protection costs are also the same as under the base-extra capacity cost method.

Table III.1-4 presents an example of how the rate base is allocated to various cost components under the commodity-demand method. In this example, the functionalized rate base for each facility is the same as used in the base-extra capacity method presented in Table III.1-1. Each element of the utility plant is assigned to commodity, demand, customer, or direct fire service functions. Investment in pumping plant, treatment plant, and transmission mains, which are generally designed to meet maximum-day demands, are assigned 100 percent to the maximum-day demand component. Treated-water distribution mains, which serve maximum-hour demands, are assigned 100 percent to the

Table III.1-4 Allocation of rate base—Commodity-demand method (test year)

Line No.	Item	Total	Commodity	Capacity Maximum Day	Capacity Maximum Hour	Customer Meters & Services	Direct Fire Protection Service
	Intangible						
1	Organization	$18,000	$9,000	$3,000	$3,000	$3,000	$0
	Source of Supply						
2	Land	1,269,000	1,269,000				
3	Reservoir	1,221,000	1,221,000				
	Pumping						
4	Land	69,000		69,000			
5	Structures	1,107,000		1,107,000			
6	Electrical Pumping Equipment	1,128,000		1,128,000			
7	Other Pumping Equipment	471,000		471,000			
	Water Treatment						
8	Structures	1,278,000		1,278,000			
9	Water Treatment Plant	11,496,000		11,496,000			
	Transmission & Distribution						
10	Land	105,000			105,000		
11	Structures	144,000			144,000		
12	Distribution Storage	3,060,000			3,060,000		
13	Transmission Mains	7,010,000		7,010,000			
14	Distribution Mains	10,516,000			10,516,000		
15	Services	6,792,000				6,792,000	
16	Meters	2,988,000				2,988,000	
17	Hydrants	1,212,000					1,212,000
	General						
18	Land	12,000		8,000	2,000	2,000	
19	Structures	570,000	28,555	257,805	158,006	111,786	13,849
20	Other Pumping Equipment	387,000	19,387	175,036	107,278	75,897	9,403
21	Net Plant in Service	50,853,000	2,546,942	23,002,841	14,095,283	9,972,682	1,235,252
	Plus:						
22	Materials & Supplies	873,000	43,734	394,849	241,998	171,208	21,211
23	Cash Working Capital	855,000	42,832	386,707	237,009	167,678	20,773
24	Construction Work in Progress	312,000		218,400	93,600		
	Less:						
25	Contributions and Advances	(4,335,000)				(4,335,000)	
26	Test-Year Rate Base	$48,558,000	$2,633,508	$24,002,797	$14,667,890	$5,976,569	$1,277,236

maximum-hour demand cost component. The rate base for distribution storage is also assigned 100 percent to the maximum-hour demand component. It should be noted that under the commodity-demand method, costs are typically assigned to one cost component, without any consideration of the incremental (or extra capacity) elements.

Table III.1-5 Allocation of depreciation expense—Commodity-demand method (test year)

Line No.	Item	Total	Commodity	Capacity Maximum Day	Capacity Maximum Hour	Customer Meters & Services	Direct Fire Protection Service
	Source of Supply						
1	Reservoir	$35,400	$35,400	$0	$0	$0	$0
	Pumping						
2	Structures	28,800		28,800			
3	Electrical Pumping Equipment	31,800		31,800			
4	Other Pumping Equipment	12,600		12,600			
	Water Treatment						
5	Structures	33,000		33,000			
6	Water Treatment Plant	251,400		251,400			
	Transmission & Distribution						
7	Structures	3,600			3,600		
8	Distribution Storage	85,500			85,500		
9	Transmission Mains	193,300		193,300			
10	Distribution Mains	290,000			290,000		
11	Services	146,700				146,700	
12	Meters	64,500				64,500	
13	Hydrants	36,900					36,900
	General						
14	Structures	14,700	736	6,649	4,075	2,883	357
15	Other Pumping Equipment	13,800	691	6,242	3,825	2,706	335
16	Total Depreciation Expense	$1,242,000	$36,828	$563,790	$387,000	$216,789	$37,592

Table III.1-5 presents an example of how depreciation expense is allocated to cost components under the commodity-demand method. The categories of items of depreciation expense are allocated to cost components in the same manner as described in the allocation of rate base.

Table III.1-6 presents an example of how O&M expense is allocated under the commodity-demand method. In general, O&M expense for each facility is allocated to cost components in a manner similar to that for rate base. However, chemical costs, which generally tend to vary with the amount of water produced, are assigned 100 percent to the commodity-cost function. Pumping power costs are allocated 71 percent to commodity cost and 29 percent to maximum-day demand cost, recognizing that power costs vary with demand. Note that under the commodity-demand method, the entire 29 percent of demand-related power costs are assigned to the maximum-day cost component, not the incremental 10 percent (29% × 35%) used on the base-extra capacity method.

In the example, administration and general expense is allocated to cost components in a manner similar to that described for the base-extra capacity method, that is, on the basis of all other expenses, exclusive of power and chemicals.

Comparison of Base-Extra Capacity and Commodity-Demand Methods

The decision for which methodology to use might be based on the unique circumstances of the utility in question and typically relates to total volume and peak-demand characteristics

Table III.1-6 Allocation of O&M expense and nonrate revenue—Commodity-demand method (test year)

Line No.	Item	Total	Commodity	Extra Capacity Maximum Day	Extra Capacity Maximum Hour	Customer Costs Meters & Services	Customer Costs Billing & Collection	Direct Fire Protection Service
1	**Source of Supply**	$270,000	$270,000	$0	$0	$0	$0	$0
	Pumping							
2	Purchased Power	777,000	551,670	225,330				
3	Other	579,000		579,000				
	Water Treatment							
4	Chemicals	363,000	363,000					
5	Other	471,000		471,000				
	Transmission & Distribution							
6	Storage	78,000			78,000			
7	Transmission Mains	156,000		156,000				
8	Distribution Mains	234,000			234,000			
9	Meters & Services	465,000				465,000		
10	Hydrants	39,000						39,000
11	Other	216,000		60,480	43,200	103,680		8,640
	Customer Accounting							
12	Meter Reading & Collection	741,000					741,000	
13	Uncollectable Accounts	132,000	26,400	54,120	9,240	17,160	23,760	1,320
	Administrative & General							
14	Salaries	582,000	51,022	227,326	62,734	100,846	131,645	8,428
15	Employee Benefits	531,000	46,551	207,406	57,237	92,009	120,109	7,689
16	Insurance	405,000	35,505	158,191	43,655	70,176	91,608	5,865
17	Other	798,000	69,958	311,694	86,017	138,273	180,502	11,556
18	Total O&M Expenses	6,837,000	1,414,105	2,450,547	614,083	987,143	1,288,624	82,498
19	Nonrate Revenue	($78,000)	($7,000)	($30,000)	($8,000)	($14,000)	($18,000)	($1,000)

of the customer classes in question. The same method should be applied to all rate classes. The base-extra capacity method and the commodity-demand method result in roughly comparable charges for water service if customer class peaking factors do not vary significantly, and assuming that all cost components are properly allocated. Table III.1-7 demonstrates the differences between the two methods. Although customer cost components and direct fire protection costs are very similar, the costs allocated to the maximum-day and maximum-hour components differ substantially. This is largely due to the recognition in the base-extra capacity method that a significant portion of system costs are also related to the provision of base or average annual usage demands, while the commodity-demand method assigns those costs in their entirety to either the maximum-day or maximum-hour demand cost components.

An advantage in using the base-extra capacity method is that it identifies in the base cost component the minimum unit volume cost of service (the unit cost of meeting average-day demand). Such a unit cost would apply as a rate only if a perfect load factor or constant rate of use could be achieved. Therefore, the unit base cost provides a measure of the lowest potential charge in a schedule of rates for delivery of uniform service. As such,

Table III.1-7 Summary comparison of allocated costs

Base-Extra Capacity Method of Cost Allocation

Line No.	Item	Total	Base	Extra Capacity		Customer Costs		Direct Fire Protection Service
				Maximum Day	Maximum Hour*	Meters & Services	Billing & Collection	
1	Rate Base	$48,558,000	$23,572,110	$11,175,548	$6,558,537	$5,974,569	$1,277,236	$0
2	Return on Rate Base	$2,623,320	$1,273,471	603,753	$354,321	$322,773	$69,002	$0
3	Depreciation	1,242,000	548,063	271,740	167,816	216,789		37,592
4	O&M	6,837,000	3,202,390	955,048	319,072	989,367	1,288,624	82,498
5	Nonrate Revenues	(78,000)	(29,000)	(12,000)	(4,000)	(14,000)	(18,000)	(1,000)
6	Total	$10,624,320	$4,994,924	$1,818,541	$837,210	$1,514,929	$1,339,626	$119,090
7		100.0%	47.0%	17.1%	7.9%	14.3%	12.6%	1.1%

Commodity-Demand Method of Cost Allocation

Line No.	Item	Total	Base	Capacity		Customer Costs		Direct Fire Protection Service
				Maximum Day	Maximum Hour	Meters & Services	Billing & Collection	
1	Rate Base	$48,558,000	$2,633,508	$24,002,797	$14,667,890	$5,976,569	$1,277,236	$0
2	Return on Rate Base	$2,623,320	$142,274	$1,296,738	$792,425	$322,881	$69,002	$0
3	Depreciation	1,242,000	36,828	563,790	387,000	216,789		37,592
4	O&M	6,837,000	1,414,105	2,450,547	614,083	987,143	1,288,624	82,498
5	Nonrate Revenues	(78,000)	(7,000)	(30,000)	(8,000)	(14,000)	(18,000)	(1,000)
6	Total	$10,624,320	$1,586,207	$4,281,075	$1,785,508	$1,512,813	$1,339,626	$119,090
7		100.0%	14.9%	40.3%	16.8%	14.2%	12.6%	1.1%

*Maximum-hour demand in excess of maximum-day demand.

the unit base cost is an important guide in preventing utilities from establishing a charge that could result in the sale of water below cost.

An advantage of the commodity-demand method would be found in those instances where a utility has numerous wholesale or contract customers whose rates include a demand charge. The commodity-demand method provides for a direct maximum-day or maximum-hour demand unit charge to be applied to the actual metered demands of such customers. The base-extra capacity method requires that the annual usage be first known or computed before the extra-capacity demand can be determined or calculated. This requires that a "settle-up" analysis be performed at the end of the year to determine the actual basis charge, which must of necessity be based on estimated annual usage amounts prior to the close of the fiscal year period.

SPECIAL CONSIDERATIONS

Some water utility systems have customers with water-use characteristics that require special consideration in allocating costs.

Customers provided with firm water service (i.e., unlimited service in the amounts and at such times as desired) should be charged rates adequate to recover the full cost to the utility of providing such service. In establishing charges for non-firm service, such as off-peak or interruptible service, utilities should consider charging special rates that are less than the rates for firm service. Such rates might consist of those direct additional costs, such as for power and chemicals, associated with providing water from existing facilities;

however, charges should reflect some recognition of capacity-related and other costs, in addition to purely incremental costs.

In areas where irrigation or other seasonal uses impose significant demands on the system, utilities might consider separate charges for such use. Costs associated with seasonal use might be recovered through rates applied to separate metering for such services or through surcharges applied to consumption over and above an established normal use.

When allocating the costs of service between inside-city and outside-city customers, government-owned utility systems should give special consideration to factors such as the facilities required, the extent and nature of service, ownership, risk, and other special items. A general approach to this situation is the use of the utility basis to assign appropriate cost responsibility to outside customers. More detail on these issues is presented in section VI of this manual.

In certain utility systems, the service area may be subdivided into pressure zones or districts because of the geophysical characteristics of the area. Under these conditions, the utility may want to assign and analyze the costs related to specific facilities to each pressure zone. The results of such detailed studies will indicate if significant differences occur in the costs of providing service to each pressure zone.

In some instances, the utility should consider the responsibility for reserve capacity in the system. A typical example would be where a significant portion of the system is being held for the future growth needs of a specific customer or class of customers. Means of recognizing reserve capacity vary from one situation to another but are important to an equitable allocation of costs.

It is also useful to consider the distinctions between variable and fixed cost categories in performing base-extra capacity or commodity-demand cost allocations. Variable costs are those costs that tend to vary directly with the volume of water produced, or perhaps also with the number of customers or bills. Examples of variable costs include chemicals used in treatment and the energy portion of the costs of power used in pumping. Water purchased on a charge per unit of volume basis is also a variable cost. Postage and certain other customer-related costs may also be considered as variable costs. Fixed costs are those capital and operating costs that remain relatively unchanged over a given operating period, such as a year. Fixed costs typically include all capital costs such as debt service, or depreciation expense, as well as costs of operating and maintaining system facilities.

Categorizing expenses as either variable or fixed is useful to understanding how the utility incurs costs. This data can help utilities recognize the effect on revenues of significantly changing volumes of production and the revenue instability that may result. Moreover, minimum required revenue levels, based on fixed cost needs, can be evaluated with respect to each customer class. Contractual charges to large-volume customers, which include a fixed cost component, can be appropriately evaluated. Finally, the evaluation process itself provides a useful consideration of a utility's revenue requirements, potentially leading to improved record keeping, budgeting, and recognition of the nature of the utility's costs.

Chapter **III.2**

Distributing Costs to Customer Classes

The preceding chapters explained how utilities determine revenue requirements and how to allocate both operating and capital-related costs to cost components (e.g., base, extra capacity). This chapter presents the final step in the cost-of-service process: distributing allocated cost components to customer classes of service (e.g., residential, commercial).

The ideal solution to developing rates for water utility customers is to assign cost responsibility to each individual customer served and to develop rates that reflect that cost. Unfortunately, it is neither economically practical nor often possible to determine the cost responsibility and applicable rates for each individual customer served. However, the cost of providing service can be reasonably determined for groups or classes of customers that have similar water-use characteristics and for special customers having unusual or unique water-use or service requirements. Rate-making endeavors to assign costs to classes of customers in a nondiscriminatory, cost-responsive manner so that rates can be designed to closely meet the cost of providing service to such customer classes.

CUSTOMER CLASSES

In establishing customer classes, water utilities consider service characteristics, demand patterns, and whether service is provided to customers both inside and outside the owning city's jurisdictional limits. Service characteristic differences may be illustrated by recognizing that customers using treated water require facilities that raw-water customers do not need. Similarly, large-volume industrial customers, wholesale customers, and other large users are often served directly from major treated-water transmission mains, whereas smaller users are served by both large and small distribution mains. Utilities should consider these and other factors when establishing customer classes and their costs of service.

Demand patterns of various customers differ, depending on their maximum-day and maximum-hour rates of demand relative to average demands. For example, the residential customer class, placing summer lawn irrigation loads on the system, typically has a much higher peak-demand requirement, relative to the average demand, than does a large manufacturing facility, which may require water on a relatively uniform basis throughout the year. These differences in demand patterns can create differences in the cost to serve those customers.

The classification of water customers as either inside or outside the city limits is related to each major group's responsibility for overall costs. As explained in section VI, this classification is important in the allocation of costs of service for government-owned utilities and, in some instances, may have a bearing on investor-owned utilities.

Utilities may need to recognize certain customer classifications from an accounting standpoint because of legal requirements or customs; such requirements can be accommodated in rate studies. However, general service characteristics, facility requirements, demand patterns, and location with regard to city limits are generally the principal considerations in customer classification.

General Classes

It is common for water utilities to have three principal customer classes: residential, commercial, and industrial. Utilities may define these general customer classes differently, but, in very broad terms, the following definitions are common.

- **Residential:** One- and two-family dwellings, usually physically separate
- **Commercial:** Multifamily apartment buildings and nonresidential, nonindustrial business enterprises
- **Industrial:** Manufacturing and processing establishments

Some utilities may break down these general classes into more specific groups. For example, the commercial customer group may be separated into multifamily customers and commercial customers, or multifamily apartments may be considered part of the residential class. Sometimes this distinction is based on ownership with small owner-occupied apartments considered to be in the residential class and larger nonowner-occupied buildings are part of the commercial class. Similarly, the industrial customer group may be subdivided into small industry, large industry, and special, the latter typified by some unique characteristic(s). Lastly, municipal accounts may be considered separately in some studies.

Many systems, particularly larger ones, have customers with individual water-use characteristics, service requirements, or other factors that differentiate them from other customers with regard to cost responsibility. These customers should have a separate class designation. These classes may include large hospitals, universities and colleges, military establishments, and other such categories.

Because the classification of some customers may be difficult and because there may be large variations within the commercial class, some utilities now classify customers based on meter size. In this case there may be a small meter class (e.g., ⅝-in. and ¾-in. meters), a medium meter class (1–3 in.), and a large meter class (>3 in.). Classifying customers in this manner can eliminate any confusion between a bank and water park that may both be commercial but have very different demand characteristics.

Other Classes

In addition to the general classes of service previously described, water utilities often provide service to certain special classes of customers. Four such classes are wholesale service, fire protection service, irrigation, and outside city limits.

Wholesale service. Wholesale service is usually defined as a situation in which water is sold to a customer through a master meter at one or more major points of delivery for resale to individual retail customers within the wholesale customer's service area. Usually, the wholesale customer is a separate municipality or water district adjacent to the supplying utility, but it may be in an area within the jurisdiction of the supplying utility. A more detailed discussion of outside-city and wholesale service considerations is provided in section VI.

Fire protection service. Fire protection service has characteristics that are markedly different from other types of water service. The service provided is principally of a standby nature—that is, readiness to deliver relatively large quantities of water for short periods of time at any of a large number of points in the water distribution system.

Costs allocated to fire protection service as a class can be subdivided to those related to public fire protection service and private fire protection service. The reader should refer to chapter IV.8 for further discussion of fire protection rates and charges.

Irrigation. Irrigation is characterized by the relatively high demands it places on the water system, usually during the early morning and evening hours. Throughout most of the United States, both lawn and agricultural irrigation are very seasonal in nature. Such usage is most pronounced during the summer months and, in some areas, virtually nonexistent during the winter months.

In many instances, irrigation service is not separately metered from other service; therefore, the high peaking characteristics of lawn irrigation need to be recognized as a part of each class's water-use characteristics. However, establishment of a separate class designation is warranted when separate metering for lawn irrigation is available, as is often the case for automatic lawn sprinkling systems, parks, fields, and golf courses, and where such loads are significant in the system. In this case, the significant demands caused by irrigation can be recognized and reflected in the cost to provide this service.

Service outside city limits. Many government-owned utilities recognize in their rate structures the differences in costs of serving water users located outside the corporate limits of the supplying city or jurisdiction compared with those located within the corporate limits. In many cases, a government-owned utility may be considered to be the property of the citizens within the city. Customers within the city are effectively the owner customers, who sometimes must bear the risks and responsibilities of utility ownership. Outside-city customers are nonowner customers and, as such, may bear a different responsibility for costs than do owner customers.

The costs to be borne by outside-city (nonowner) customers are similar to those attributed to the customers (nonowners) of an investor-owned utility. Such costs include operation and maintenance (O&M) expense, depreciation expense, and an appropriate return on the value of property devoted to serving the outside-city customers. Section VI provides a more in-depth discussion of the treatment of outside-city or nonowner customers.

UNITS OF SERVICE

The total cost of each cost component, such as the base cost, is divided by the appropriate total customer service requirements or units of service for all customer classes for each cost component to express a unit cost of service for each cost component. The unit costs of each component serve as a basis for calculating the cost of serving each customer class as well as for designing rates. As a basis for distributing component costs to customer classes, the units of service attributable to the respective classes must be established for the test year. To do so, the utility must determine or estimate the total quantity of water to be used by each class in the test year and the peak rates of use by the class. Peak rates of use are usually designated by maximum-day and maximum-hour rates of use. (In some systems, maximum-week or other peak use periods may be appropriate.) In addition, the utility must determine the number of equivalent meters and services by class, as well as the number of bills by class.

Maximum rates of use may be expressed in terms of a *peaking factor*, that is, a percentage relationship of the estimated class maximum rate of use to average annual rate of use. Thus, if a customer class maximum-day rate of use is 2.5 times its average annual daily rate, it is said to have a maximum-day peaking factor of 250 percent. Stated another way, using this same example, a class with an average day use of 1.0 million gallons would have a maximum-day peak use of 2.5 million gallons.

To estimate customer class peaking factors, utilities need to investigate and study all pertinent sources of information. Such data should include daily and hourly system pumping records, recorded rates of flow in specific areas of the system, studies and interviews of large users regarding individual and group characteristics of use, special demand metering programs, and experience in studies of other utilities exhibiting like characteristics. Recent technology improvements in automated meter reading have provided utilities with far greater opportunities to collect demand data applicable to cost-of-service studies. In addition, sound and logical inferences can be drawn from customer billing information, provided billing periods are sufficiently short to reflect seasonal differences, usually not to exceed three-month periods, with monthly billing being preferable for these analyses. Appendix A provides some techniques that can be used to determine reasonable estimates of the maximum-day and maximum-hour peaking factors for each customer class using available system demand data for the utility and customer class billing records.

The total annual volume of water used for fire service is usually negligible, at least in relation to that of other classes; however, peak requirements for fire service can be quite significant. The Insurance Services Office periodically defines desired rates of flow for fire service, which is a good source of maximum-capacity requirements for fire service. These data must be applied judiciously to achieve practical cost allocations.

Customer-related costs for meters and services may be properly distributed among customer classes by recognizing factors that are generally responsible for those costs being incurred. As an example, one method for distributing meter-and-service costs to customer classes is in proportion to the investment in meters and services installed for each customer class, based on the number of equivalent meters. Distribution of customer costs by equivalent meter-and-service ratios recognizes that meter-and-service costs vary, depending on considerations such as size of service pipe, materials used, locations of meters, and other local characteristics for various sized meters as compared to ⅝-in. meters and services. In this example, typical customer meter-and-service equivalent ratios based on investment are as follows:

Meter Size, in.	Equivalent Meter Size Ratios Based on Investment
⅝	1.0
¾	1.1
1	1.4
1½	1.8
2	2.9
3	11.0
4	14.0
6	21.0
8	29.0

Table III.2-1 Units of service—Base-extra capacity method (test year)

Line No.	Customer Class	Base Units		Maximum-Day Units			Maximum-Hour Units			Customer Units	
		Annual Use, 1,000 gal	Average Rate, 1,000 gpd	Peaking Factor, %	Total Capacity, 1,000 gpd	Extra Capacity, 1,000 gpd	Peaking Factor, %	Total Capacity, 1,000 gpd	Extra Capacity, 1,000 gpd	Equivalent Meters & Services	Bills
	Inside City:										
1	Retail Service										
2	Residential	968,000	2,652	250	6,630	3,978	400	10,608	3,978	15,652	185,760
3	Commercial	473,000	1,296	200	2,592	1,296	325	4,212	1,620	1,758	14,640
4	Industrial	1,095,000	3,000	150	4,500	1,500	200	6,000	1,500	251	420
5	Fire Protection				840	840		5,040	4,200		
6	Total Inside City	2,536,000	6,948		14,562	7,614		25,860	11,298	17,661	200,820
	Outside City:										
7	Residential	95,000	260	280	729	468	420	1,093	364	1,580	18,240
8	Wholesale	230,000	630	225	1,418	788	375	2,363	945	34	48
9	Total	2,861,000	7,838		16,708	8,870		29,316	12,608	19,275	219,108

Appendix B further discusses how to develop the meter-and-service cost ratios previously shown, as well as equivalent meter ratios based on factors such as meter demand capacity.

Costs related to meter reading, billing, and collecting may be distributed among customer classes based on the total number of bills or equivalent billing units rendered to the respective classes in a test year. In some instances, billing ratios are used to recognize that billing, metering, and collection costs for larger services may be greater than for smaller meter-size services. This may be due to difficulty in accessing the meter facility, replacement of meters, multiple dial meters, more customer service time associated with dealing with larger meter customers, and other factors.

Table III.2-1 illustrates the development of the test-year units of service for the example utility, using the base-extra capacity method of cost allocation and distribution. Test-year units of service reflect the prospective average annual customer water use and other service requirements during the test-year study period considered in this example. For purposes of the examples in this manual, it is assumed that retail service and fire protection service are provided inside the city to residential, commercial, and industrial classes. Outside-city service is provided on both a retail and wholesale basis (see section VI for a more detailed discussion). The annual usage and number of customers by customer class were previously developed in Table II.2-2.

DISTRIBUTING COST COMPONENTS TO CUSTOMER CLASSES

Table III.2-1 shows, under the heading "Base Units," the total annual water use in thousand gallons for each customer class, as well as the average rate in thousand gallons per day. Maximum-day peaking factors are applied to average-day rates of flow to develop total maximum-day capacity by class. *Maximum-day extra capacity* is defined as the difference between total maximum-day capacity and the average day rate of use. Fire protection service is considered to require negligible flow on an average annual basis but 840 thousand gallons per day (1,000 gpd) on a maximum daily basis (3,500 gpm for 4 hours).

Maximum-hour extra peaking factors for each customer class are applied to average-day rates of flow, and the *maximum-hour extra capacity units* are defined as the difference in

Table III.2-2 Units of service—Commodity-demand method (test year)

Line No.	Customer Class	Commodity		Maximum Day			Customer Units		
		Annual Use, 1,000 gal	Average Rate, 1,000 gpd	Peaking Factor, %	Total Capacity, 1,000 gpd	Peaking Factor, %	Total Capacity, 1,000 gpd	Equivalent Meters & Services	Bills
	Inside City:								
1	**Retail Service**								
2	Residential	968,000	2,652	250	6,630	400	10,608	15,652	185,760
3	Commercial	473,000	1,296	200	2,592	325	4,212	1,758	14,640
4	Industrial	1,095,000	3,000	150	4,500	200	6,000	251	420
5	Fire Protection				840		5,040		
6	Total Inside City	2,536,000	6,948		14,562		25,860	17,661	200,820
	Outside City:								
7	Residential	95,000	260	280	729	420	1,093	1,580	18,240
8	Wholesale	230,000	630	225	1,418	375	2,363	34	48
9	Total	2,861,000	7,838		16,708		29,316	19,275	219,108

the total maximum-hour capacity and the maximum-day capacity. Maximum-hour units for fire protection service assumes that flow for fires is 5,040 thousand gpd (3,500 gpm expressed as a gpd rate = 3,500 gpm × 60 min × 24 hours). *Maximum-hour extra capacity units for fire protection* is defined as the total maximum-hour capacity less total maximum-day capacity, similar to the other classes of service.

Equivalent meters and services are derived by applying equivalent meter-and-service cost ratios to the number of meters of each size by class. The number of bills is simply the total number of bills rendered annually for each class. If customers are billed at different frequencies, care must be taken to reflect this. For example, large-volume customers may get 12 bills per year and smaller-volume customers may get 4 bills per year.

Table III.2-2 shows the development of the units of service that apply to the commodity-demand method of cost allocation. Table III.2-2 differs from Table III.2-1 only in that the incremental maximum-day and maximum-hour extra capacity columns are excluded. Under the commodity-demand method, the total maximum day or maximum hour is used.

In this example, the maximum total capacity, on both a maximum-day and maximum-hour basis, for the total system (shown in Tables III.2-1 and III.2-2) is an estimate of the sum of noncoincident peaking requirements on the system. That is, it is the sum of the peaks for each class, regardless of the day or hour in which such peaks may occur. Again, appendix A provides a more thorough discussion of the noncoincident peaking requirements by customer class and their development.

UNIT COSTS

Unit costs of service are based on total costs previously allocated to each of the cost components and divided by the total number of applicable units of service for the test year. The development of unit costs of service for the base-extra capacity method is presented in Table III.2-3. As explained in the previous chapter, the following tables contain capital cost allocations based on the utility-basis method of determining revenue requirements. This is because the example includes outside-city, nonowner customers. As described more fully in section VI, it is appropriate to use the utility basis of revenue requirements for nonowner customers to assess them a fair rate of return in determining the costs of

Table III.2-3 Unit costs of service—Base-extra capacity method (test year)

Line No.	Unit Cost Component	Rate of Return Percentage	Total	Base	Extra Capacity — Maximum Day	Extra Capacity — Maximum Hour*	Customer Costs — Meters & Services	Customer Costs — Billing & Collection	Direct Fire Protection Service
	Units of Service								
1	Total System			2,861,000 1,000 gal	8,870 1,000 gpd	12,608 1,000 gpd	19,275 equiv. meters	219,108 bills	
	O&M Expense								
2	Total		$6,837,000	$3,202,390	$955,048	$319,072	$989,367	$1,288,624	$82,498
3	Unit Cost, $/Unit			$1.1193	$107.6701	$25.3081	$51.3290	$5.8812	
	Depreciation Expense								
4	Total		$1,242,000	$548,063	$271,740	$167,816	$216,789		$37,592
5	Unit Cost, $/Unit			$0.1916	$30.6353	$13.3107	$11.2472		
	Nonrate Revenue								
6	Total		($78,000)	($29,000)	($12,000)	($4,000)	($14,000)	($18,000)	($1,000)
7	Unit Rate Base, $/Unit			–$0.0101	–$1.3529	–$0.3173	–$0.7263	–$0.0822	
	Rate Base								
8	Total Rate Base		$48,558,000	$23,572,110	$11,175,548	$6,558,537	$5,974,569		$1,277,236
9	Unit Rate Base, $/Unit			$8.2391	$1,259.9070	$520.2078	$309.9647		
	Unit Return on Rate Base								
10	Outside City, $/Unit Return on Rate Base (Input)	8.00%		$0.6591	$100.7926	$41.6166	$24.7972		
11	Outside-City Units of Service			325,000	1,256	1,310	1,614		
12	Outside-City Rate Base		$5,441,904	$2,677,713	$1,582,650	$681,258	$500,283		
13	Outside-City Return on Rate Base		$435,352	$214,217	$126,612	$54,501	$40,023		
14	Inside City, $/Unit Return on Rate Base (Input)	5.07%		$0.4181	$63.9352	$26.3984	$15.7295		
15	Inside-City Units of Service			2,536,000	7,614	11,298	17,661		
16	Inside-City Rate Base		$43,116,096	$20,894,398	$9,592,898	$5,877,279	$5,474,286		$1,277,236
17	Inside-City Return on Rate Base		$2,187,968	$1,060,306	$486,801	$298,248	$277,798		$64,815
18	Total System Return on Rate Base (Calculated)	5.40%	$2,623,320	$1,274,523	$613,413	$352,749	$317,821		$64,815
19	Inside City, $/Unit (Line 3 + 5 + 7 + 14)		$1.7189	$200.8877	$64.7000	$77.5793	$5.7991	$183,905	
20	Outside City, $/Unit (Line 3 + 5 + 7 + 10)		$1.9599	$237.7451	$79.9182	$86.6471	$5.7991		

*Maximum-hour demand in excess of maximum-day demand.

providing service to such customers. The residual cash needs are the total cash expenses after deducting the revenues from outside-city customers. These residual cash needs may then be recovered from the "owners" or inside-city customers.

Most government-owned utilities, particularly those that do not have outside-city service, may choose to allocate their costs based on their cash needs, because most of these utilities use the cash basis of revenue requirement determination. In using the cash-needs revenue requirements, instead of including depreciation and return on rate base as the capital costs, a government-owned utility can replace these items with debt service (including any coverage requirements) and annual capital outlays. Because the annual costs of debt service or cash-financed capital outlays can vary significantly from year to year, revenue requirements under the cash-needs approach can also vary significantly. To conform to the objective of rate continuity, those capital costs can be allocated to base and extra capacity components, or to commodity and demand cost components, in the same overall proportion or ratio as the allocation of total net plant investment or rate base. It is assumed that future capital projects (whether debt or cash financed) will be in rough proportion to the past investments in the system, or the net plant value, and the use of the cumulative net plant-value allocation basis for annual capital costs will tend to "dampen out" the variations in the annual additions to the net plant value and will provide for rate continuity.

Unit costs are determined simply by dividing the test-year O&M and capital cost components by the respective total system units of service for the test year. For example, in Table III.2-3 under the base-extra capacity method, the base unit cost for O&M expense of $1.1193 per thousand gallons may be derived by dividing the allocated base O&M expense of $3,202,390 by the total base-component units of service of 2,861,000 thousand gallons. Similar computations are made to determine unit costs for all other O&M expense and depreciation expense. Using the utility-basis approach, the resulting average unit costs for O&M expense and depreciation expense apply to all customers, both inside and outside the city. Allocation of O&M expense and depreciation expense to cost components is presented in chapter III.1. As shown in Table III.2-3, unit return on rate base is determined by first calculating the unit cost for rate base. The rate base for each cost component is divided by the respective total system units of service to yield unit costs for rate base. Subsequently, unit return on rate base is derived by applying the appropriate inside-city and outside-city rates of return to the unit costs for rate base. As discussed in chapters I.1 through II.5, for the government-owned utility to meet total cash revenue requirements under the hybrid utility-basis approach or residual cash-needs approach, the required level of return in the example would be $2,623,320. Based on a total rate base of $48,558,000, the overall required rate of return is approximately 5.40 percent. In this example, it is assumed that the utility provides service to both inside-city and outside-city customers. Generally, where inside-city owners provide service to outside-city nonowners, a differential rate of return is appropriate. In this example, a rate of return of 8.0 percent is assumed and applied to component unit costs for rate base to determine the outside-city unit return on rate base.

In some cases, it may be desirable to calculate the outside-city and inside-city rates of return under the hybrid approach. Total outside-city return is calculated by determining total outside-city rate base and applying the 8.0 percent rate of return. According to the base-extra capacity method, total outside-city rate base is derived by applying the unit costs for rate base from Table III.2-3 to the respective outside-city units of service presented in Table III.2-1. Application of the 8.0 percent rate of return to an outside-city rate base of $5,441,904 results in an outside-city return of approximately $435,352. Once outside-city return is determined, the inside-city rate of return can be calculated as a level sufficient to derive the balance of the total required return or cash needs. In the example, the total required return is $2,793,000. Subtracting the outside-city return of $435,352 leaves a residual amount of $2,187,968, which is the net revenue requirement for inside-city customers.

The inside-city rate of return can be determined by dividing the total return from inside-city customers of $2,187,968 by the inside-city rate base. The inside-city rate base is calculated in a manner similar to that described for developing the outside-city rate base and totals $43,116,096. As a result, the total inside-city rate of return is determined to be 5.07 percent.

Returning to the unit-cost approach presented in Table III.2-3, inside-city unit return on rate base is developed by applying the 5.07 percent rate of return to the unit costs for rate base. The differential in inside-city versus outside-city rates of return reflects in part the municipality's risk in the ownership of facilities constructed to serve outside-city customers, as well as a return on paid-up equity in system facilities to inside-city customers.

Total unit costs of service are comprised of the O&M, depreciation, the credit for nonrate revenues, and return on rate-base unit costs of service and are shown at the bottom of Table III.2-3 for inside-city and outside-city customers on Lines 19 and 20, respectively. Also included in the table are the costs of service directly allocated to fire protection service. See chapter IV.8 for details on direct and indirect fire protection costs.

Unit costs of service for the commodity-demand method are developed using an approach similar to that used for the base-extra capacity method. Total unit costs of service for inside-city and outside-city customers under the commodity-demand method are summarized at the bottom of Table III.2-4.

DISTRIBUTING COSTS BY BASE-EXTRA CAPACITY METHOD

The costs of service are distributed to the utility's customer classes by applying unit costs of service to individual customer class units of water service. The total units of service and the unit costs of service for the test year, from Tables III.2-1 and III.2-3, respectively, are summarized in Table III.2-5.

As discussed previously, base costs are costs that would be incurred in supplying water at a perfect load factor (i.e., at a continuous, uniform rate), without costs incurred in providing extra plant capacity for variation in the rate of use beyond a uniform rate. The resulting distribution of cost responsibility for base costs is simply a function of the volume of water used by each class.

As shown in Table III.2-5, residential customers are projected to use 968,000 thousand gallons of water in the test year; commercial customers, 473,000 thousand gallons; and industrial customers 1,095,000 thousand gallons. Applying the inside-city unit base cost of $1.7189 per thousand gallons to the respective units of service yields the distributed customer-class base cost of service. By definition, the *unit base cost* is the minimum rate at which water could be sold (if perfect load-factor use could be achieved) after customer costs are recovered. Outside-city distributed base costs are derived from applying the unit base cost of $1.9599 per thousand gallons to the outside-city base unit-of-service requirements. The higher unit base cost reflects the rate of return differential discussed previously.

Extra capacity costs for maximum-day and maximum-hour service are incurred in providing facilities to furnish water at varying rates above the average. Customer class responsibility for extra capacity costs is determined by applying the unit costs of service to the individual customer-class units of service in a manner similar to that used for determining customer class base costs.

Customer costs, which include the categories of meters and services and billing and collection costs, are generally treated separately in rate studies. Customer costs associated with meters and services (both capital and O&M costs) may be distributed to customer classes on the basis of equivalent meter-and-service cost factors. Meter-and-service costs are based on the total number of equivalent ⅝-in. meters and are applied to customer class equivalent meter units of service to determine allocated costs of service. Units based on equivalent ⅝-in. meters allow for the fact that customer costs will vary and tend to increase with the size of the customer meter and service.

Billing and collection costs may be related to the number of bills issued and, in turn, distributed to customer classes on the basis of the number of bills rendered to customers within each class. For the example, customer class responsibility is determined by

Table III.2-4 Unit costs of service—Commodity-demand method (test year)

Line No.	Unit Cost Component	Rate of Return Percentage	Total	Commodity	Capacity — Maximum Day	Capacity — Maximum Hour*	Customer Costs — Meters & Services	Customer Costs — Billing & Collection	Direct Fire Protection Service
	Units of Service								
1	Total System			2,861,000 1,000 gal	16,708 1,000 gpd	29,316 1,000 gpd	19,275 equiv. meters	219,108 bills	
	O&M Expense								
2	Total		$6,837,000	$1,414,105	$2,450,547	$614,083	$987,143	$1,288,624	$82,498
3	Unit Cost, $/Unit			$0.4943	$146.6647	$20.9470	$51.2136	$5.8812	
	Depreciation Expense								
4	Total		$1,242,000	$36,828	$563,790	$387,000	$216,789		$37,592
5	Unit Cost, $/Unit			$0.0129	$33.7427	$13.2010	$11.2472		
	Nonrate Revenue								
6	Total		($78,000)	($7,000)	($30,000)	($8,000)	($14,000)	($18,000)	($1,000)
7	Unit Rate Base, $/Unit			–$0.0024	–$1.7955	–$0.2729	–$0.7263	–$0.0822	
	Rate Base								
8	Total Rate Base		$48,558,000	$2,633,508	$24,002,797	$14,667,890	$5,976,569		$1,277,236
9	Unit Rate Base, $/Unit			$0.9205	$1,436.5626	$500.3369	$310.0684		
	Unit Return on Rate Base								
10	Outside City, $/Unit Return on Rate Base (Input)	8.00%		$0.0736	$114.9250	$40.0270	$24.8055		
11	Outside-City Units of Service			325,000	2,147	3,456	1,614		
12	Outside-City Rate Base		$5,612,545	$299,158	$3,083,690	$1,729,247	$500,450		
13	Outside-City Return on Rate Base		$449,004	$23,933	$246,695	$138,340	$40,036		
14	Inside City, $/Unit Return on Rate Base (Input)	5.06%		$0.0466	$72.7328	$25.3319	$15.6987		
15	Inside-City Units of Service			2,536,000	14,562	25,860	17,661		
16	Inside-City Rate Base		$42,945,456	$2,334,351	$20,919,107	$12,938,644	$5,476,118		$1,277,236
17	Inside-City Return on Rate Base		$2,174,316	$118,188	$1,059,129	$655,080	$277,254		$64,666
18	Total System Return on Rate Base (Calculated)	5.40%	$2,623,320	$142,120	$1,305,824	$793,420	$317,290		$64,666
19	Inside City, $/Unit (Line 3 + 5 + 7 + 14)			$0.5513	$251.3447	$59.2070	$77.4332	$5.7991	$183,756
20	Outside City, $/Unit (Line 3 + 5 + 7 + 10)			$0.5783	$293.5370	$73.9021	$86,5400	$5.7991	

*Maximum-hour demand in excess of maximum-day demand.

applying the billing and collection unit cost to the total estimated number of bills in each customer class rendered for the average rate year.

The base-extra capacity and customer costs, summarized by customer class, constitute the costs of service to be recovered from the respective classes of customers involved. This summation also identifies the responsibility of each class for the functional costs.

Table III.2-5 Cost distribution to customer classes—Base-extra capacity method (test year)

Line No.	Item	Total Cost of Service	Base Demand	Extra Capacity Maximum Day	Extra Capacity Maximum Hour*	Customer Costs Meters & Services	Customer Costs Billing & Collection	Direct Fire Protection Service
	Inside City:							
1	Unit Costs of Service, $/Unit		$1.7189 1,000 gal	$200.8877 1,000 gal	$64.7000 1,000 gal	$77.5793 per equiv. meters	$5.7991 per bill	
	Residential							
2	Units of Service		968,000	3,978	3,978	15,652	185,760	
3	Allocated Costs of Service	$5,011,889	$1,663,851	$799,148	$257,382	$1,214,272	$1,077,236	
	Commercial							
4	Units of Service		473,000	1,296	1,620	1,758	14,640	
5	Allocated Costs of Service	$1,399,435	$813,018	$260,328	$104,805	$136,384	$84,898	
	Industrial							
6	Units of Service		1,095,000	1,500	1,500	251	420	
7	Allocated Costs of Service	$2,302,435	$1,882,146	$301,332	$97,050	$19,472	$2,436	
	Fire Protection Service							
8	Units of Service			840	4,200			
9	Allocated Costs of Service	$624,390		$168,746	$271,740			$183,905
10	Total Inside-City Allocated Cost-of-Service	$9,338,150	$4,359,015	$1,529,554	$730,977	$1,370,129	$1,164,570	$183,905
11	**Outside City:**							
12	Unit Costs of Service, $/Unit		$1.9599 1,000 gal	$237.7451 1,000 gal	$79.9182 1,000 gal	$86.6471 per equiv. meters	$5.7991 per bill	
13	**Residential**							
14	Units of Service		95,000	468	364	1,580	18,240	
15	Allocated Costs of Service	$569,369	$186,189	$111,382	$29,121	$136,902	$105,775	
16	**Wholesale**							
17	Units of Service		230,000	788	945	34	48	
18	Allocated Costs of Service	$716,801	$450,773	$187,265	$75,539	$2,946	$278	
19	Total System Allocated Costs of Service	$10,624,320	$4,995,977	$1,828,201	$835,637	$1,509,977	$1,270,624	$183,905

*Maximum-hour demand in excess of maximum-day demand.

DISTRIBUTING COSTS BY COMMODITY-DEMAND METHOD

As noted in the previous chapter, there are two generally accepted methods of allocating costs to cost components: the base-extra capacity method and the commodity-demand method. Costs are distributed to customer classes under the commodity-demand method using the same process previously discussed to distribute base-extra capacity costs. Table III.2-6 summarizes the application of units of service to unit costs of service, as developed in Tables III.2-2 and III.2-4 for the commodity-demand method.

In the commodity-demand method, commodity costs are distributed to customer classes on the basis of total annual use. Demand-related costs are distributed to the various classes in proportion to the class total-demand responsibility; this is not the extra or incremental demand over the base use, but the total maximum-day or maximum-hour demand. The method of distribution demand cost responsibilities is an important differentiator between the base-extra capacity method and the commodity-demand method.

Table III.2-6 Cost distribution to customer classes—Commodity-demand method (test year)

Line No.	Item	Total Cost of Service	Commodity	Capacity		Customer Costs		Direct Fire Protection Service
				Maximum Day	Maximum Hour*	Meters & Services	Billing & Collection	
	Inside City:							
1	Unit Costs of Service, $/Unit		$0.5513 1,000 gal	$251.3447 1,000 gal	$59.2070 1,000 gal	$77.4332 per equiv. meters	$5.7991 per bill	
	Residential							
2	Units of Service		968,000	6,630	10,608	15,652	185,760	
3	Allocated Costs of Service	$5,117,409	$533,658	$1,666,450	$628,081	$1,211,984	$1,077,236	
	Commercial							
4	Units of Service		473,000	2,592	4,212	1,758	14,640	
5	Allocated Costs of Service	$1,382,580	$260,764	$651,430	$249,359	$136,128	$84,898	
	Industrial							
6	Units of Service		1,095,000	4,500	6,000	251	420	
7	Allocated Costs of Service	$2,111,837	$603,673	$1,131,051	$355,242	$19,436	$2,436	
	Fire Protection Service							
8	Units of Service			840	5,040			
9	Allocated Costs of Service	$693,289		$211,130	$298,403			$183,756
10	Total Inside-City Allocated Costs of Service	$9,305,116	$1,398,095	$3,660,062	$1,531,085	$1,367,547	$1,164,570	$183,756
	Outside City:							
11	Unit Costs of Service, $/Unit		$0.5783 1,000 gal	$293.5370 1,000 gal	$73.9021 1,000 gal	$86.5400 per equiv. meters	$5.7991 per bill	
12	**Residential**							
13	Units of Service		95,000	729	1,093	1,580	18,240	
14	Allocated Costs of Service	$592,156	$54,942	$213,920	$80,786	$136,733	$105,775	
15	**Wholesale**							
16	Units of Service		230,000	1,418	2,363	34	48	
17	Allocated Costs of Service	$727,048	$133,017	$416,179	$174,632	$2,942	$278	
18	Total System Allocated Costs of Service	$10,624,320	$1,586,053	$4,290,161	$1,786,503	$1,507,223	$1,270,624	$183,756

*Maximum-hour demand in excess of maximum-day demand.

As noted previously, the base-extra capacity method uses the difference between class contribution to the average demand and peak demand, whereas the commodity-demand method uses the class contribution to the total maximum demand. These are clearly two separate and distinct perspectives regarding customer class demand responsibilities.

Customer costs are distributed based on equivalent meter and billing requirements. Commodity costs, which tend to vary with the annual quantity of water produced, are distributed to inside-city customer classes by applying the inside-city commodity unit cost of $0.5513 per thousand gallons to the respective inside-city class units of service. Likewise, demand-related costs for maximum-day and maximum-hour service requirements are distributed to the classes based on the application of total estimated class service demands and the unit costs of demand.

Customer costs for meters and services and for billing and collection are the same under both the base-extra capacity and commodity-demand methods and are distributed similarly in both methods. Meter-and-service costs are distributed to classes in

Table III.2-7 Allocated cost to customer classes—Base-extra capacity and commodity-demand comparison

Line No.	Customer Class	Base-Extra Capacity		Commodity-Demand	
		Allocated Cost of Service	Percentage of Total	Allocated Cost of Service	Percentage of Total
	Inside City:				
1	Residential	$5,011,889	47.2%	$5,117,409	48.2%
2	Commercial	1,399,435	13.2%	1,382,580	13.0%
3	Industrial	2,302,435	21.7%	2,111,837	19.9%
4	Fire Protection Service	624,390	5.9%	693,289	6.5%
5	Total Inside-City Allocated Cost of Service	9,338,150	87.9%	9,305,116	87.6%
	Outside City:				
6	Residential	$569,369	5.4%	$592,156	5.6%
7	Wholesale	716,801	6.7%	727,048	6.8%
8	Total System Allocated Cost of Service	$10,624,320	100.0%	$10,624,320	100.0%

proportion to the number of equivalent ⅝-in. meters, whereas billing and collection costs are distributed on the basis of the number of bills rendered. Cost of service for outside-city service may also be derived by applying the outside-city unit costs of service to outside units of service.

A summation of the distributed costs for each cost component for inside-and outside-city customers yields the total distributed customer class cost-of-service responsibility and appears in the "Total Cost of Service" column in Table III.2-6.

A word of caution should be added that may prevent misinterpretation of the commodity cost of $0.5513 per thousand gallons. Under no circumstances does the commodity cost equate to the base cost of service for water. Even with perfectly uniform use, demand or capacity costs must be added. The base-extra capacity method clearly identifies the base cost of service for water.

A summary comparison of the distribution of costs to customer classes under the base-extra capacity and commodity-demand methods is provided in Table III.2-7. As discussed in chapter III.1, depending on the unique total demand and customer peaking factor characteristics of the utility in question, the base-extra capacity and commodity-demand methods may result in reasonably similar allocation of cost of service to class and the resulting water rates.

This page intentionally blank.

Chapter **III.3**

Emerging Trends in Water Rate-Making

The first edition of this manual was written in 1960, and over the course of the five subsequent editions it has changed to reflect important evolutions in the water utility industry. Though these editions vary—quite considerably in some respects—they are founded on durable fundamental principles that have withstood the tests of time. This chapter continues that tradition of outlining how rate-setting methodologies may evolve to continue to ensure that rates are set in a cost-based and equitable manner as emerging trends change the landscape of the water utility industry. This chapter highlights emerging issues affecting the industry and reviews implications for the water rate-setting community.

Water rate development can and should be tailored to address policy objectives and unique local circumstances. This flexibility has implications for each major phase of the rate-setting process, from the determination of revenue requirements through cost allocations and rate design. As the water utility industry itself evolves, it is important that rate-setting practices be reviewed and refined to ensure adequate revenue recovery and the equitable distribution of cost responsibilities. In this chapter, several emerging trends in water rate-setting practice are introduced. Although some of these trends are mentioned in other sections of this manual, their presentation here is to offer guidance on how rate-setting practice is evolving in response to the challenges and opportunities facing the utility industry.

The evolution of rate setting is being built on a foundation of established practice that has well served the industry. The principles articulated in this manual have provided a basis for ensuring that water utilities have adequate financial resources to deliver reliable, high-quality services and that responsibilities for paying for those services are distributed equitably across customer classes. As an analytical framework, rates derived through cost-of-service analyses establish a benchmark for assessment of rate equity and defensibility that has been accepted by governmental entities and legal courts throughout North America.

The concepts behind revenue requirements and cost allocation have been used for more than 100 years. Legal precedents have solidified this analysis as a industry-accepted method of developing rates. However, as successful as traditional cost-of-service analysis has been, technical advances and evolving perspectives invite improvement and refor-mulation. For example, to the extent that utilities' current cost structures fail to recognize environmental externalities, imperatives for climate change resiliency, or even long-term reinvestment needs, system revenue requirements may be understated. Cost allocation processes rely extensively on judgments and assumptions about everything from the shares of costs allocable to given utility functions to rate-of-return determination. Some of these judgments and assumptions are sound; others are imprecise, misplaced, or even questionable. Most utilities continue to employ customer classification structures that group customers based on assumed similarities in water-use patterns or simple historical inertia. In addition, rate designs—now often constrained by both meter reading and bill-ing system limitations—may be enhanced as technological advances provide higher res-olution data on which to base cost allocations and improved capabilities to send tailored price signals.

As the water utility industry faces new challenges and embraces new opportunities, generally accepted rate-setting practices and methodologies are being adapted to reflect these emerging trends while continuing to ensure equitable distribution of cost responsi-bilities. These emerging trends and challenges include but are not limited to

- **resource scarcities** that have precipitated development of water supplies from new sources (e.g., desalination), various forms of water reuse, and continuing emphasis on water conservation pricing;
- **system investment/reinvestment requirements** that range from renewal and rehabilitation of aged water transmission and distribution networks, to plant upgrades for meeting increasingly stringent regulatory requirements, to imple-menting climate change adaptation measures and enhanced security features; and
- **affordability issues** that have become more pronounced with the general rise of water (and related wastewater and stormwater) service rates at a pace well in excess of income growth in many communities.

These (and other) challenges are complemented by new opportunities and initiatives that hold the prospect for the water utility industry to continue to economically deliver reli-able, high-quality services. These initiatives include but are not limited to

- **information technology** that can provide high-resolution information on facility operations (through supervisory control and data acquisition systems), customer demand patterns (through advanced metering infrastructure systems), and new methods to send customer pricing and usage signals (through automatic phone dialing and texting);
- **water management approaches** that recognize that water utilities may provide a diverse range of services beyond potable water delivery, including water reuse and other "fit-for-use" services that help ensure environmentally responsible and sustainable use of limited water resources; and
- **utility consolidation and collaboration** that provides mechanisms to achieve both operational and capital project efficiencies by leveraging economies of scale and joint purchasing power.

As these dynamics reshape the water utility industry, approaches to rate develop-ment are evolving not only to keep pace, but also to help appropriate price signals be conveyed. Whether through use of advanced metering technologies to inform cost alloca-tions and tailor rates or through asset management programs that better define revenue requirements to ensure long-term system sustainability, these dynamics are manifested in corresponding revisions to rate-setting practices.

REVENUES

Among the trends facing the North American water industry (not noted specifically above) is the gradual, persistent decline in (residential) use per capita over the last two decades, and which has been most noticeable since 2008 (Rockaway et al. 2011, Beecher 2015). This trend has complicated demand forecast and revenue projections on a system and customer-class-level revenue for many utilities. In response, many utilities have looked to diversify their revenue portfolio and make revenue recovery less reliant on volumetric charges or have investigated strategies for developing a more resilient business model (Hughes et al. 2014; discussed further in chapter IV.7).

Diversification is also indicative of a general recognition by water utilities that they are not merely purveyors of potable water services but are vital economic participants in the communities they serve. Water utilities are increasingly viewing their role as providers of a whole range of water-related services. These new sources of funding include, but are not limited to, the following:

- **Service line insurance.** This involves offering protection for water service line failures or breaks within the customer's property boundary (and therefore the property owner's responsibility to repair or replace). Subscribing customers pay regular fees often included on monthly utility service billings to ensure that service lines (and potentially indoor plumbing problems) are repaired without additional costs.

- **Laboratory services.** This involves water quality and other laboratory testing for private sector entities or other water utilities requiring water quality testing. This service involves leveraging specialized expertise and equipment for detection of contaminants.

- **Point-of-use devices and bottled water.** Notwithstanding the exceptional quality of tap water, these revenue generation options recognize market perceptions and consumer demands. Point-of-use service involves installation and regular maintenance of devices providing added filtration of tap water within customers' residences and places of business. Utility plumbers or contracted plumbers may be deployed to install equipment on subscribing customers' property and meter reading or field crews deployed to render regular maintenance. Bottled water generally involves providing additional treatment of a utility's water, bottling either by utility staff or under contract, and retail sales and distribution of the bottled water product.*

Though typically not major revenue sources, to the extent that these noncore sources of revenue are not subject to the same influences that impose volatility in potable water system revenue streams, they afford a measure of revenue resiliency. From a rate development standpoint, they require careful cost allocation procedures but may also provide nonrate revenue sources that mitigate the increasing pressures on service rates imposed by increasingly stringent water quality regulations, system reinvestment requirements, and other factors.

---

* In some cases, eschewing the revenue generation potential and policy issues associated with competing for sales with private bottled water providers, a utility will provide bottled water at local community events free of charge as a form of public relations and education regarding the quality of tap water not subject to further treatment. See, for example, Louisville Water Company's Pure Tap program (www.louisvillepuretap.com/).

RESERVES

Establishing and maintaining adequate reserves is an important financial management practice of a water utility. Reserves typically include operating reserves, capital/construction/depreciation reserves, and bond reserves. Reserves, particularly operating reserves, have traditionally been maintained to address cash-flow needs and the lag between expenses incurred and revenues received.

In recent years, utilities have been challenged financially by two emerging trends. First, utilities have experienced declining per capita use. In addition, many water utilities have been faced with water supply shortages and, in some cases, severe droughts, leading to voluntary or mandatory reductions in use. Both of these trends have led to reduced sales and revenues that, in turn, have prompted utilities' desire for greater revenue stability from their rates.

Reserve funds can address short-term fluctuations in revenue levels until such time that rates may be adjusted to address utilities' reduced sales volumes, if implemented correctly. However, in using this approach, utilities need to establish and maintain reserve levels above those established for "normal" cash-flow fluctuations. This additional amount of reserves should be established in relation to the potential volatility of rate revenues of the particular utility. Much like a water reservoir, if these reserve funds are drawn down in a particular rate-setting period, their replenishment should be funded in a following rate-setting period. Unlike a water reservoir, the refilling of financial reserves requires commitment to fiscal stability on the part of utility managers and governing boards.

REVENUE REQUIREMENTS

The increasing pressures on rate levels and reserve requirements, compounded by new and increasing demands for efficiency, resiliency, and environmental accountability, hold the prospect for changing the structure of utility revenue requirements. Traditional rate-setting practices focused on well-defined, familiar expenses associated with system operations and infrastructure development financing. However, new expense categories and/or new ways that traditional expenses will be incurred may be anticipated as interest in alternative valuation approaches as a basis for rates, holistic water management, climate change adaptation, and sustainability gain currency.

Alternative Rate-Base Valuation Methodologies

Utility rate regulation allows investors or owners to earn a reasonable rate of return on the value of their investment. *Value* in this context may be open to different interpretations, but the connotation centers on concepts of investment value and fair value. One issue related to the valuation of utility plant in service is whether original cost (i.e., the capitalized value of utility plant as recorded in financial records) or an estimate of current value should be used. Original cost is generally accepted and is, by far, the most common basis for determining annual depreciation expense, accumulated depreciation, and the net value of rate base assets under the utility-basis approach to revenue requirement determination. However, current or fair value approaches to determine utility plant-related capital costs (rate base) are occasionally used and of increasing interest as the industry addresses the need to replace built infrastructure at costs substantially higher than original cost values.

In some circumstances, the rate-making provisions of wholesale water supply or water wheeling contracts may require that utility plant in service be valued at replacement cost, typically as determined by the application of historical construction cost inflation factors to original cost values. In other cases, a wholesale contract may require that utility plant in service be valued at fair market value, often estimated based on a combination of original cost and current replacement cost. In many cases, these types of contractual requirements are intended to mimic the regulatory practices once followed by state public utility commissions who allowed investor-owned electric power and natural gas utilities to deviate from the original cost approach to rate base valuation.

Regardless of its genesis or the specific calculation methodology employed, the ultimate outcome of using a current or fair value approach will be an increase in capital-related revenue requirements to be recovered from rates (assuming the allowed rate of return on rate base assets is not adjusted downward correspondingly). This outcome, which may be entirely appropriate depending on the specific circumstances in question, will occur because the value of net rate base assets under a current value approach is almost always much higher than if these same assets were valued using original (investment) cost. All else equal, the result is both a level of higher depreciation expense and a higher return on rate base being included in the utility revenue requirement.

Understated/Excluded Costs

Although utility revenue requirements represent the funding through rates required (immediately) to sustain utility services, they may be viewed as systematically understating the true costs of utility services. A more expansive view of the costs to serve—and an emerging trend—internalizes what have traditionally been regarded as market externalities. Utilities that maintain or develop additional water supplies are increasingly being required to prevent or mitigate the environmental consequences of flow diversions. Water utilities' uses of electricity—to deliver raw water supplies, treat water to potable standards, and send potable water to customers' taps (under pressure)—are now recognized as having a significant carbon footprint. Prospective revenue requirements may incorporate the costs of various mitigation or compensation measures. Similarly, to the extent that climate change adaptation requires new infrastructure investments (as well as emergency response protocols), utility revenue requirements will be affected—with associated questions regarding appropriate cost allocations.

Alternative Project Delivery

In addition, as cost pressures and risks mount, many utilities are looking to alternative project delivery mechanisms to deliver capital projects and services, potentially imposing structural changes on utility revenue requirements. For example, where traditional water treatment plant development costs would readily be designated as a capital expense and plant operations designated as operating expenses, the rate-making treatment of the costs of services delivered under a build-own-operate-transfer model are not as readily delineated.

Alternative Funding Sources

The advent of alternative project delivery mechanisms complements a broadening range of capital financing mechanisms from changes in the eligibility of projects funded through traditional State Revolving Fund loan programs, to the Water Infrastructure Finance and Innovation Authority program (see Copeland 2015, Curtis 2014), to the use of private equity. Although these funding sources will not likely have significant effects on the procedures used for allocations of cost responsibilities, they are affecting the trajectory of rate levels and the structure of the marketplace within which utilities operate.

Regionalization

Regionalization refers to the consolidation of utilities, utility assets, and/ or utility operations within a given geographic area. There are many reasons why utilities may wish to consolidate, but the most frequently cited motives relate to system revenue requirements. Regionalization may achieve operational efficiencies and economies of scale, and avoid duplication of substantial capital investments. Whether such goals can be met depends on the nature of the consolidation efforts, the types of assets to be consolidated, the levels of service to be provided regionally, and the governance structure used to manage the regionalized assets and operations.

Regionalization may bring about difficult and often complex issues related to the cost-of-service principles discussed at length in this manual. The key considerations tend to fall into three categories: economics, levels of service, and governance. Economic considerations include the range of issues around costs of services, equitable allocation of those costs, and the business case for (or against) the proposed regionalization effort. A beneficial regionalization should result in lower long-run costs per unit of service, irrespective of potential short-term anomalies, for all of the parties involved. Level-of-service considerations relate to the types of services provided and the quality of those services. Levels of service (and associated service rates) may vary in terms of treated water quality (e.g., potable, "fit-for-use"), reliability, and other overall system performance criteria. Governance considerations cover a range of issues from organizational structure to political and legal frameworks. Informal agreements may require no political buy-in and have limited effects on rate setting while a full merger will almost certainly involve significant rate-setting changes, a formal vote of governing bodies, and a host of legal actions.

Regionalization, alternative project delivery and financing methods, and changes in the composition of costs are all emerging trends that are affecting water utility revenue requirements. In some cases, these trends are simply altering the levels and trajectory of rate changes; in other situations, they are impacting the distribution of cost responsibilities across customer classes. Complementing these drivers of system revenue requirements are emerging changes to cost allocation practices that are leveraging new technologies and approaches to service delivery.

COST ALLOCATION

Although cost allocation practices have been relatively stable during years of significant change in the water industry, the cumulative effects of technology, staffing, regulatory, and customer demand pattern changes, among many other factors, are causing some utilities to consider modifications in how they allocate costs. This section introduces some of the ideas being explored to enhance and extend equity in cost allocation.

Recognition of Improved Data to Support Cost Allocations

One of the most powerful drivers of new cost allocation approaches is the dramatic improvement in the quality and availability of relevant information. Improvements are being driven by two key utility management initiatives: advanced metering infrastructure and asset management.

- **Advanced metering infrastructure (AMI).** Utilities measure customers' demands on their systems in a variety of ways. Demands are not only associated with volumetric consumption but also actual and potential claims on capacity, customer service requirements, proximity to the system, and even the value of structures being served. Historically, information on customer or customer class demand characteristics was limited to quarterly or monthly observations. Route/cycle meter reading protocols and billing system constraints further contributed to demand statistics and utility billing data sets that provided less than optimal foundations for cost allocations.

AMI installations, also referred to as "fixed network systems," provide frequent (e.g., four or more times per hour) data readings through fixed radio networks. This represents a significant improvement in measurement accuracy and available data resolution. In many communities, rate analysts are able to access detailed customer class consumption profiles—actual measurements of peak-day and peak-hour demands—rather than rely on conceptual analysis or estimated industry-wide demand characteristics. These information improvements may enhance rate analyses as well as demand analyses, leak detection, and conservation monitoring and education. Customer service may also be enhanced by AMI-enabled customer feedback mechanisms that deliver timely information on customers' consumption patterns (via home dashboards or even cell phone applications), effectively eliminating the disconnection between the timing of customer demands and traditional quarterly or monthly billed price signals.

Material implications for rate-making could include enhancements in the ability to characterize customer class contributions to system peaks—both coincidental and noncoincidental, as described in appendix A—and the potential to build more homogeneous customer classes. These changes could represent the most significant improvement in the potential to enhance equity in cost recovery since the widespread adoption of water meters.

- **Asset management.** Historically, local government utilities tended to track investments in capital assets with less detail and accuracy than was required of investor-owned utilities where the determination of rate base plays a key role in regulated rate setting. With the issuance of Statement 34 by the Governmental Accounting Standards Board, and more generally with the evolution of accounting and management practices, local government utilities have embraced asset management and improved the quality of information on assets used to provide service. Rather than using depreciation schedules used for accounting purposes, asset management takes into consideration many factors, including condition assessments and risk factors to determine needed system investment over an extended period of time.

  Asset management initiatives, oriented to minimize the life-cycle costs of capital assets at acceptable levels of risk (NACWA et al. 2002), represent a significant business improvement and, when integrated into financial and rate-planning processes, can help more equitably allocate cost responsibilities. Asset management initiatives take a wide variety of forms but typically enable utilities to document the investments they have made by year, location, and function, as well as providing significantly enhanced information on asset condition and value. This improved information on both historic investment and future needs provides the potential for enhanced cost allocation accuracy through improved data on investment by key functions. An additional benefit will be the simplification of obtaining updated information as assets in service change over time.

Recognition of Cost Differentials

In some cases, improved information accuracy will allow utilities to recognize cost differentials in rate-making that were previously impossible to support with available data. The transition from manual records to digital records, and increasingly to more detailed, higher resolution digital data sets will be of benefit in cases where the investment to serve different customer classes deviates significantly from typical patterns.

Although not every differential in costs warrants recognition in cost allocation, and given that the water industry's established practice of aggregating customers into classes continues to be valid and appropriate, emerging data acquisition and management capacities hold considerable promise. Customer classifications may be enhanced to reflect differences in demands and associated cost to serve not previously acknowledged in cost allocation. Three notable examples are distance, elevation, and seasonal cost concepts.

1. **Distance from source of supply or treatment facilities.** This potential cost allocation factor may be used in cases where specific investments are required to serve a single customer or well-defined subset of customers defined by distance characteristics and material deviations in related costs. Though potentially problematic, distance* is obviously a cost driver, and the combination of ease of location tracking for each account (e.g., geographic information system, better customer data) and improved network modeling offers the potential for some utilities to consider distance-based pricing. Prudence dictates the development of boundary conditions to prevent the drawing of irrelevant distinctions, but a utility with an extended distribution system may soon have the capability of recognizing such cost differentials.

2. **Elevation (pumping costs) differentials.** As with distance, elevation has been used in limited and selected cases where specific investments are required to serve a single or well-defined subset of high-elevation customers. Although elevation factors may be problematic, information technology enhancements hold the potential to recognize cost-of-service differences associated with delivering water service to higher elevations. These enhancements include real-time monitoring and control of pumping facilities and customer demand profiles, improved network models, and other analytical tools that may facilitate elevation-related cost allocations.

3. **Seasonal cost concepts.** Utilities often face widely divergent costs of supply at different times in the year and nearly always face different costs of meeting peak relative to average-day demands. Examples of cost divergences include wholesale supply contracts with seasonal pricing differences or supplemental sources of supply called on only "in season." When seasonal or peak-demand differences are associated with material differences in costs, cost-of-service analyses may appropriately consider these effects. Improved information on class behavior during system peak periods, drawn from higher-resolution monitoring of daily and hourly demands by class relative to specific capacity limitations, could allow recognition of associated cost differences when performing cost allocations.

Improved data will not resolve all of the hard questions required to allocate costs equitably across customer classes, but the data are presenting new opportunities to refine allocations and rate structures to reflect better understood, system-specific realities. Information improvements are also presenting new opportunities for customer classification.

---

* Distance is often used as an example of a factor with as many potentially negative as positive attributes. The downsides include the potential for unending calls for refinements and consideration of nuances. A "system-wide" approach dispenses with such non-equity-enhancing work by embracing a level of service standard that recognizes that all customers throughout the geographically distributed system are receiving the same benefit.

Customer Classification

The emerging aspect to be addressed in this section is prompted in large part by the greater ability to disaggregate traditional customer classes with better technology that yields greater data resolution to recognize diversities in traditional classifications. On the wastewater side, this may also involve recognition of the resource recovery value of contributed water streams.

Utilities of the future are not limited to reliance on customer classes of the past. Though traditional customer classes have enabled defensible and equitable cost allocations, it may be possible to create more precise groupings of customers for rate-making purposes as new information and billing system capabilities evolve. The dramatic increase in consumption and other customer data (made available, for example, by AMI systems) will empower some utilities to explore a variety of customer class refinements:

- Variability in demand patterns within the residential customer class is often not recognized in customer billing systems. It may be desirable to distinguish between single-family and several different versions of multifamily housing, and perhaps between different single-family housing units to reflect different peak and average demand characteristics or other water usage determinants (e.g., lot sizes, plumbing fixture units).

- Commercial, industrial, wholesale, and contract customers exhibit significant diversity in consumption patterns. Water uses reflect needs ranging from that of the proverbial dress shop to a water theme park. Irrigation is a key differentiator, as it is in residential classes, and equally relevant to cost allocations. The ability to better track individual customers' usage characteristics may reveal obvious clustering that suggests new customer classifications or confirms similarities within a utility's existing classes.

- Nontraditional customer classification could be structured to address other customer characteristics beyond those related to metered consumption. In some cases, customer classes could reflect potential demand, or even desired levels of demand, as refinements or extensions to more common demand concepts. In cases of extreme conservation objectives, some utilities might consider differentiation to reflect the uses to which water is applied, or usage levels determined to be "excessive" given local supply and cost considerations. Equity and cost allocation issues remain, but improvements in the breadth, quality, and ability to analyze information are stimulating new conversations and examinations.

- Utilities could have the potential to identify certain selected affordability criteria and create an explicit affordability-related class. Challenges and risks associated with affordability programs are identified in chapter V.4, but for purposes of this section, if rates are to be a part of a utility's affordability strategy, customer classifications informed by better information on household demographic characteristics could be leveraged.

RATE DESIGN

The "art" of rate-making tends to be seen through the development of structures of rates and charges that provide for adequate revenue recovery and best meet competing pricing objectives. The technological innovations and changing perspectives previously noted both affect the balancing of objectives and afford new opportunities to send more effective price signals to customers.

Some long-standing rate-design considerations, such as the reexamination of trade-offs between base and volumetric charges, have regained such immediate importance that they warrant mention in this chapter. Other rate-design options are just emerging, and the direction of the industry is far from established. Examples relate to the potential for greater disaggregation of customer classes, and the potential to perform better-informed, higher resolution cost allocation procedures. These changes provide important foundational knowledge required for more complex rate designs, and they could dramatically change rate schedules in the future. On the other hand, many utilities' responses to greater revenue volatility and declining per capita usage involve returning to, and reinvigorating, tried-and-true, and often more simple, rate structure options.

Fixed Versus Variable Charges

Most water utilities have a portion of their rate structure as a flat or fixed fee that a customer pays regardless of the amount of water used*, often graduated based on meter size. The other components of most rate structures are variable charges based on the volume of water used. The ratio of revenue recovered from base versus volumetric charges is a major factor in utility revenue stability. A relatively small proportion of revenue coming from base charges imposes more financial vulnerability, especially where there is also an imbalance between fixed costs and fixed revenues. Designing rates so that a higher proportion of the utility's revenue comes from base charges is advantageous from the standpoint of revenue stability. However, higher base charges may dampen conservation price signals and affect the affordability of minimal levels of service.

Tailored fixed charges (reflecting peak usage). In the traditional model, all customers in the residential class with the same meter size pay the same base charge. However, some suggested rate-design models challenge the concept of equal base charges for all customers within the same class or with the same meter size. Studies tracking individual customer usage have shown that installed meter size within the residential class does not capture the variation in use (and cost impact on the system) among these customers (Boyle et al. 2011). Given that peaking drives much of a utility's expenses, models where each customer has a unique base charge, depending on the peak usage or peaking pattern of that customer, are being explored. For example, in one approach inspired by power utilities' demand ratchet charges, a customer's base charge could be set based on a three-year rolling average of that customer's peak month of demand. This would create a unique base charge for each customer. The utility would still charge variable commodity charges, but they could constitute a lower proportion of a customer's bill. This could represent a way to increase revenue stability while recognizing the value of allocating a significant portion of total costs to reflect peak period use of the system. This model could allow a utility to build more of its cost recovery into the base charge while still promoting customer conservation and efficiency. In particular, it would encourage consistent customer water use as well as more precisely allocate cost responsibilities within the residential customer class—an increasingly important concern as the share of costs recovered through base charges increases (Hughes et al. 2014).

Alternative approaches for developing cost-of-service-based base charges. While many utilities have a base charge that is determined by meter size, another approach regaining currency as utilities look to achieve greater revenue resiliency is the concept of

---

* Some utilities include a minimum quantity allowance, typically 1,000–3,000 gallons, in their base charges. These consumption allowances, when discounted, have been a way for utilities to respond to concerns about affordability. However, many communities have eschewed the notion that any quantity of water use should be included "free" with payments of fixed charges, and non-rate-structure programs are increasingly recognized as a means to provide more focused and more effective opportunities to address service affordability.

a "minimum bill." In this case, the utility may calculate the customer's bill based purely on volume consumed. If the calculated bill is more than the minimum bill, the customer is charged at the calculated amount. However, if the calculated amount is less than the minimum bill, the customer is charged the minimum bill amount. This approach recognizes the substantial fixed costs to serve customer accounts that would not be recovered through volumetric charges that fail to exceed certain minimum levels.

Similarly, "readiness to serve" charges perhaps connote something more comprehensive than simple "base charges" in conveying the incurrence of fixed costs to service customer accounts. Both terms relate to charges that aim at capturing the costs of having a system in place to provide water to the customer regardless of whether the customer consumes any water in a given service period. Common inputs for both charges include costs such as

- billing costs (meter reading, mailing bills, accounting, collecting, and customer service),
- debt-service cost (allocating at least a portion of the annual utility debt service), and
- fire protection (allocating public fire protection costs for the oversizing of distribution facilities).

In developing readiness-to-serve charges, one can go as far as analyzing the minimum distribution system required to serve water customers. This is a concept that is also inspired by the electricity industry. The rationale is that a minimum amount of distribution system investment and operation and maintenance (O&M) expenses are required to enable the system to be ready to serve. As the number of customers to a system increases, so does O&M, and fixed capital costs may be spread over larger populations. However, the minimum system requirements may be considered customer-related costs recoverable through the readiness-to-serve charge. One method for calculating the minimum system concept in the water sector could be to calculate the cost of distributing one gallon of water per day to customers (Gould and Grace 2011). That theoretical minimum investment can then be compared to the total current utility investment to determine the customer-related portion of distribution lines. Such an approach allows the utility to establish a base charge that relates more closely to the cost of providing water service.

Individualized Rate Setting

Customer classes are created to provide an equitable means of cost recovery through a manageable rate schedule. Associating users with similar demand profiles is at the heart of class creation, and this practice continues to render equity in cost recovery. But aggregation of customers into classes necessarily obscures some level of detail. With modern data systems, it is possible in some cases to create a more customized cost recovery plan.

One approach already adopted by some utilities is to recognize "load factor" concepts to reward stable usage and push costs toward those users who make larger contributions to system peaks. A variety of rate structure options are possible. One is a set of increasing blocks with individualized breakpoints reflecting each customer's usage pattern. A residential customer could be provided with a first tier consumption approximating their consumption during a time of year when irrigation is not common. The individual amounts would differ within the class, reflecting the stable usage portion of that individual customer's consumption pattern. Further breakpoints could be set at increments to first tier levels, providing a stepped conservation incentive uniquely reflecting each customer's demands. The objective of this approach would be to push costs of meeting peak water demands to those individual customers contributing the most to those peaks. If customers as a whole respond by changing their consumption patterns, the utility would essentially reacquire capacity; and if peak usage was a key constraint, this would enhance the utility's ability to serve new customers and advance economic development opportunities. If customer responsiveness to the structure was low, the utility would gain by having reallocated costs to better reflect cost–causation and potentially increase revenue generation from price-insensitive customers.

Similarly, isolation of the irrigation component of usage will be increasingly possible for utilities seeking to allocate costs differentially based on the uses to which water is put. This is the core of the "water budget" concept under which utilities are managing scarce resources by allocating capacity to meet some measure or estimate of customer need. The ability to capture a high level of detail on consumption could allow a utility to explore differing rates for indoor and outdoor usage based on an algorithm reflecting individualized consumption patterns. A simple "indoor/ outdoor" structure, customized to each individual customer's usage pattern that can be easily communicated to the public, may render support as a focused conservation tool.

Following a similar track, an allocation of peak-related costs could be made through a base charge component reflecting individual customers' usage in some past period. Base charges could then be augmented by volumetric charges (in varying forms) that match recovery of peak-related costs with behaviors contributing to system peaks.

Any form of more individualized rate-setting approach will introduce additional uncertainty that must be managed. Revenue instability could be increased if rate structure changes contribute to material fluctuation in customer demands. This could be the case whether the changes result in class instability, or even if limited to material changes in billable volumes for key classes. As a result, careful planning and analysis is a prerequisite for any significant change toward individualized rate structures.

Customer Choice Rate-Design Options

A concept with the potential to greatly contribute to ratepayer support of alternative rate structures involves customer "opt-in" provisions. Letting customers have some choice in the selection of their rate schedule provides both an increased connection with customers and an enhanced level of communication of the utility's pricing and cost recovery objectives. Many potential customer selection options could be applicable to utilities in different circumstances, each requiring careful thought and analysis to support revenue-sufficient, cost-based allocations.

One form of this strategy is a capacity allowance, and such programs are in effect in some communities as part of their impact fee programs. Capacity costs are paid as a condition of service, and usage is monitored in the future (through effective use of modern billing systems). If demands exceed the specified amount—generally with some allowance for variability—an additional capacity payment is required. As long as trigger conditions are carefully set, equity enhancements would be possible, as well as increases in customers' awareness of their water use. Customers with self-selected capacity allowances are more likely to be aware of their peak usage and more fully engaged in monitoring their consumption behavior.

Another example might be applicable to a utility with a significant seasonal residential component of their customer base. Some customers are concerned with the base charges due when they are out of town for an extended period and might appreciate a rate option that allowed for a certain number of turn-ons and turn-offs each year, recovering costs but also providing a sense of control to the customer. To fully recover all costs appropriately, the net financial impact might be minimal, but an improvement in customer satisfaction could result.

One more example might be an "aspirational" conservation class stipulating best practices in water usage and conservation, associated with appropriately lower cost-based allocations. Rewarding customer commitment to conservation could contribute not only to conservation, but also to enhancing a utility's image in the customer base at large.

Drought Surcharges

Drought changes water use although not always in an easily predictable direction. If a utility in a drought area has ample water supply and no obligations to enact water-use restrictions, the utility's financial condition can actually improve with more revenue from increased demand. On the other hand, where supply level is threatened or regulations call for curtailments, revenue under-recovery may result. A utility in the latter scenario may offset the revenue losses due to conservation during water shortage periods by implementing drought surcharges. The surcharge is a temporary and higher rate for water that is removed when the drought condition is alleviated. The surcharge has the dual purpose of discouraging water use, as well as increasing the revenue from the water that is used. This concept is discussed in further detail in chapter V.3.

Drought surcharges have been successful in many drought-stricken communities but have been seen as insufficiently refined tools in others. Challenges have included

- mismatches between billing cycles and times of drought impact,
- difficulties in equitably implementing unanticipated rate changes,
- confusion in customer understanding of the rate schedule, and
- targeting surcharges to customers contributing disproportionately to water supply impacts.

New data and billing tools could provide significantly enhanced precision and clarity to utilities and their customers and thereby enhance the effect of drought surcharge programs on consumption. New billing tools, supplemented by different, timelier, and more effective communication strategies, may enable a community to send current price signals that are effective forms of drought pricing. These drought surcharges may improve revenue resilience and enable utilities to meet their water resource management obligations.

SUMMARY AND CONCLUSIONS

In some ways, historical limitations of water rate-setting practices are simultaneously indicative of both water utility industry success and failure. As noted, traditional cost-of-service analysis has been a hallmark of an industry with a profound history of success. Water utility service throughout most of North America is economical, reliable, and high quality. Service costs, with few exceptions, are affordable by almost every metric. Water service that meets stringent potable water quality standards is reliably delivered in most communities on a continuous (24/7) basis. Pricing of services to recover average embedded costs of service under a cost-causative framework, as contemplated through cost-of-service analysis, ensures against exacting monopoly rents and generally provides for utility financial viability and sustainability—an attribute of an effective utility. The water industry's historical practices are not broken.

At the same time, changes in environmental and technological conditions, as well as in management, customer, and regulatory perceptions, provide new challenges and suggest some need for water rate-setting practices to evolve in concert with industry dynamics. These changes offer both opportunities and risks, emphasizing the need for both open-minded exploration and cautious analysis. The success and historic evolution of this manual testifies to the water industry's ability to embrace progress while retaining core principles and successful techniques.

REFERENCES

Beecher, J. 2015. *How Low Can It Go? Implications of Falling Usage for Water Utilities.* East Lansing, Mich.: Institute of Public Utilities, Michigan State University. Revised March 17, 2015.

Boyle, Christine E., Shadi Eskaf, Mary Wyatt Tiger, and Jeffrey A. Hughes. 2011. Mining water billing data to inform policy and communication strategies. *Journal AWWA* 103, no. 11 (2011): 45-58.

Copeland, C. 2015. *Water Infrastructure Financing: The Water Infrastructure Finance and Innovation Act (WIFIA) Program.* Washington, D.C.: Congressional Research Service. August 6.

Curtis, T. 2014. Open Channel—WIFIA: Now We Put It to Work. *Journal AWWA*, 106(9):10.

Gould, T., and G. Wilcox. 2011. Back to the Future: Revenue Stability and "Readiness to Serve Charges. In *Proceedings of the 2011 AWWA/WEF Utility Management Conference.* Denver, Colo.: AWWA.

Hughes, J., M. Tiger, S. Eskaf, S.I. Berahzer, S. Royster, C. Boyle, D. Batten, P. Brandt, and C. Noyes. 2014. *Defining a Resilient Business Model for Water Utilities.* Denver, Colo.: Water Research Foundation.

NACWA, AWWA, AMWA, and WEF (National Association of Clean Water Agencies, American Water Works Association, Association of Metropolitan Water Agencies, and Water Environment Federation). 2002. *Managing Public Infrastructure Assets to Minimize Cost and Maximize Performance.* Washington, D.C.: Association of Metropolitan Sewerage Agencies.

Rockaway, T.D., P.A. Coomes, J. Rivard, and B. Kornstein. 2011. Residential Water Use Trends in North America. *Journal AWWA*, 103(2):76–89.

Section IV
Rate Design

This page intentionally blank.

Chapter **IV.1**

Selecting Rate Structures

A utility is presented with a major challenge when it sets out to select a rate structure that is responsive to the philosophy and objectives of both the utility and its community. Rates and rate structures are subject to legal requirements and typically consider various other criteria (see Corssmit 2010 for details). It is important for the utility and its customers to select the appropriate rate structure because the majority of the utility's revenues are collected through water rates and because pricing policies may support a community's social, economic, political, and environmental concerns.

A *water rate structure* is a user charge or schedule of user charges designed, among other things, to recover the utility's costs. Rate structures vary from utility to utility but generally include three elements. First, they include consideration of the classifications of customers served (i.e., residential, commercial, and industrial). Second, they establish the frequency of billing. Third, they identify the charges or schedule of charges each classification of customer will be assessed. It is this final element of a rate structure, the schedule of charges, on which utilities and customers tend to focus. These charges vary by utility in level (how high or low) and in design (how customers are charged). For water utilities that use a cost-based approach, which is highly recommended, the level of the utility's rates is a function of the utility's costs and customer demands. The design, however, is a function of many diverse and sometimes competing objectives.

When diverse and competing objectives are well understood and evaluated, a utility has the opportunity to design a rate structure that does more than simply recover its costs. A properly selected rate structure should support and optimize a blend of various utility objectives and should work as a public information tool in communicating these objectives to customers.

PLANNING THE RATE STRUCTURE STUDY

The process of selecting the most appropriate rate structure for a particular utility and its customers is not simple. The selection is complex because there are so many types of rate structures. No one rate structure meets all utility objectives equally, and not all objectives are valued the same by the utility or its customers. Even within a single utility, because of these objectives, each customer class may not use the same rate structure. For example, to appropriately reflect the different costs of serving various customer classes, it may be most appropriate for residential customers to be charged using an increasing (tiered) block rate structure, while commercial customers are billed under a uniform rate structure. In addition, a rate structure may or may not be appropriate for a specific customer class. For example, in establishing a conservation-oriented rate structure, greater use does not necessarily imply "inefficient or wasteful" use given that a utility's largest water consumers may be some of the most conservation-oriented and efficient users on the system. For those reasons, a "one size fits all" approach to rate structures may not be appropriate within a utility that has a diverse customer base and usage patterns. Because selecting the most appropriate rate structure is an important undertaking, it is advisable that the utility spend some time up front planning the approach for the selection process. The process described in this chapter divides the study approach into three steps. It is important to note that there is no one correct way to design a study of this nature. Among other things, planning the study approach is a valuable exercise that will identify ideas and obstacles. The actual study may deviate somewhat from the plan, but the plan should help keep the study moving in the right direction. As with any decision, selecting the appropriate rate structure depends on at least the following three components:

1. Defining the goals and objectives of the rate structure
2. Evaluating the available alternatives in meeting these goals and objectives
3. Understanding and communicating the potential effects on customers

Based on these three components, a rate selection process might include the following steps.

Step 1. Defining Goals and Objectives

This critical starting point is often difficult. Questions such as "Why is the study being conducted?", "Is there a problem with the existing structure?", and "What is the goal of the study?" must all be addressed to focus the study scope. As part of this step, it is important to have a clear understanding as to why alternative rate structures are being considered. To determine if the existing method or an alternative rate structure best meets the utility's needs, there must be a comprehensive understanding of the utility's operations, its economic and legal environment, and the customers it serves. It is also important to understand

- the utility's history,
- how customers responded to existing and previous rate structures and rate adjustments,
- who are the major classes and major customers,
- contractual rate obligations,
- the availability of water resources,
- the level of current or future costs,
- customer and utility concerns,
- socioeconomic status and concerns of customers, and
- legal constraints on the utility.

These factors play an important part in determining which rate structure best meets the utility's goals.

Next, the utility must determine its rate structure objectives. Rate structures can perform several functions that support the utility's overall objectives. Rate objectives common to many utilities and their customers include

- yielding necessary revenue in a stable and predictable manner;
- minimizing unexpected changes to customer bills;
- discouraging wasteful use and promoting efficient uses;
- promoting fairness and equity (i.e., cost-based);
- avoiding discrimination;
- maintaining simplicity, certainty, convenience, feasibility, and freedom from controversy; and
- complying with all applicable laws.

Evaluating and weighing alternative rate structures and effects against these objectives is, perhaps, the most important part in the process of selecting a rate structure (Bonbright, Danielsen, and Kamerschen 1988).

Step 2. Evaluating Available Alternatives

The first item to assess when evaluating alternative rate structures is the level of effort allotted to the study. The availability of resources and time and the inclusion and degree of public involvement are primary drivers in determining this level of effort. More rigorous and technically complete studies, involving significant public input, require ample resources and time.

Public involvement (discussed in detail in chapter VIII.1) can take many forms, but it often includes a core group of individual volunteers who study the issue as a committee and periodically report and consult with the general public at open meetings. Typically, a committee should also have representation from utility management, finance staff, the governing board, and customer groups that would be affected by the rate structure. The composition of this committee is crucial if the results are to be meaningful and responsive to the utility's overall objectives. The committee must have credibility with the key parties involved with the utility, as well as with constituencies in the community they represent.

Next, a list of alternative rate structures needs to be identified. Although rate structures are generally composed of three components (who is charged, how often, and how much), most discussion about rate structures centers around the structure's consumption charge. Typically, there are four basic types of consumption-based rate structures: uniform, decreasing block, increasing block, and seasonal. These are discussed in detail in chapters IV.2 through IV.5. In chapter IV.6, a distinctly different increasing block rate approach is discussed—water-budget rates. With these different types of consumption charges, combined with the additional option of service charges, meter charges, or minimum charges, as well as the potential for various customer class configurations, there are numerous rate structures from which to choose. To facilitate the selection process, the study must focus on a reasonable number of suitable alternatives.

Finally, evaluation criteria may be developed and prioritized to provide a rational method of determining how well each alternative rate structure meets the selected rate objectives. Evaluation criteria can be both quantitative (e.g., provides conservation incentive) and qualitative (e.g., simple and easy to understand). Some criteria must be met regardless of other evaluation principles. For example, compliance with legal requirements and revenue sufficiency must be met. It is commonly thought that a cost-based quantitative analysis is less subjective than a qualitative analysis and is, therefore, more defensible. However, most quantitative analyses are based on certain assumptions and data limitations. Hence, a quantitative analysis should not necessarily be construed as precise. In developing evaluation criteria, both quantitative and qualitative analyses may be appropriate depending on the objective being measured. For example, a quantitative analysis might be developed to measure a rate structure's effects on the objective of revenue stability; a qualitative analysis would be used to measure perceived fairness of a rate structure.

Step 3. Understanding and Communicating Outcomes

Most evaluations of rate structures have a technical format. The tendency when presenting the technical trade-offs, such as the revenue effects or typical customer bills under various rate structures, is to present the information in a quantitative format. For many audiences, however, a numerical presentation of an evaluation is overly complicated and may not be well understood. The message often becomes lost in the numbers. Simple charts, graphs, and matrix presentations tend to work well for a wide range of audiences because the display reinforces the message and the numbers add information. For diverse audiences (including decision makers) to understand them, technical outcomes must be presented in easily understood formats that express and support the technical analysis in nontechnical terms.

RATE STRUCTURE VARIABLES AND CONSIDERATIONS

Availability and Quality of Data

The importance of the availability and quality of data cannot be overemphasized. To perform a good rate structure evaluation, there must be reliable and ample data resources. Key types of information are: past and projected cost records, water sales data by billing period and customer class, revenue data by billing period and type of charge, and other customer account data. Ideally, this data will also include bill tabulation information. A bill tabulation compiles the distribution of accounts and usage levels under current conditions (see appendix C) and can be used in evaluating rate-design alternatives. This information is often presented by customer class, meter size, month, season, or year. These data are necessary not only to determine the cost to serve each customer class, but also to estimate the billing effects of various rate structures to different types of customers. See chapter VIII.2 for a detailed discussion of the data requirements for conducting a comprehensive water rate study.

Customer Diversity

The water utility's total system demands, seasonal demands, facility needs, and the resulting costs are a function of the diverse demands among a water utility's customers. Recognizing and recovering the costs associated with different types of demand from the appropriate customer classes avoids subsidies among customer classes and minimizes potential subsidies within customer classes. Differences in demand patterns and facility requirements are typically the basis for distinguishing customer classes. This diversity of demand among classes is what results in different costs of service per unit of water sold.

Seasonality of Revenues and Costs

The seasonal variability of operating expenses and revenues should be reviewed when selecting a rate structure. It is likely that a utility's revenues will fluctuate to a greater extent over the course of a year than do the utility's operating expenses. The financial integrity of a utility requires that the utility's rate structure, along with other financial controls, support the cash-flow needs of the utility by not jeopardizing the utility's ability to meet its annual and seasonal expenses.

It is also important to draw the distinction between operating expenses as they relate to both cash flow and a cost-of-service analysis. Although the operating expenses on a cash-flow basis may not fluctuate dramatically, a cost-of-service analysis may indicate that a portion of the utility's costs are associated with meeting peak demands. For example, the payroll expense at the treatment plant may occur at a relatively level amount each month, but, based on cost-of-service principles, some of this cost may be allocated to peak demands.

Ability to Send Price Signals

Many of the desired outcomes of a rate structure depend on customers receiving a price signal or an understanding of the cost of their consumption. For a utility to maximize its price signal, customers must have timely information, and the signal must be meaningful to customers.

The element of time is critical to sending a price signal. As long as utilities maintain monthly and bimonthly billing cycles, a customer's bill lags the actual time of consumption by, at best, one to two months. The customer's ability to quickly respond to the price signal is limited because the signal arrives after the fact. Over the long term, however, it may be possible for customers to adjust their water consumption habits based on previous price signals.

Price Elasticity of Demand

Price elasticity of demand is a measurement of how buyers respond to changes in price. Under normal conditions, as the price of a product increases, buyers demand less of the product. This relationship, measured in percentages between the change in price and the change in demand, is called the price elasticity of demand.

All products have a different price elasticity of demand. Products that are nonprice responsive (i.e., as the price changes, the relative change in demand is small) are *price inelastic*. This is generally considered to be the case for water. See chapter V.7 for more detailed discussion of price elasticity.

Weather Risks

For many communities, weather is a major concern when estimating annual water sales and revenues. It is important for a utility to examine the extent to which variations in weather may affect customer usage patterns and the utility's ability to meet its financial obligations. It is equally important for the utility and its customers to realize that some rate structures result in greater revenue and bill volatility because of seasonal weather patterns.

Implementing an Alternative

Before selecting an alternative structure, it is important to evaluate the time and cost of implementing the alternative. Elements of the new rate structure that might require additional time include collecting additional data, reclassifying customers into new classes, programming the utility's billing and accounting systems, and developing the rates.

SUMMARY

In general, a utility should determine how its rate structure can support its goals and objectives, which might include the following:

- Yielding total revenue in a stable and predictable manner
- Minimizing unexpected changes to customers
- Discouraging wasteful use and promoting efficient use
- Promoting fairness and equity
- Avoiding unjust discrimination
- Maintaining simplicity, certainty, convenience, feasibility, and freedom from controversy
- Complying with all applicable laws

The level of effort allotted should be determined when a comprehensive study of alternative rate structures is undertaken, including evaluating the availability of data and how the public will be involved. This step includes listing alternatives to be studied and criteria to evaluate how each alternative meets the selected rate objectives. Finally, the trade-offs for each alternative rate structure need to be evaluated, measured, and communicated to decision makers.

The remaining chapters of this section are designed to evaluate the benefits and detriments of various alternative rate structures. Selecting the most appropriate rate structure is a function of unique circumstances facing each utility and no one rate structure meets all objectives equally. In selecting a rate structure, a utility must evaluate the strengths and weaknesses of each rate structure and select the one that maximizes the overall objectives of the utility while still satisfying all applicable legal requirements.

REFERENCES

Bonbright, J.C., A.L. Danielsen, and D.R. Kamerschen. 1988. *Principles of Public Utility Rates*, 2nd ed. Arlington, Va.: Public Utilities Reports.

Corssmit, C.W. 2010. *Water Rates, Fees, and the Legal Environment*, 2nd ed. Denver, Colo.: AWWA.

Chapter **IV.2**

Uniform Rates

A uniform, uniform-volume, or uniform-commodity rate is a constant unit price for all metered volumetric units of water consumed on a year-round basis. Unlike flat fees or charges, uniform rates require metered service and can be applied to all customer or service classifications, such as residential, commercial, industrial, wholesale, and so on. Alternatively, uniform rates by class provide separate uniform-volume rates within a customer or service classification. Figure IV.2-1 illustrates a uniform rate for three customer classifications.

The term *uniform rates* sometimes refers to applying a common rate structure to non-interconnected (as well as interconnected) systems operated by the same water utility, a practice also known as *single-tariff pricing*. Single-tariff pricing can involve any of the rate structures described in this manual.

GENERAL CONSIDERATIONS

A uniform water rate is expressed as constant price per thousand gallons or per hundred cubic feet (see Figure IV.2-1). Potential cost-of-service differentials among customer or service classifications are not recognized when designing a uniform rate applicable to all general water service customers. To capture class-based, cost-of-service differentials, uniform rates must be designed by customer class. The rate usually accompanies a fixed charge per billing period, commonly referred to as a customer charge, meter charge, service charge, or administrative charge. Fixed charges can vary by customer class, meter size, or other service characteristics, but not by the amount of water consumed.

Uniform rates are relatively simple for water utilities to implement and for customers to understand. A uniform rate also sends customers a usage-based price signal. Although the unit price is constant, customer bills will escalate with increased water use. However, in comparison to block rates (where unit prices vary with the level of consumption), the uniform rate also implies that all increments of water provided are associated with the same unit cost of service.

Utilities might consider a uniform rate for all customers when

- customer groups or service classes exhibit similarities in usage (demand) characteristics,

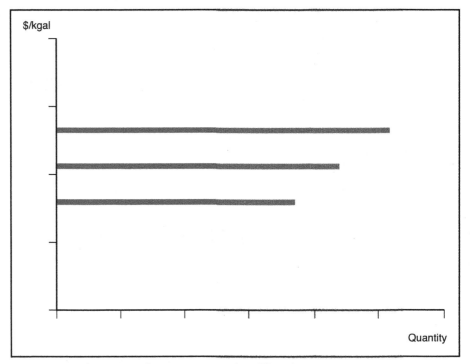

Figure IV-2.1 Uniform rate by customer classification

- varying rates by customer or service classification are undesirable from equitability or other perspectives,
- simplicity and customer understanding of the rate structure are valued highly,
- rate uniformity adequately addresses economic efficiency and conservation concerns,
- rate structures that vary charges by usage block or other means are not justifiable, or
- cost and usage data by customer or service classifications are not available or too costly to develop (i.e., costs outweigh potential benefits).

The feasibility and ease of implementing a uniform rate structure depends on a variety of factors. Metering is required, as is cost allocation by customer class if uniform rates by class are developed. The transition to uniform rates from block rates affects customer bills. For example, large-volume customers with decreasing block rates pay more under a uniform rate structure, but uniform rates by customer class could mitigate this effect.

HISTORICAL PERSPECTIVES

Historically, many water utilities began charging for service without the benefit of metering. Property taxes and, eventually, flat fees or charges were used to collect utility revenues. Some utilities began approximating the cost of service by varying user charges according to equivalent residency units, fixture units, or even number of livestock.

With metering came the potential to charge for water on a per-unit basis, and many smaller water utilities opted for the simplicity of the uniform rate. During the 1960s, many middle-sized and larger water utilities used decreasing block rate structures. Decreasing block rates were often justified on the grounds that large-volume customers typically had favorable demand and cost-of-service characteristics.

By the late 1970s, concerns about conservation in the energy and water sectors led many legislators and regulators to rethink the prudence of decreasing block rates. The Public Utility Regulatory Policies Act of 1978, among other things, required investor-owned electric utilities to justify the continued use of decreasing block rates over innovative rate-design alternatives that were considered more conservation oriented. State public utility regulators began considering economic efficiency in the context of utility pricing and planning.

At the same time, economic efficiency emerged as an important consideration in the water sector as well. Metering and volume-based rates are considered vital steps toward efficient water production and consumption. Conservation advocates believe that decreasing block rates do not send an appropriate pricing signal to encourage conservation. In addition, some consumer advocates believe that decreasing block rates are unfair to residential customers. In the 1990s, many utilities reconsidered uniform rates as a cost-effective way to simplify rate design. Uniform rates were accepted and approved for use by many unregulated and regulated water utilities.

Historically, some utilities and individuals did not consider a uniform rate structure to be conservation oriented. Water industry thinking and opinion have changed over time, and a uniform rate structure is now considered conservation oriented when a majority of the revenue derived from the rate structure is from the volumetric portion of the rate structure as opposed to being generated from the fixed-charge portion of the rate structure.

ADVANTAGES AND DISADVANTAGES

This section provides a discussion of the benefits and detriments of uniform rates, including considerations of simplicity, equity, revenue stability, conservation, and implementation.

Simplicity

Simplicity is one of the chief advantages of uniform rates. Uniform rates are easily understood and implemented. Other utility functions, such as cost analysis, customer service, and regulatory proceedings, are also simplified with less complex rate forms.

Equity

Uniform rates are usually considered equitable because all customers pay the same unit price for general water service. Uniform rates also might be perceived as equitable during periods of rising costs. Political and public opposition might be less with uniform rates than with other rate structures. With uniform rates across all customer classes, the appearance of large-volume customers subsidizing small-volume customers, or vice versa, is avoided.

Uniform rates might not be perceived as equitable when variations in the cost of serving different customer groups are substantial. Unless a community's customers all show relatively similar demand patterns, the use of uniform rates by customer class should be considered to reflect the variations in the costs to serve different customer demands.

Revenue Stability

Uniform rates provide utilities with a degree of revenue stability in comparison to increasing block rates and other more complex rate forms. Barring adverse economic or other conditions causing usage to fluctuate widely, uniform rates provide a dependable revenue

Table IV.2-1 Uniform rates for all customers

Without Price Elasticity Adjustment	All Customers
Cost of Service	$6,179,060
Anticipated Sales, 1,000 gal	2,536,000
Uniform Charge, $/1,000 gal	$2.44

Table IV.2-2 Uniform rates by customer class

Without Price Elasticity Adjustment	Residential	Commercial	Industrial
Cost of Service	$2,720,381	$1,178,152	$2,280,527
Anticipated Sales, 1,000 gal	968,000	473,000	1,095,000
Uniform Charge, $/1,000 gal	$2.81	$2.49	$2.08

stream. However, the transition to a uniform rate from a flat fee or decreasing block structure can potentially result in short-term revenue instability.

Conservation

A uniform rate facilitates conservation because customer bills vary with the level of water usage. Thus, uniform rates are considered superior to flat fees or charges. In general, uniform rates also provide a more conservation-oriented rate signal than decreasing block rates. The actual efficiency of the uniform rate depends on the circumstances of the individual utility.

Conservation advocates might believe that the conservation orientation of water prices could be enhanced by more complex rate forms. For example, seasonal or increasing block rates are sometimes favored because higher prices are charged for higher usage.

Implementation

With metered water service in place, uniform rates are easily implemented. A uniform rate across all customer classes avoids the expense of detailed cost allocation. Public education and customer service may also be somewhat easier with uniform rates.

DETERMINING A UNIFORM RATE

Developing a uniform rate is relatively straightforward. Some costs can be identified with customer service functions (such as meter reading, billing, and revenue collection), as well as with fire protection. These costs can be recovered through the fixed component of the bill. The uniform rate, based on consumption, applies to general water service. Further allocation of costs to base-extra capacity functions (or to commodity and demand components) is not required, unless class-based rates are developed.

EXAMPLE

Table IV.2-1 provides a sample calculation of a uniform rate for inside-city customers. In this instance, the total cost of inside-city retail customer service to be derived from volume charges to residential, commercial, and industrial customers ($6,179,060) is divided by the anticipated amount of total sales (2,536,000 thousand gallons) to arrive at a volume rate of $2.44 per thousand gallons. In this particular example, the same rate is charged for all classes of customers or service. A usage response (price elasticity response) to the change in price is not included in this example; consideration of customer adjustments in response to a significant change in price should be part of any utility's analytical process.

Table IV.2-2 provides a sample calculation of separate uniform rates by customer class. In this instance, differences in the cost of serving residential, commercial, and industrial customers are taken into account. A separate unit price is established for each class based on costs allocated by customer class, within the cost-of-service analysis, and the anticipated metered sales to each class. In this example, the lower costs of serving commercial and industrial customers, because of the lower peaking factors applicable to those classes of customers relative to the residential customer class, result in lower unit prices than for residential customers.

To calculate the effect of the rate on total customer bills, the uniform rate is multiplied by the volume of water usage, and the resulting amount is added to the monthly customer charge. As previously indicated, monthly customer charges often vary by customer class or meter size.

SUMMARY

The uniform rate structure has gained relatively wide acceptance. Uniform rates also afford water utilities a degree of revenue predictability and stability.

As with any rate structure, the effect of a change to uniform rates varies depending on the magnitude of the change and how it is implemented. A transition from unmetered service can be facilitated by a customer education program. Water-use reductions should be anticipated. A transition from block rates can be accomplished by gradually reducing the number of rate blocks and the differentials among them. A phased approach can reduce rate shock, particularly for large-volume customers served previously under decreasing block rates.

A uniform rate might not be preferred by every water user. Large-volume customers might believe that favorable cost-of-service characteristics justify the use of decreasing block rates. Conservationists might believe that efficiency and environmental concerns justify the use of increasing block rates. In balancing these perspectives, uniform rates or uniform rates by customer class can present a compromise.

This page intentionally blank.

Chapter **IV.3**

Decreasing Block Rates

A decreasing (or declining) block rate is a rate structure in which the unit price of each succeeding block of usage is charged at a lower unit rate than the previous block(s). The number of rate blocks and the size and pricing of each block vary among utilities, depending on the specifics of the customers or classes of customers to which the rate structure is applied. Figure IV.3-1 illustrates a decreasing block rate.

GENERAL CONSIDERATIONS

As with any rate structure, the decreasing block rate can be appropriate given certain situations and cost considerations. In an era when conservation and efficient use of water resources has received significant emphasis, water rate surveys show that decreasing block rate structures are still used by many utilities in some parts of North America. However, application of the decreasing block rate structure appears to be more selective than in the past, and utilities are moving away from the use of this structure in most parts of North America.

Many customers unfamiliar with the rate-design process consider the decreasing block rate structure to be a quantity discount or "anti-conservation" and favorable to large-volume users of water. In actuality, when properly designed, the decreasing block rate structure reflects the manner in which costs are incurred by the utility and can reflect the cost of service where larger-volume users have lower peak-demand requirements than smaller-volume customers. It assesses costs associated with the usage patterns and demand requirements of the various classes of customers served. The decreasing block rate is often used to develop a single rate schedule that takes into account the different cost and usage characteristics of all customers, yet it is equitable to all customers. However, as is true with all rate structures, over time, maintaining equity between customers with a single rate and rate structure (i.e., decreasing block) requires periodic reviews.

The size of the rate blocks and the variability of the decreasing unit prices should reflect the types of customers served and the cost differences between peak and average

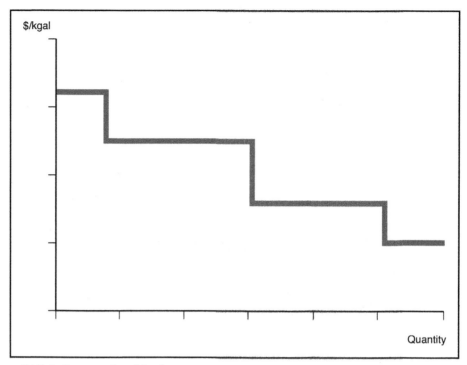

Figure IV-3.1 Decreasing block rate

use for the different classes of customers. An initial block may be designed to recover costs associated with the volumetric use and demand requirements of residential and small commercial customers. Subsequent blocks may be selected to encompass the water use and associated demand costs for other classes of customers.

Utilities may consider using a decreasing block rate structure when the following conditions exist:

- A single rate structure is preferred for all customer classes of service.
- A class of service has an array of customers with varying usage and demand requirements (e.g., a class of service containing both small and large commercial customers).
- System costs decline with increasing water usage (i.e., economies of scale).
- Economic circumstances dictate that price incentives be provided to encourage specific large-volume customers to remain on the system (e.g., a large-volume customer that can develop its own source of supply by drilling a well). This consideration may be characterized as an economic incentive rate.

A decreasing block rate structure is generally not difficult to administer, depending on the number and size of the blocks. In designing decreasing block rates, it is important to accumulate and maintain sound billing data to accurately predict the amount of water usage to be billed in each block.

HISTORICAL PERSPECTIVES

A number of different justifications exist for decreasing block rate structures. The principal justification is when a single rate schedule is preferred for all customer classes served.

In this case, the decreasing block rate structure is designed to reflect the differences in water and capacity use for the different classes of customers served.

Generally, large-volume users, as a class, have a lower peak-to-average peaking factor (i.e., relationship of peak use to average use) with correspondingly lower extra-capacity requirements and related costs than do smaller-volume users as a class. A properly designed decreasing block rate schedule recovers revenue for each class according to how costs are incurred. Another way to view this approach is to consider the results of the cost-of-service study. Within the cost-of-service study, all base costs or annual volume-related costs should be equal for each class of service on a per-unit basis, stated in dollars per hundred cubic feet or dollars per thousand gallons. It is the peaking-related costs, stated in dollars per hundred cubic feet or dollars per thousand gallons, that vary by class of service and reflect the overall demand characteristics of each class.

Residential and small commercial customers usually have greater peaking (capacity or demand) factors than large commercial and industrial customers. As a result, a utility typically faces higher unit costs to meet the peaking requirements of residential and small commercial customers relative to large commercial and industrial customers. A properly designed decreasing block rate structure reflects the differences in usage levels and peaking-related costs between the types of customers served using the size of the blocks to establish the approximate usage levels of each class and the relative price differences between blocks to recognize demand characteristics of each class.

Another justification assumes that with increased consumption, certain economies of scale may be achieved, and these economies of scale or savings should be reflected within the rates. The economies of scale are assumed to be achieved via capacity utilization or improved capacity use with the existing capacity.

One attribute of the decreasing block rate structure sometimes cited is revenue stability. A decreasing block rate is said to provide more revenue stability when compared to an increasing (or inverted) block rate structure. Given the potential for variability in consumption between a wet and a dry summer, the decreasing block rate may minimize revenue swings. In addition, from an economic perspective, under a decreasing block rate structure, customers with the least ability to change consumption (inelastic demand) tend to consume water primarily in the highest-priced initial blocks, while those customers with the greatest ability to change consumption (elastic demands) tend to consume more water in the subsequent lower-priced blocks of the decreasing block rate structure.

Given the nature of this rate structure, there are mixed views regarding its appropriateness. While proponents of the structure argue that it reflects the costs incurred by the system, critics argue that a decreasing block rate structure encourages waste and in some cases provides a subsidy to large-volume users. Careful thought and analysis should go into developing the size and unit price of the decreasing blocks to justify them from a cost and usage characteristic basis.

ADVANTAGES AND DISADVANTAGES

The following paragraphs discuss the pros and cons of decreasing block rates.

Simplicity

For the most part, the decreasing block rate structure is fairly easy for the customer to understand and for the utility to administer. Designing the rate does require information and analysis of customer usage patterns and peaking requirements, a portion of rate development that can be fairly complex. In addition, ensuring that the proposed rate design collects the appropriate level of revenues is an important test.

Equity

A decreasing block rate schedule is designed to recover, as a single rate schedule applicable to all retail customers of the utility, the costs of serving different classes of customers while maintaining reasonable equity between customer classes. As discussed previously, decreasing block rate structures are not designed to provide quantity discounts or lower rates simply because water is sold in large volumes. The decreasing block rate structure offers a mechanism to recover cost differences based on class water use and demand characteristics in a fair and equitable manner.

Utilities should carefully select the proper block sizes and associated rates, for each block can dramatically affect the equity of the rate design. In addition, as consumption patterns or the composition of the customer classes change over time, the equity of the rate structure may also change. Periodic reviews of the bill frequency analysis and customer demand characteristics should address this issue.

A major underlying assumption in regard to decreasing block rate structures is that larger-volume customers have lower peaking factors, or a better relationship between peak demand and average annual demand, than do smaller-volume customers. This may or may not be true depending on the specific usage characteristics of the utility's customers. Further, the decreasing block rate structure assumes a direct relationship between volumetric consumption and peaking characteristics. In other words, the lowest-volume customer has the highest peaking factor, while, in contrast, the highest-volume customer has the lowest peaking factor. Whether or not this average-to-peak-demand relationship holds true should be determined by each utility.

The final issue in regard to equity is customer perception. While a decreasing block rate may be properly designed to be cost based and equitable, some customers may still perceive it to be inequitable. This is particularly true for the low-volume user being charged at the highest rate per consumption unit.

Revenue Stability

A properly designed decreasing block rate should be able to adequately meet target revenue levels of the utility. Additionally, decreasing block rate schedules could have the positive attribute of minimizing revenue volatility in wet or dry weather conditions.

Conservation

Many believe that a decreasing block rate structure conflicts with the goals of efficient water use and resource conservation. Because decreasing block rates may be perceived as promoting consumption rather than conservation, they are often viewed negatively in regard to conservation. During the last decade, utility industry practices have relied less on decreasing block rate structures, especially in water-stressed regions.

During periods of water scarcity or emergencies, the focus may be shifted away from a decreasing block rate structure to a rate structure perceived to be more conservation oriented (e.g., uniform rate or perhaps even an increasing block structure). A shift from a decreasing block structure may be implemented in phases to limit billing effects on selected customers.

Implementation

The decreasing block rate structure may be difficult to implement if the utility does not already have the rate structure in place. If local water supply conditions are such that conservation is a key factor in establishing rates and a rate policy, perceptions and current industry thinking regarding this rate structure may make approval at the regulatory level challenging.

Table IV.3-1 Derivation of typical inside-city cost per 1,000 gallons by water-use blocks (test year)

(1)	(2)	(3)	(4)	(5)	(6)	(7)	(8)
Line No.	Consumption Block Threshold, 1,000 gal	Base Cost, $/1,000 gal	Maximum-Day Extra Capacity*	Maximum-Day Extra Capacity Cost, $/1,000 gal†	Maximum-Hour Extra Capacity‡	Maximum-Hour Extra Capacity Cost $/1,000 gal†	Total Cost, $/1,000 gal
1	Block 1 (first 15)	$1.7189	150	$0.8256	150	$0.2659	$2.8103
2	Block 2 (next 1,485)	$1.7189	100	$0.5504	125	$0.2216	$2.4908
3	Block 3 (over 1,500)	$1.7189	50	$0.2752	50	$0.0886	$2.0827

* In excess of average day.

†Values determined by dividing Allocated Cost of Service from Table III.2-5 for each respective class by the Base Demand, Units of Service, also from Table III.2-5.

‡ In excess of maximum day.

Implementing this particular rate structure also requires that the utility analyze its current metering, billing, and data processing systems to ensure compatibility.

DETERMINING DECREASING BLOCK RATES

In developing decreasing block rate structures, the key issue is the number and size of rate blocks within the rate structure. As noted earlier, the decision on the number and size of blocks depends on the number of customer classes served by the utility and the variations in demand characteristics of those classes. At the same time, consideration should be given to developing a decreasing block rate structure that is not overly complex.

Consumption patterns of each class must be reviewed and analyzed to determine the number of blocks and their sizes. This is generally accomplished with a bill frequency analysis or bill tabulation. The bill frequency analysis provides the total amount of consumption, system-wide or by class of customer, within given intervals of customer usage. It also has the number of bills or customers that fall within these consumption intervals. Generally, rate blocks should be set at logical break points. These logical break points may be dictated by many considerations. Often, issues such as the average usage within a customer class, the number of customers falling in each block, and the seasonal use or load profile of the class of service help make this determination. See appendix C for an example of how to develop a bill tabulation or frequency analysis.

After the number of blocks and their sizes are determined, the level or amount of consumption that falls within each rate block must be computed. The decreasing block rate structure can then be developed to meet the target revenue, using the average peaking factors for each class to establish the differential in rate block unit charges.

EXAMPLE

Tables IV.3-1 and IV.3-2 illustrate an approach that may be used to design a decreasing block rate structure. The example provided is fairly straightforward, but contains the elements required for effective rate design. The first item to determine is the total revenue requirement for each class that the rates are to collect from volume-related charges. The number of consumption charge blocks may vary in number and size. In this example, three rate blocks reflect the usage characteristics of the three classes of customers. Consumption levels for each class of customer within each rate block must be analyzed and determined.

Table IV.3-2 Summary of customer water use by rate block and application of proposed rates (test year)

Line No.	Consumption Block Threshold, 1,000 gal	Percentage of Use	Annual Water Use, 1,000 gal	Proposed Rates, $/1,000 gal	Proposed Revenue	Cost of Service	Percentage of Cost
	Inside City:						
1	Residential	Service Charge			$2,290,751		
2	First 15	94.0%	909,920	$2.81	2,556,875		
3	Next 1,485	6.0%	58,080	$2.49	144,619		
4	Over 1,500	0.0%	0	$2.11	0		
5	Total	100.0%	968,000		$4,992,245	$5,011,889	99.6%
6	Commercial	Service Charge			$221,192		
7	First 15	15.0%	70,950	$2.81	199,370		
8	Next 1,485	79.0%	373,670	$2.49	930,438		
9	Over 1,500	6.0%	28,380	$2.11	59,882		
10	Total	100.0%	473,000		$1,410,882	$1,399,435	100.8%
11	Industrial	Service Charge			$21,894		
12	First 15	0.2%	2,190	$2.81	6,154		
13	Next 1,485	13.8%	151,110	$2.49	376,264		
14	Over 1,500	86.0%	941,700	$2.11	1,986,987		
15	Total	100.0%	1,095,000		$2,391,298	$2,302,435	103.9%
16	Public Fire-Protection Service						
17	Annual Charge for	1,155	hydrants		$624,390	$624,390	100.0%
18	at	$540.60	per hydrant				
19							
20	**Total Inside City**		2,536,000		$9,418,816	$9,338,150	100.9%
21	**Outside City:**						
22	Residential	Service Charge			$242,677		
23	First 15	94.0%	89,300	$3.44	307,192		
24	Next 1,485	6.0%	5,700	$2.73	15,561		
25	Over 1,500	0.0%	0	$2.11	0		
26	Total	100.0%	95,000		$565,430	$569,369	99.3%
27	Wholesale	Service Charge			$2,914		
28	All Use	100.0%	230,000	$3.10	713,577		
29	**Total Outside City**		230,000		$716,491	$716,801	100.0%
30	Total		2,861,000		$10,700,737	$10,624,320	100.7%

An initial volumetric charge is determined for each rate block, based on the unit costs developed in the cost-of-service study. Final unit volumetric charges typically must be adjusted slightly to recognize, especially for larger-use customers, that they are paying somewhat more than the average unit cost of service attributable to the large-user (industrial) class in the earlier rate blocks.

Table IV.3-1 shows the initial calculation of the average unit volumetric charge applicable to each customer class, recognizing the peaking factors assigned to each class as applied to the unit costs of service. Lines 1, 2, and 3 of Table IV.3-1 show the development of the average unit cost of service for residential, commercial, and industrial classes, with the total unit cost for each class shown in column 8. These average unit costs are applied to the distribution of consumption by customer class for each of the selected rate blocks to project annual revenue from each customer class.

As indicated in Table IV.3-2, because initial usage of larger-volume customers must first pass through the lower-use rate blocks before reaching the final rate block consumption level, initial rate blocks over-recover costs for these customers. Accordingly, the actual unit rate for the last rate block must be reduced from the average volumetric rate for the class to avoid over-recovery of revenue from the industrial class. Table IV.3-2 also shows the final determination of volumetric rates that recover, as closely as practicable, the total cost of service from each customer class.

In practice, developing rates that result in revenue meeting costs within the limits indicated in Table IV.3-2 may involve adjustments to the number of rate blocks, usage allowances in each of the various blocks, and individual block rates within the schedule.

SUMMARY

The decreasing block rate structure remains in use and can be appropriately structured to reflect a utility's cost structure. However, utilities continue to move away from this rate design for various reasons, including customer perceptions of inequity, cost justification for its use, and conservation considerations.

This page intentionally blank.

Chapter **IV.4**

Increasing Block Rates

Increasing block rates (also known as ascending, inclining, inverted, or tiered block rates) charge increasing volumetric rates for increasing consumption. Increasing block rates require metering and defining consumption blocks over which rates increase. Increasing block rates should usually be designed by customer classes (i.e., groups with similar usage patterns). Figure IV.4-1 illustrates an increasing block rate.

GENERAL CONSIDERATIONS

Although increasing block rates can be more complicated to design than other types of rates, they also provide flexibility in rate design, particularly when designed by customer classes. Properly designed increasing block rates recover class-specific cost of service while sending a more conservation-oriented price signal to that class. This flexibility places larger analytical demands on the rate analyst, especially when accounting for potential demand responses to block rate differentials (see chapter V.7). Increasing block rates can be coupled with fixed or service charges. See chapter IV.7 for further discussion of these charges.

Increasing block rates should be considered by a water utility when the utility

- is able to distinguish separate customer classes for billing;
- has the analytical capability to design block rate structures, including defining the amount of water sold per block, potential demand responses to differential rate impacts, and the development of the underlying costs of service for each block;
- has or will attain the administrative capability to apply block rate structures;
- is confronting system capacity (supply or infrastructure) constraints or potential system expansion (i.e., in cases where there is a higher payoff to demand-side management);
- would like to send a strong conservation price signal; and
- is willing to spend additional effort to communicate the nature and rationale of increasing block rates.

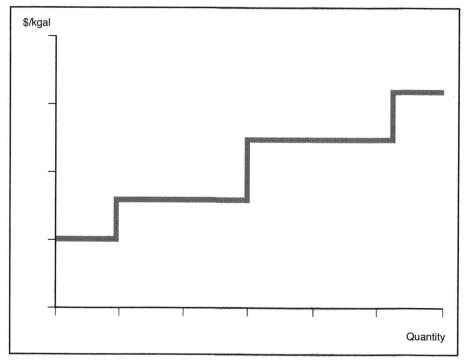

Figure IV-4.1   Increasing block rate

Increasing block rates are not a one-size-fits-all solution. Unless used with a small, highly homogeneous customer base, system-wide application of a single increasing block rate structure is likely to result in cost-of-service inequities, especially to commercial and industrial customers with relatively uniform consumption patterns (low peak demands but high total usage). These larger-volume customers may not impose costs on a water system proportional to the unit costs implied by increasing block rates. Additionally, assigning large price increases on customer classes known to have price-elastic demand can make it difficult to predict decreases in consumption. A single system-wide increasing block rate design applied to a customer base with diverse consumption patterns is more difficult to justify on a cost-of-service basis than increasing block rates designed for specific customer classes within which there are relatively homogeneous consumption patterns.

HISTORICAL PERSPECTIVES

Increasing block rate structures, designed for revenue neutrality and differentiated by customer class, may allow a utility experiencing supply cost escalations to send consistent price signals to customers. For this reason and because of the heightened interest in water conservation, increasing block rates have been progressively more favored, especially in relatively water-scarce regions.

Because a system must be constructed to meet maximum-day and maximum-hour demands, system capacity is underutilized during non-peak periods. Moreover, if the system were sized to meet the average demand only, the resource and infrastructure demands could be much smaller. Consequently, an increasing block structure may be designed to recover the cost of constructing and maintaining extra capacity for the peak demands. Because this capacity is underutilized, the per-unit cost of water is higher than for base capacity, which is used year-round. In short, a block structure can remain consistent with, if not enhance, the relationship of rates to cost of service.

ADVANTAGES AND DISADVANTAGES

The following paragraphs analyze the advantages and disadvantages of increasing block rate structures.

Simplicity

Increasing block rates are not as simple to design or explain as some other rate forms. They require information on water sales by block of consumption. This information can be developed through bill tabulation (see appendix C). They also require applying judgment and utility policy regarding the number of blocks, the point at which one block ends and the next begins, and the relative price levels of the blocks.

Equity

As with any rate design, overly simple or poorly designed increasing block rate structures run the risk of being inequitable. Increasing block rates can address various definitions of equity and provide flexibility with regard to pricing strategies for water utilities.

Revenue Stability

Increasing block rate structures tend to result in more revenue volatility than other rate structures (i.e., decreasing and uniform block rates). This revenue volatility is because an increasing block rate anticipates recovering a proportionately greater percentage of the customer class's revenue requirement at higher levels of consumption. These higher levels of consumption tend to be more subject to variations in seasonal weather and, when coupled with a higher-than-average unit pricing, customers tend to curtail consumption in these higher consumption blocks. As a result, a utility implementing an increasing block rate structure is advised to have a good understanding of the distribution of water demand by customer class and of price elasticity of demand.

A utility concerned about adverse revenue effects resulting from an increasing block rate design might consider developing a reserve, often referred to as a rate or revenue *stabilization fund*. A stabilization fund allows a utility to draw on the fund balance during revenue shortfalls that result from lower-than-expected consumption.

Conservation

Increasing block rate structures are usually considered to be conservation oriented. The most conservation-oriented rate structure maximizes the consistency of the price signal. Under a properly designed increasing block rate structure, no customer within a given class and using similar amounts of water should be rewarded more or less than another customer for saving water. If properly designed, increasing block rates can send an appropriate conservation signal to certain customer classes. However, care should be taken when determining whether increasing block rates are applicable for a particular class of customers that includes large-volume and master meter customers and those with highly diversified water-use characteristics and demand patterns.

Implementation

The implementation of increasing block rate structures is accompanied by some disadvantages, including the following:

- These rates are more difficult to design for predictable revenue streams.
- Definitions of rate blocks can be based on more than one rationale.
- The rate structure can be more difficult to communicate to customers.
- The use of customer class rates creates additional billing and customer service issues, and requires care that customers are classified correctly.

Water systems requiring more flexibility and conservation response from a rate structure may find the higher implementation cost of increasing block rate structures to be justified.

SETTING BLOCK SIZE AND PRICING

There is no single method for setting the size or unit price of the usage blocks under this rate approach; however, there are several general considerations.

Block Size

Increasing block rates are most commonly applied to residential customers because of their relatively homogeneous demand pattern. Block sizes should correspond to the utility's individual bill distribution and customers' usage patterns. For example, the first block can be set to capture a defined percentage of the annual number of bills, such as 50 percent (or median number) of all single-family residential bills. Another example would be establishing the first block to correspond to nonirrigation season (winter) water demands, which provide some indication of indoor water usage in most areas. Finally, this first block can be established to meet policy objectives, such as tying the block size to a lifeline need or essential use allowance (i.e., to correspond to the estimated basic water needs of a typical family).

Additional blocks can be set based on percentage of bills or to encourage usage reductions at the higher end of the demand curve. For example, single-family usage greater than 30 thousand gallons per month might make up 5 percent of the annual bills but 15 percent of a utility's residential water consumption. The top block could be set at 30 thousand gallons to reduce this high-end water consumption.

Block Pricing

As with any rate structure, increasing block rates must be set to recover the stated revenue requirements. Rate setting must necessarily take into account any reduction in water demands due to the price elasticity factor demonstrated by a particular customer class. Through the cost allocation, individual customer classes are assigned a proportionate share of the utility's total revenue requirement. Once that allocated amount has been determined, the utility can then establish the price of each usage block within that customer class to achieve its desired objectives.

Blocks by Customer Class

As previously stated, increasing block rates are most commonly applied to residential customers, because of their relatively homogeneous usage pattern and peaking characteristics. The utility could also create a general service customer class comprised of residential and small commercial customers. In this way, smaller residential customers can be included with smaller nonresidential customers that may have the same consumption patterns. This may also eliminate problems with inequities within the commercial class where customer demands may greatly vary (e.g., clothing store versus restaurant or hotel). Customer classes that do not demonstrate uniform demand patterns might be adversely affected by an increasing block structure.

Blocks by Meter Size

In some cases, it may be better to determine customer classes based on meter size (see chapter III.2). A utility can also implement an increasing block structure by meter size if it can demonstrate a consistent relationship or homogeneous usage pattern by meter size. For example, the first block for a ⅝-in. meter might be 7 thousand gallons while increasing to 12 thousand gallons for a 1-in. meter. As previously noted, this rate structure is best applied to customer classes that demonstrate a significant peaking pattern and might not be appropriate for industrial or commercial customers that use water at relatively consistent levels throughout the year.

EXAMPLES

The first example illustrates how an increasing two-block rate might be designed for inside-city residential customers. In this example, annual water sales are anticipated to be 968,000 thousand gallons and the consumption-related cost of service is $2,720,000 (see Table III.2-5, Residential Base Demand 1,000 gal divided into the Base, Maximum-Day and Maximum-Hour Allocated Costs of Service). While there is no single analytical method to define consumption blocks, for this example, it is assumed that the utility wishes to set the threshold between block 1 and block 2 at an amount that approximates the transition from indoor to outdoor consumption. The utility's objective is to have block 1 consumption approximate indoor usage and to charge a higher amount for outdoor usage in block 2 to promote conservation.

Based on a review of low-consumption (typically winter) billing information and a bill tabulation, the utility determines that a typical residential customer uses 7 thousand gallons per month for "indoor" use and that, on an annual basis, 80 percent of the water sales are for 7 thousand gallons or less. This equates to annual block 1 sales of 774,400 thousand gallons and block 2 sales of 193,600 thousand gallons. In this example, the utility has also conducted an analysis of supply costs and determined that block 2 rates should be set at a level 30 percent higher than block 1 to reflect the cost incurred for increased capacity costs and supply purchases. With this information it is possible to calculate block 1 and block 2 water rates as follows:

Block 1 Equation:

$$\text{Block 1 Rates} = \frac{\text{Total Consumption-Based Revenue Requirement for Class}}{\text{Block 1 Sales} + [\text{Block 2 Sales} \times (1 + \text{Price Differential})]}$$

$$= \frac{\$2,720,000}{774,400 + [193,600 \times (1 + 0.30)]}$$

$$= \$2.65 \text{ per Thousand Gallons}$$

Block 2 Equation:

$$\text{Block 2 Rates} = \text{Block 1 Rate} \times (1 + \text{Price Differential})$$

$$\$2.65 \times 1.30 = \$3.45 \text{ per Thousand Gallons}$$

Table IV.4-1 Increasing block rate design—Residential class

Consumption Block Threshold	Consumption, 1,000 gal	Consumption, %	Rate Differential	Estimated Revenue	Rate, $/1,000 gal
Block 1 (first 7,000 gal)	774,400	80	1.0	$2,053,118	$2.65
Block 2 (over 7,000 gal)	193,600	20	1.3	667,263	$3.45
Estimated Total	968,000	100		2,720,381	
Cost of Service				2,720,381	
Difference				$0	

Table IV.4-2 Increasing block rate design—Residential class marginal cost-based rate

Residential Inside City	Consumption, 1,000 gal	Consumption, %	Estimated Revenue	Rate, $/1,000 gal
Block 1 (first 7,000 gal)	774,400	80	$1,752,381	$2.26
Block 2 (over 7,000 gal)	193,600	20	968,000	$5.00
Estimated Total	968,000	100	$2,720,381	

Table IV.4-1 displays a method of verifying these calculations. Table IV.4-2 illustrates an alternative method of setting increasing block rates for the inside-city residential class using marginal cost information. (This example is purely hypothetical, and the reader should refer to chapter V.8 for a discussion of marginal cost pricing.) Block 1 in this second example is again defined as the first 7 thousand gallons of monthly water use. The second consumption block is any monthly water consumption over 7 thousand gallons. For this marginal cost example, the rate in the second block is first set equal to the sum of the three-year marginal operating cost ($3.90 per thousand gallons) plus the average incremental capital cost ($2.10 per thousand gallons), resulting in the utility's marginal cost pricing estimate of $5.00 per thousand gallons.

The revenue from block 2 water sales equals $968,000, leaving $1,752,381 ($2,720,381 − $968,000) to be recovered from block 1 water sales. Block 1 rates are then calculated by dividing revenue needed from water sales in the first block ($1,752,381) by annual water use in the first block (774,400 thousand gallons), equaling a block 1 rate of $2.26/thousand gallons.

SUMMARY

Increasing block rate structures have been used more often in areas experiencing growth in water demand that is reaching the safe yield or capacity of the system, where there has been an impetus for improved efficiency in water use. In these areas, there can be a payoff to using price as a demand management tool. Such conservation-oriented rate structures require additional analysis to avoid the over- or under-recovery of revenue requirements. When legally defensible, utilities willing to undertake the additional analysis in rate design and conduct customer communications may find that increasing block rate structures are valuable tools in the effort to provide demand-side management.

Chapter **IV.5**

Seasonal Rates

A seasonal rate is a form of time-differentiated charge or a rate that varies by time period. It establishes a higher price for water consumed during a utility's peak-demand season, usually reflecting the increased costs of providing service during those periods. The objectives of seasonal rates are to better match price and cost recovery with demand patterns, and provide a price incentive for customers to reduce their consumption during peak season or use periods. High costs are often associated with capital projects and water supplies required to meet peak demands of a water system. Seasonal rates provide a price signal for customers to conserve water during the peak season that, in turn, optimizes system resources. Figure IV.5-1 illustrates a seasonal rate.

GENERAL CONSIDERATIONS

All water utilities experience some degree of peak demands on a seasonal basis. Seasonal trends, in large part, are caused by annual weather patterns, including temperature and precipitation, that affect outdoor water use. However, in some cases, the peak season may occur during the winter months because of an influx of residents during that time or for some other regional reason (e.g., skiing) for higher demand.

Seasonal rates can be implemented to reduce peak use, or at least to appropriately charge customers for such use during peak-demand times. These rates provide a price signal to the consumer indicating the high cost of providing water resources during the peak period. Seasonal rates have received greater attention in the past several years partly because of localized water shortages and conservation awareness. Recognizing peaking requirements as a significant element of cost has also facilitated greater acceptance of seasonal rates.

The allocated cost of supplying water can vary substantially between time periods, depending on the differences in demand between time periods and the utility-specific resources available to meet those demands. Improper price signals to customers regarding the cost of providing water during peak use may compound peak-use problems and encourage inefficient use of the water system.

Given the premise that water rates should track costs as closely as possible, seasonal rates provide a price signal to consumers that may encourage them to alter their

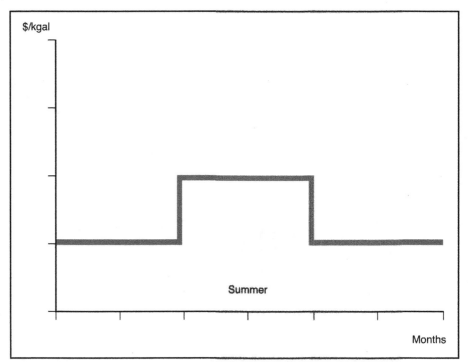

Figure IV-5.1 Seasonal rate

consumption by either reducing their overall use during the high-demand period or shifting consumption to lower-cost, low-demand periods. Because system capacity is essentially designed to meet peak demands, peak users should assume cost responsibility for capacity required to serve peak demand.

Designing a seasonal rate structure involves assigning the lower off-peak costs to the low-demand rate period and recognizing the variance in the unit cost of water between high-demand and low-demand periods. High peak costs—those associated with the higher capacity requirements needed to meet system design peak-day or peak-hour requirements—are assigned to the high-demand period rate. Differences in costs between high-demand and low-demand periods can be determined by a cost-of-service study and by a review of the resources and facility design requirement needs to meet the utility's peak-period capacity requirements.

Two approaches are common when developing a seasonal rate structure. Under either approach, care needs to be taken in defining the seasonal periods and the pricing differential between time periods:

1. *High-demand/low-demand approach.* This rate structure contains a specific rate for each season (i.e., a winter rate and a summer rate).

2. *Excess-use approach.* This rate structure may be similar to the previous approach, but customer consumption above a specified threshold per bill is charged a higher rate.

Several variations of seasonal rates are possible. For example, a seasonal rate structure may be combined with customer class rates and/or an increasing block rate structure to produce a seasonally differentiated increasing block rate structure. Seasonal pricing can be effective in several situations, including the following:

- Substantial variation occurs in costs between high-demand and low-demand periods.
- Substantial variation in demand exists between high-demand and low-demand periods.
- A utility is capacity constrained as a result of peak-period demands.
- Systems experience seasonal fluctuations in the numbers and types of customers served (e.g., tourist destinations).

Both high-demand/low-demand and excess-use approaches are effective in meeting the goals and objectives of implementing seasonal rates. Administrative considerations and data requirements may lead to the choice of one approach over the other.

Revenue generated from a seasonal rate will likely be weather sensitive and demand-response sensitive. Customer education and effective communication programs, along with the seasonal rate structure, are the most effective combination for dealing with high demand-period usage and pricing issues. Without customer education and communication programs, a seasonal rate structure may not produce desired results or meet the utility's objectives.

When considering a seasonal rate, a utility should give attention to the degree of variability in usage between seasons by the various types of customers served by the utility. This review may also provide guidance in regard to the magnitude of the difference in rate levels between seasons to bring about the desired degree of change. In some cases, certain customers have a greater ability to adjust their consumption patterns than other customers. Depending on its objectives, the utility may want to consider targeting those customer classes with the greatest ability to change their behavior and consumption.

Seasonal rates can be an attractive alternative for utilities that have significant fluctuations in usage during different times of the year. Facilities are often constructed to meet peak demands during peak season with a large portion of capacity remaining idle during off-peak season. Peak demands are typically created by lawn irrigation, public sanitation purposes, pool usage, car washing, seasonal industrial operations (vegetable processing, etc.), and, in certain areas, the influx of tourists.

Given that the objective of seasonal rates is to communicate to the customers the cost of their consumption at various times of the year and provide a proper price signal for the cost of this variation in consumption, a utility should consider customer billing frequency. As a general rule, if meters are read only quarterly, customers will not be notified quickly enough to modify their behavior. As meter-reading technology allows more frequent meter reading in a more cost-effective manner, billing cycles or other communications to the customer over shorter time periods may be even more effective in modifying customer responses.

HISTORICAL PERSPECTIVES

For water utilities, seasonal pricing has been used in areas with high irrigation demands and in those with seasonal resort activities that affect water consumption and peak demands. Seasonal rates have also been commonly used for commercial customers where a conservation-oriented rate design is desired and, due to the diversity of the commercial customer group, where an increasing block rate structure or similar rate structure may not be suitable. In general, however, seasonal pricing for water service in the United States has not been as quickly accepted or placed into practice as for other types of utilities, such as those providing natural gas or electricity. The reason for this slow acceptance is primarily related to the water industry's historic ability to provide adequate supply at affordable costs.

However, in recent years, utilities have experienced larger capital needs and higher construction costs. Furthermore, in some regional areas there is strong competition for water resources due to their growth patterns. Water utilities are becoming more open to the advantages of seasonal rate designs in mitigating or controlling peak demands. Given that alternative or additional sources of water supply usually come at a higher price, it is important that rates reflect the cost of providing water. Seasonal rates provide an important tool that can be used to defer the need for these additional sources of supply.

ADVANTAGES AND DISADVANTAGES

This section provides a discussion of the advantages and disadvantages of seasonal rate designs.

Simplicity

There are two perspectives regarding the simplicity of implementing a seasonal rate. From the customer's perspective, seasonal rates need to be understandable to be effective, which could require an education program by the utility. From the utility's perspective, seasonal rates may not be simple to administer and will depend on its billing system capabilities. The billing system must be capable of addressing issues associated with a customer's billed consumption, including consumption before and after the change of seasons (i.e., proration between seasons).

One approach to dealing with seasonal rates is to prorate the customer's consumption during the transition period for the seasons and bill the customer based on the number of days in each season during the transition billing period. This approach requires a billing program capable of handling the proration issue. An alternative approach is to have a stated policy that all meters read after a specific date will be computed at the higher peak-season rate levels. Regardless of the methodology, seasonal rates may only result in conservation or lower demand if the customer sees a clear relationship between usage and bill amounts.

Equity

A seasonal rate structure may be equitable from a cost-of-service perspective, because the customers responsible for the higher peak-demand-related costs are charged for such costs. Care should be exercised not to adopt seasonal rate structures that disregard intra-class and intergenerational rate equity norms.

Revenue Stability

Implementing seasonal rates can place revenue stability at risk, depending on the differential in the peak-season rate and customer response to the higher rate. Variations in metered revenue levels are typically associated with the swings of peak-season consumption, given wet or dry conditions. Because the peak-use period charge is, by definition, the highest rate under the seasonal rate approach, changes in peak-season consumption can potentially have a large effect on revenue.

A utility concerned about the adverse seasonal revenue effects resulting from a seasonal rate design might consider establishing a reserve fund, often referred to as a rate or revenue stabilization fund. A stabilization fund allows a utility to draw on the fund balance during revenue shortfalls that result from lower-than-expected customer consumption.

Conservation

Seasonal rates tend to affect those customers that exhibit relatively higher peak-demand to average-demand characteristics, and seasonal rates will result in higher bills if customers do not modify their consumption behavior. Customers who exhibit relatively low peak-demand to average-demand characteristics during the peak season may see a reduction in their water bills.

In the long run, a seasonal rate may reduce the cost of water to all customers. If customers conserve water in response to seasonal rates, the utility may be able to delay or avoid construction of additional supply or peak-capacity-related projects that would have otherwise been required. Even if demand is not reduced, customers contributing to peak demands pay the cost associated with that demand.

Implementation

The implementation of a seasonal rate structure requires identifying peak system consumption periods, determining associated costs, providing accurate and frequent (monthly is preferred) meter readings and billings, and educating and notifying customers. As discussed previously, the administrative issue of the change in billing periods is an important consideration. Ideally, meter readings should be scheduled to coincide as closely as possible with the beginning and end of the peak season. If the excess-use approach is used, the issue of what the threshold is for *low demand* will need to be resolved for new customers. Residential customers are usually considered to be typical of the class, and the residential class average is used until customer-specific data are collected. Average use by meter size is a potential way to facilitate estimating the correct threshold for nonresidential customers.

The utility should communicate with all customers before each high-demand season to increase customers' awareness of the intent of seasonal rates and the impending higher charges.

DETERMINING SEASONAL RATES

Many methods exist to quantify the seasonal rate component of the rate structure. One technique is to determine excess costs associated with supplying water during peak months. This approach could look at the specific costs associated with peaking facilities (e.g., wells used only in the summer).

A utility might also use the base-extra capacity allocations to determine the cost of supplying water beyond average-day demands. Excess capacity costs attributed to delivering incremental peak seasonal demands plus base costs during the peak season, divided by the total quantity of water sold during the peak season, can yield a cost basis for charging on a seasonal basis.

Once the structure and amount of a seasonal rate has been determined, estimates of and adjustments for potential consumer demand response to seasonal pricing should be made. These estimates can be based on management judgment and the results of detailed customer response or elasticity studies.

Developing seasonal rates is not an overly complex exercise but does have many considerations that make it more complex than other rate structure alternatives. The following is a discussion of some of the more important considerations in this process, along with a numerical example for developing a seasonal rate structure.

Rate Types

As noted previously, there are two basic types of seasonal water rates. The simplest type has a higher charge for the high demand, or peak period, as compared to the low-demand period. Under this approach, the price differential between seasonal periods could be based on an analysis of additional costs required to meet peak demands. This can be determined by comparing average demands to peak demands, or by reviewing various resources and facilities used exclusively during high-use periods (e.g., peak-use wells). From this cost information, an initial determination can be made as to the cost difference between meeting high-demand and low-demand periods.

A more sophisticated and complex method to develop seasonal rates is the excess-use approach. Excess-use charges have a schedule of charges for high demand-period use, which includes an additional charge during this period for use in excess of a specified threshold consumption amount. One of the more challenging aspects of developing the excess-use-charge rate structure is determining the basic level of usage allowable before excess-use charges apply. Typically, the low-demand period is analyzed to determine the basic level of usage. By reviewing the low-demand period, usage related to lawn irrigation, recreational activities, and so forth, is typically reduced or eliminated. The excess-use approach may not be appropriate or equitable for a general service or commercial type class of service with large variations in usage, but it may be appropriate for classes of service with homogeneous or similar usage characteristics.

Basic use and excess use are usually determined by customer class. For example, a review of single-family residential customer consumption patterns may indicate that the monthly basic usage should be 10,000 gallons. Excess usage would be defined as all consumption above this base. Another more rigorous approach to determining basic use and excess use is on an individual customer basis. This is a much more sophisticated approach and raises many complex administrative and billing issues.

A variation on the excess-use approach entails granting an additional allowance, above the computed basic level of use, to allow customers some limited additional use at basic level rates. This approach may also make the rate more acceptable from the customer's perspective. The allowance above the basic level of usage is a policy decision. Provisions may also be made to account for permanent changes in a customer's basic low-demand-period usage, which could occur with an expansion of operations, new operations, or a reduction of operations.

Defining Periods

An important consideration in developing a seasonal rate involves defining seasonal periods. To do this, many issues and considerations should be addressed. The first issue is frequency of meter readings. Monthly meter reading is preferred to provide customers with timely feedback regarding consumption patterns and the effects on their water bills. The utility should consider the basis for the billing and whether bills will be prorated between seasonal rate periods or, conversely, whether bills will be based on the rate in effect at the time the bill is calculated or the meter is read.

Next, the number of seasonal time periods should be administratively feasible. A simple definition for winter and summer time periods should be sufficient for most utilities. Utilities attempting to more closely match cost to price may consider more than two time periods. For example, time periods could be defined as high demand (June–September), low demand (November–February), and shoulder demand (October; March–May). In making a final determination, other related issues to consider include the practicality of the definition, customer understanding of the approach, and potential administrative constraints and added costs related to metering, billing, and data processing.

Determining Cost Basis

Determining the cost basis for the cost differential is the last step in developing seasonal rates. Given that sufficient variation exists between high-demand and low-demand periods, and that the seasonal months can be defined, the next step is to allocate operating and capital costs between high-demand and low-demand periods. No single method exists for performing this step, but the following three basic approaches can be used to make this determination:

1. Using the base-extra capacity cost-of-service method
2. Directly allocating or assigning costs to seasonal periods
3. Reviewing specific facilities and costs

The first approach uses the base-extra capacity method of cost allocation, which is described in depth in section III. By definition, base costs include operation and maintenance (O&M) and capital costs associated with meeting average load conditions. O&M and capital costs incurred to meet peak use should not be included as a base cost. Extra capacity costs are those related to meeting rate-of-use requirements in excess of average-day demands.

The next method is to directly allocate or assign costs to seasonal periods. Under this approach, the cost-of-service methodology may, for example, split demand-related costs between summer-demand and winter-demand costs. This approach requires detailed cost accounting information that allows costs to be split between seasonal periods.

Another method to determine cost differences between seasonal periods is a use-of-facilities approach. Often, the major cost differences between seasonal periods are a function of water supply resources. Certain water supply resources may be in place to meet base-demand or year-round demand requirements. In contrast, utilities may have resources used only during peak-use periods to meet high-demand requirements. These costs should be assigned to the high-demand period, creating the cost differential between seasonal time periods.

EXAMPLES

The numerical examples for developing seasonal rates that follow show that the analytical process is similar to the other rate-design approaches discussed in this manual. Both examples use the base-extra capacity cost-of-service method to determine the level of the seasonal rates.

Table IV.5-1 develops seasonal rates using the high-demand/low-demand approach for the inside-city residential class. In this example, the utility has determined that the peak or high-demand period (summer) is five months long, from May through September, and the low-demand period is the remaining seven months, from January through April and October through December. During the summer period, the residential customers are estimated to use 580,800 thousand gallons (60 percent of the annual consumption), and during the winter period, they are expected to consume 387,200 thousand gallons.

The base-extra capacity allocations, as calculated earlier in Table III.2-5, indicate the consumption-related cost of service for the residential class totals $2,720,381. This total cost includes $1,663,851 of base costs and $1,056,530 for maximum-day and maximum-hour costs (extra capacity costs).

In this example, the utility's objective is to have a higher rate in the summer (peak-use period) than in the winter (nonpeak-use period) and to set the rate at a level reflecting the increased cost of providing water during high-demand periods. A separate cost

Table IV.5-1 Seasonal residential class rates—Peak and off-peak approach

Seasons	Consumption, 1,000 gal	Consumption, %	Allocated Cost	Rate, $/1,000 gal	Estimated Revenue
Winter (off-peak)	387,200	40	$929,675	$2.40	$929,280
Summer (peak)	580,800	60	1,790,708	$3.08	1,788,864
Estimated Total	968,000	100	$2,720,383		$2,718,144

Table IV.5-2 Seasonal residential class rates—Excess-use approach

Seasons/Blocks	Consumption, 1,000 gal	Consumption, %	Rate, $/1,000 gal	Estimated Revenue
Winter (off-peak)	387,200	40	$2.40	$929,673
Summer (peak)				
Block 1				
First 10,000 gal/month	290,400	30	$2.40	696,960
Block 2				
Over 10,000 gal/month	290,400	30	$3.77	1,094,808
Estimated Total	968,000	100		$2,721,048

analysis was conducted of typical plant operations, and the utility determined that winter (low-demand) rates should recover base costs in proportion to winter consumption, plus 25 percent of extra capacity costs. The allocated winter costs therefore equal $665,540 of the base costs and $264,135 of the extra capacity costs for a total of $929,675. This cost divided by the expected winter consumption equals a rate of $2.40 per thousand gallons. Next, estimated summer costs equal $1,788,864, divided by summer consumption of 580,800 thousand gallons to yield a summer rate of $3.08 per thousand gallons. The projected winter and summer revenue differ slightly from the allocated cost of service because of rounding in the rates.

Table IV.5-2 provides a second example of seasonal rates using the excess-use approach. In this example, the summer charge includes two rate blocks. Block 1 of the summer rate is set equal to the winter rates, based on the concept that there is an average or basic level of usage throughout the year that should be priced at one level regardless of the season for residential customers. Summer usage in excess of this basic level is considered to be excess use and is priced at a higher rate. Using the same information as for the first example, the winter rate and block 1 of the summer rate are both set at $2.40 per thousand gallons. Summer consumption must then be divided into a basic-use amount and an excess-use amount per customer. In this example, the utility determined that the basic amount per customer was 10,000 gallons per month. Summer basic use equals 30 percent of the annual water sales for the residential class, or 290,400 thousand gallons. The remaining 290,400 thousand gallons are determined to be excess use. As a result, summer water consumption in block 1 will yield $696,960. To generate the remaining $1,094,808 needed to meet the consumption-based revenue required for the residential class, the excess-use rate (summer block 2 rate) equals $3.77 per thousand gallons and generates an estimated $1,094,808.

Both approaches reflect typical examples of seasonal rates. Each may be developed based on available utility information, in conjunction with specific goals, objectives, and judgments of the utility. Although no single method exists to determine the level of differential between the high-demand and low-demand periods, these two examples are based on dividing the base-extra capacity costs into seasonal costs as part of rate design. Often it is more efficient to calculate seasonal allocations of base-extra capacity costs as part of the cost-of-service allocations. Performing a seasonal allocation of base-extra capacity costs provides a utility with an indication of the seasonal cost differences based on the allocation method.

SUMMARY

Most utilities experience some differences in cost throughout the year, particularly in meeting peak capacity requirements. Seasonal rates attempt to pass on cost differences to the customers creating the demand. While there are distinct advantages to allocating costs to the customer as the utility incurs them, there are also some disadvantages worth considering before implementing seasonal rates. The primary concern is revenue stability, which can be adversely affected by weather conditions. Seasonal rates can bring about significant long-term savings if peak demands are reduced and new capital facilities required to meet peak demands can be postponed.

This page intentionally blank.

Chapter **IV.6**

Water-Budget Rates

A water-budget rate structure is a form of increasing block rates where the amount of water within the first block or blocks is based on the estimated efficient water needs of the individual customer. Water-budget rates differ from other metered water rate designs in two key ways. First, the blocks are established based on points that represent varying levels of each customer's efficient water use. Second, water-budget rates require the utility to set specific standards for what is, and what is not, considered efficient water use for an individual customer. Other metered rate designs may address efficient water use, but not in this direct manner, nor do they directly account for efficiency of use when determining a specific customer's bill.

The goal of water-budget rates is to encourage efficient water usage for each individual customer. To do this, a utility must establish a standard for efficient usage and then establish a budget for each individual customer. Typically, water-budget rates do not limit the amount of water a customer can consume; rather, a water budget is established for each customer that defines how much water is considered efficient. Customers with usage above this efficient usage budget generally pay a significantly higher rate for their "inefficient" or "wasteful" usage.

An individual customer's water budget can be based on several customer-specific factors and, for the purposes of this chapter, are organized into two categories of water use: indoor use and outdoor use. The sum of indoor and outdoor usage, or needs, establishes the customer's water budget. Water budgets may also vary throughout the year based on seasonal variables, such as weather, economic activity, and/or other industrial processing requirements. In some applications, individual customer water budgets may vary based on daily weather conditions.

Water-budget rates (see Figure IV.6-1) focus on charging customers the same commodity charge for similar uses of water (e.g., efficient indoor and outdoor use, and inefficient or wasteful use, as defined by the utility). A traditional increasing block rate design, on the other hand, generally charges all customers, within the same customer class, the same commodity rate for predetermined and set volumes (e.g., 0–5,000 gallons, 5,000–15,000 gallons) regardless of individual efficiencies.

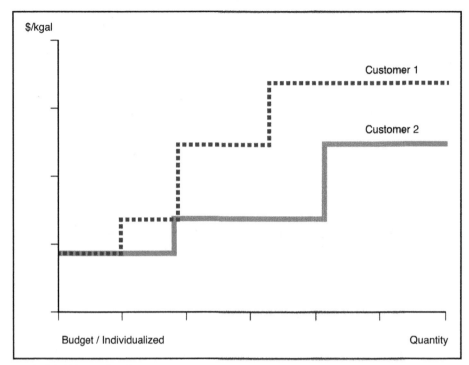

Figure IV-6.1 Water-budget rates

GENERAL CONSIDERATIONS

As with other increasing block rate designs, the decision of whether to implement water-budget rates normally depends on the extent to which a utility needs to encourage water conservation, the cost of implementation and administration, customer acceptance, the need to address equity concerns, and other factors.

Water-budget rates require more data on customers and their usage factors or behavior than other rate designs. As a result, water-budget rates will generally be more costly to implement and maintain, and in some cases significantly more, depending on several factors and the level of detail and complexity of the water budget. This additional data can include persons per household (PPH), irrigable landscape area, evapotranspiration* (ET) requirements, and so on.

In some cases, utilities lack the individual customer data required to create individualized water budgets for each customer. In those cases, water budgets may be developed using default values for the customers (e.g., PPH, landscape area). Where default values are used to develop water budgets, a water-budget rate design operates much like other increasing block rate designs with fixed thresholds for blocks.

Like other conservation-oriented rate designs, utilities employ water-budget rates to encourage consumers to use water more efficiently. Water-budget rates do this by establishing individualized usage targets (i.e., individual water budgets) for water consumption in homes, businesses, public facilities, and for crop and landscape irrigation. Because water-budget rates focus on individualized water budgets for customers, they can also be used by utilities to manage water use during extended supply restriction periods or droughts.

---

* Evapotranspiration is the amount of water that transpires through plant leaves combined with the amount that evaporates from the soil in which it is growing. ET is used as a guide for how much water a plant needs per day/week/year due to the loss of water from soil evaporation and transpiration from plants.

Similar to other conservation-oriented rate structures, water-budget rate structures are often employed to achieve conservation objectives while addressing other concerns utilities may have. By pricing water according to efficiency of use, efficient customers (as determined by comparing their use to their defined budget) can be charged less than those customers that the utility determines to be wasting water. This relationship to efficiency allows the utility to provide an economic incentive to change the behavior of those customers using water inefficiently without increasing the bills of those customers who use water efficiently.

HISTORICAL PERSPECTIVES

Water-budget rate designs have been in limited use since the 1980s. Water utilities using water-budget rate designs typically chose them to encourage water conservation while, in some cases, laying the groundwork for future drought-response programs.

Recent trends indicate that water-budget rates are more common in areas where water supplies are limited. More utilities are considering water-budget rates as pressure on water supplies mount, and as environmental concerns increase the uncertainty of current and future water sources.

ADVANTAGES AND DISADVANTAGES

The following paragraphs examine the advantages and disadvantages of water-budget rate designs.

Simplicity

Water-budget rates can be more complex to plan, implement, and maintain than most other rate designs because specific water budgets are often set for each individual customer. The complexity of the rate design poses challenges to both the political feasibility of achieving acceptance by policymakers, and for staff and customer understanding during the initial implementation. This complexity continues with the ongoing administration and maintenance of the data.

Water-budget rates employ terminology and concepts not traditionally used by water utilities or its customers. These include the concepts of ET, crop coefficients, and irrigation efficiencies. In addition, water-budget rates can require the maintenance of significantly more information about customers than other rate designs (e.g., PPH, landscape area), and they require individual calculations to determine each customer's water budget based on estimates of appropriate indoor and outdoor usage. Consequently, water-budget rates are more complex and require more sophisticated customer billing systems than many other rate designs. In many instances, a utility's existing billing system will not be capable of billing a water-budget rate structure and thus will require modification, upgrade, or replacement. Entities that have implemented water-budget rates have found it necessary to also establish *variance* policies and processes to address errors, changes in customer data over time, and extenuating circumstances.

Equity

As with any rate design, poorly designed water-budget rate designs can result in inequities. If properly developed, water-budget rates can be equitable and cost based. In addition to achieving equity by allocating costs to customers based on cost-causation principles, water-budget rates can result in the sharing of limited water supplies while preserving customer choice. Water-budget rates represent a departure from traditional rates because customers may be charged different amounts for the same volume of use. Depending on how the individual water budgets are calculated, it is possible that differences will exist in the amount customers within the class pay for the same volume of water.

Water-budget rates may also have other limitations with respect to equity. For example, if the water budgets are based on "default values" for household size or irrigated areas (in the case of residential customers) or based on past usage patterns (as is common for nonresidential budgets), it is possible that inefficient users will receive larger water allowances and efficient users will receive smaller ones. Furthermore, this effect can be exacerbated if larger users pay less in total than small users, which is a situation that can occur if the rate differentials among the blocks are large enough. In addition, large users may pay a lower marginal rate than small users, which may present issues with customer understanding and acceptance.

Like other rate structures, there are issues about how to apply water-budget rates fairly and equitably between residential and nonresidential customers. Developing water budgets for nonresidential customers is often quite challenging because of the variety of uses within the class and the difficulty in defining *efficient* versus *inefficient* water use. For large commercial or industrial customers, large volumes of use do not necessarily imply inefficient use. This challenge is not unique to water-budget rates and can be an important consideration in selecting different rate approaches for different customer classes.

Revenue Stability

With the effectiveness of conservation programs, including education and pricing, revenue stability has become a growing concern for many utilities. Increasing block rate structures, such as water budgets, are sometimes viewed as providing a lower level of revenue stability when compared to other rate forms. However, proponents of water-budget rates argue that this rate design may provide an added degree of stability in that the revenues from the efficient-use blocks are generally predictable; but the relatively small number of systems with water-budget rates does not provide a definitive answer to this question as of this writing.

Conservation

Water-budget rates are considered to be one of the more effective rate structures to discourage wasteful use. Some utilities have reported demand reductions as high as 40 percent in poorly managed irrigation accounts. Utilities using water-budget rates have reported demand reductions from 10 to 25 percent across customer classes (Pechiney and Chesnutt 1997). Notably, similar savings have also been reported by utilities using other rate designs, (e.g., increasing block and seasonal rates). Communication to customers about the conservation objectives and the cost of water (i.e., via the amount of their water bill) is key to the success of any conservation program. Water-budget rate designs typically require more in-depth knowledge about the customer base and usually involve a heightened level of customer outreach and involvement during the implementation phase. These efforts help to inform the customer base and potentially lead to wiser water use by a community; this can then be reinforced over time by a water-budget rate design.

Water-budget rates can also be an effective tool in times of drought. Drought management requires the ability to reduce demands to match the reduced water supply; this must frequently be done quickly and for durations that are not predefined. Under normal weather and supply conditions, water budgets identify efficient and inefficient usage by customers. During periods of drought, water-budget rate designs allow the utility to use the established budgets to apportion demand reductions (during the drought) among customers with different needs. Drought management can then be supported through the utility's billing system by informing customers of the required demand reductions and bill impacts. As such, water-budget rates can be a tool for drought plan enforcement by penalizing inefficient use (Mayer et al. 2008). Depending on the severity of the drought, utilities can reduce each customer's water budget to ensure an equitable sharing of the system-wide targeted demand reductions. As drought severity varies, water budgets allow the utility to target reductions in outdoor use, indoor use, or a combination of both.

Implementation

Utilities implementing water-budget rates may incur significant costs for additional computer hardware and software, database development, and staff training. Additional customer service personnel may also be required during the transition to assist customers in understanding their new water bills and in the customer "variance" process.

IMPLEMENTING WATER-BUDGET RATES

The following sections provide details for implementing water-budget rates.

Initial Design Considerations

Implementing a water-budget rate design begins by considering which customer classes should be on a water-budget rate. Dedicated landscape irrigation customers are typically targeted for application of this rate design because these accounts are single-purpose water users (i.e., irrigation only) and relatively few in number (when compared to the number of residential accounts), their water savings from efficiency gains can be substantial, and their water budgets are fairly simple to determine. Residential customers are also commonly included in water-budget rate designs, often with budgets for efficient indoor and outdoor usage. However, nonresidential customers can pose challenges because of the diversity of use among them and greater complications with determining efficient usage.

Developing the water budgets for nonresidential customers often relies on proxies for efficient water use. Although it is feasible to use factors that are correlated with water usage (e.g., number of seats in a restaurant) as proxies for efficient use, these proxies can be challenging to obtain, maintain, and justify. As a result, nonresidential customers are often excluded from the water-budget rate design or their budgets are based on their historical average annual water use or average winter water use. Nonresidential customers may participate in the water-budget rates by setting budgets for their outdoor use when they have separate irrigation meters.

Other initial design considerations include the availability of data for water budgets, the capabilities of the existing billing system, and an initial assessment of legal requirements that might prevent the implementation of water-budget rates. An assessment of public attitudes, understanding, and communication needs are an important part of the initial rate-design process.

Setting Indoor and Outdoor Water Budgets

A customer's water budget typically includes an allowance for indoor and outdoor use as well as variances for specific circumstances.

Indoor budget. Indoor water budgets are most often formulated for individual customers within a customer class. Residential indoor water budgets are relatively easy to calculate, but as previously noted, the nonresidential classes present several challenges.

Residential. Two general methods are used for determining the indoor budget for residential customers. The most common is based on PPH data. Household sizes may be based on customer surveys, US census data, default assumptions, or through empirical analysis based on winter-time water consumption. For example, an indoor budget might range from 50 to 80 gallons per capita per day (gpcd); however, utility-specific factors and/or data should be considered.

In some climates, historical indoor water use by individual customers can be derived from average winter consumption of water and used to set the indoor budget. This approach is applicable in climates that have minimal or no outdoor water use in the winter. This approach implicitly determines the household size based on actual indoor water consumption. A disadvantage to this method may be diminished equity; households that have historically been inefficient with water use during the winter may be given a disproportionately large budget relative to the actual number of residents. An upper limit can be placed on each household's indoor water budget to reduce the impact of this potential inequity.

Another complication of using average winter water consumption is that some households may be vacant during the winter (e.g., so-called snowbirds going to locations with warmer climates) or have increased winter use (e.g., skiing destinations with increased winter activities). In general, having seasonal use as a base in areas with large variations in seasonal customers makes this approach more difficult.

The methods for developing indoor water budgets for multifamily residential (MFR) are generally similar to single-family residential (SFR). In some cases, the default value for PPH for MFR is lower than SFR. A separate assessment may be conducted for MFR customers regarding the gpcd value because it is common that the average gpcd is lower for MFR than SFR. These lower average gpcd for MFR may be the result of off-site laundry, differences in demands for culinary and sanitary uses, and so forth. Again, the methods and resulting values should be utility specific.

Nonresidential. Nonresidential customers can be grouped into subcategories (e.g., restaurants, big-box retail, steel fabrication, office buildings, and car washes) and/or by meter size. Fewer utilities have implemented water-budget rates for nonresidential customers because of the challenges posed by the diversity of water needs among, and even within, nonresidential subcategories. Utilities that have implemented nonresidential water-budget rates have, for lack of a better alternative, generally based water budgets on historical use for individual customers. While this approach provides a benchmark to price current usage against past usage, it does not account for historically inefficient water use or increases in water use that may be efficient and may result from a growing business.

Outdoor budget. Many approaches can be used for setting the outdoor budgets. One of the more complex options sets outdoor budgets based on four variables: size of the customer's landscaped area, an ET value, a crop coefficient (K_c), and an irrigation efficiency coefficient. With these four variables in place, the outdoor water budget for each customer can be calculated as follows:

$$\text{Outdoor Budget} = [\text{Landscaped Area (ft}^2)] \times [\text{ET (ft)}] \times [\text{Kc (\%)}] \times [\text{1/Irrigation Efficiency (\%)}]$$

Setting outdoor budgets can be simplified by adopting basic assumptions for quantifying the variables in this equation, as explained in the following section.

Landscaped area. Depending on available resources, obtaining measurements of the landscaped area of each individual customer can be among the most challenging tasks of implementing a water-budget rate design. Data collection requirements can range from simple approaches (e.g., estimating the lot size based on the customer's meter size) to moderate (e.g., estimating the landscaped area based on total lot size), to the more complex (e.g., directly measuring the landscape area of each individual property/customer).

The simple approaches are reasonable when lots sizes and uses are sufficiently similar across the customers to whom they apply. In some cases, utilities have estimated landscaped areas for customers based on the average value of a representative sample of directly measured lots. This approach has limited application because there are few utilities for which the customers within the customer classes are sufficiently similar. A more precise and more costly method is to use parcel data. There are two general approaches to calculating landscaped area when using parcel data. The first is to assume that the landscaped area for each customer is a predetermined percentage of the customer's lot size. This percentage can be established by conducting a survey of lot sizes compared to landscaped areas for specific land-use categories. This technique is appropriate when land use in the service area is relatively similar throughout the customer class.

The second approach is to estimate the landscaped area based on the estimated footprint of the recorded building. In some cases, the footprint is used to develop stormwater charges. Alternatively, the building footprint can be estimated from data on a building's square footage and number of floors. The landscaped area can be estimated by subtracting this footprint estimate, and further assumptions on additional impervious areas, from the lot size.

A more precise and costly method is to directly measure each individual property. Given that direct, on-the-ground measurements are often infeasible, geographic information system and satellite imaging technologies have been used to accomplish this task.

Evapotranspiration. ET is a measure of the amount of water a plant loses to the atmosphere through evaporation and transpiration; it is a good indication of how much water a plant needs to regain to maintain its health and appearance. ET is typically based on several factors, including temperature and humidity; therefore, use of ET as a factor generally increases water budgets during the summer.

Utilities can use four typical approaches to address ET in water budgets. The first is to simply ignore ET. Ignoring ET effectively means the outdoor allocation for water use will be constant throughout the year. Although this is simple to implement, it may not address efficiency concerns, because the amount of water allocated for outdoor usage will remain constant throughout the year. Also, not using ET may contribute to revenue instability, because customers will demand different amounts of water under differing weather conditions. For instance, on a warmer day, customers will appropriately demand additional water, which produces extra revenue. The reverse is also true; on cooler or wetter days, outdoor demand will be reduced. This revenue instability is compounded as the incremental price of the outdoor consumption increases.

The second approach is to use historical ET averages for the billing period. This method will have the outdoor allocations increasing in the summer months and decreasing in the winter months. Although it is relatively simple to use historical ET values, it may lead to problems such as allocating excessive water during wet and cool years and insufficient water during hot and dry years.

The third approach is to use real-time ET data from local weather stations. Daily ET readings are collected by the utility and then summed to obtain the total ET for each billing period. As such, the total allocation for a given period is not known until the end of the billing cycle. Approximations, based on historical averages, can be provided prior to the billing cycle. A further step could include subtracting effective precipitation from the allocation because ET does not account for rainfall. Use of real-time ET adds another degree of complexity and equity but may require a more advanced billing system that can interface with an ET database; it may also add to customer confusion and a blunting of the price signal as the usage blocks change from month to month. This would add significant complexity to the task of revenue forecasting as the usage blocks change from month to month.

The fourth approach is to combine historical ET with actual ET to provide predictability to customers for their outdoor water uses. According to this technique, a utility uses the greater of either historical or actual ET in setting the water budget. With this method, a utility can provide a customer the minimal amount of outdoor water requirement for the next billing period.

Crop coefficient. Types of vegetation significantly affect the actual rate of ET. Crop coefficients (K_c) are used to modify the reference ET (ET_o) rates into specific crop ET (ET_c) rates. ET_c is calculated by multiplying the K_c for a given plant by the ET_o of a given climate. Local ET_o rates and K_c values are available from a variety of sources (in the United States, this information is available from most state land-grant colleges).

The K_c values that are adopted by a utility can either be specific to each customer or based on a type of plant that is deemed to be appropriate for a given climate. In agricultural applications, the K_c value is often specific to the crop being grown. Residential applications, however, normally use a single K_c value based on a target vegetation type (e.g., turf grass) because tracking the actual vegetation for each customer may be impractical; dedicated irrigation customers fall somewhere in between these two extremes.

Irrigation efficiency. An irrigation efficiency coefficient is included to account for irrigation systems that are inherently imperfect; typically, a single system-wide or customer-class-specific value is used. The most common inefficiencies are attributable to water losses and uneven (nonuniform) application. By including an irrigation efficiency coefficient in the outdoor water-budget calculation, the utility concedes that there is an acceptable level of inefficiency in every system. Determining the value of the coefficient can be based on records of actual observations by local landscape professionals and water auditors or based on a prescriptive level set by the utility. Irrigation efficiencies can generally range from 35 percent (very poor) to 80 percent (very good).

Policy decision for outdoor budgets. The following are examples of policy decisions that may need to be made when determining outdoor budgets.

Nonirrigation. Outdoor budgets are often based on the assumption that all permeable surfaces on a lot require an irrigation budget. Modern landscapes, especially in water-scarce areas, frequently have areas that require no irrigation (a rock garden or wooded lot). In such cases, should these utilities determine whether the customer is given an outdoor allocation based on their lot size or irrigable area, and if so, how does that decision support efficient and inefficient usage?

Outdoor irrigation caps. Some utilities have chosen to apply a cap or a declining amount of water for the outdoor budget of large landscaped areas (e.g., 1-acre residential lots). For example, a water utility may cap the landscaped area for outdoor budgets. Under a cap, the water budget for a customer only includes enough water to irrigate the maximum area capped. Any use above the cap is considered inefficient and priced outside the customer's water budget.

Variance Procedures

Initial water budgets often need to be modified to meet the specific water needs of some customers. Establishing a variance process with clear rules is helpful. (Even if it is decided that no variances are allowed, the rule should be clearly communicated.) Utilities may consider granting variances for extenuating circumstances (see the example later in this chapter) or to address errors in the data used to create the customer's water budget.

Extenuating circumstances. The extent to which customers are allowed to request variances to their water budget depends on the specific policy goals of the utility and the availability of resources to make adjustments to individual customers. The following are some examples of variances that may be considered.

- Persons per household
- Irrigated area
- Medical needs
- Home businesses
- Large animals

The specificity of water-budget rate designs could potentially increase the number or variety of special exemptions requested by customers as compared to the level of requests under other rate designs. The list of extenuating circumstances adopted by a utility could itself become a source of concern and even opposition to a proposed water-budget rate program.

Setting the Number of Consumption Blocks

The number of consumption blocks in a water-budget rate design is determined by the utility and often varies from two to five (or more) blocks. Changes in the number of blocks have an impact on the width of each block (i.e., the allowed water budget or the water-use allowance in each block).

Two-block rate design. In the case of a two-block rate design, the first block would most often be equal to the total water budget (indoor and outdoor use) and the second block would represent all water use in excess of the established water budget. The quantity of water allocated to the last block is always infinite because the purpose of a water budget does not include limiting the amount of water that can be purchased.

Three-block (and more) rate design. When employing a rate design with more than two blocks, the first two are generally tied to the customer's indoor and outdoor budgets, respectively, and the remaining blocks have quantities of water that are a percentage of the water budget (e.g., 125 percent of the block 2 amount) or directly tied to a specific water resource.

Setting the Rate for Each Block

Utilities use many methods for setting the relative rates for each block of a water-budget rate design. Some utilities use unit costs from a cost-of-service analysis to estimate the cost of providing water for indoor versus outdoor use. Other utilities use a marginal-cost type approach to establish the relative rates by block (see chapter V.8). In all cases, the price (rate) for each block should be based on cost-of-service principles and be cost based. Simply multiplying the price of the first or second block by a fixed multiple to create a punitive price is not cost based or in keeping with the cost-of-service principles endorsed within this manual. Failure to develop rates for each block (efficient and inefficient) using cost-based principles and cost-of-service methodologies may lead to rates that are not cost justified or legally supportable.

EXAMPLE

This example illustrates how a water-budget rate might be designed for the residential class. In this example, annual inside-city residential water sales are anticipated to be 968,000 thousand gallons; and based on the results of the cost-of-service analysis, the consumption-related cost of service is $2,720,381 (see Table III.2-5 earlier in this manual). While there is no single analytical method to define consumption blocks, it is assumed for this example that the utility wishes to set the thresholds for blocks 1 and 2 at amounts that approximate the total of the estimated indoor and outdoor budgets of the customers

Table IV.6-1 Water-budget rates

Blocks	Forecast Consumption, 1,000 gal	Consumption, %	Rate Differential	Revenue	Rate, $/1,000 gal
Block 1 (indoor)	387,200	40	1.0	$809,248	$2.09
Block 2 (outdoor)	435,600	45	1.3	1,183,525	$2.72
Block 3 (inefficient)	96,800	10	2.0	404,624	$4.18
Block 4 (wasteful)	38,720	4	3.0	242,774	$6.27
Block 5 (unsustainable)	9,680	1	4.0	80,925	$8.36
Estimated Total	968,000	100		2,721,096	
Cost of Service				2,720,381	
Difference				$715	

in this class. The utility's objective is to have block 1 consumption approximate indoor usage and to charge a higher amount for outdoor usage in block 2 to promote outdoor conservation. Similarly, the utility will charge higher rates for consumption beyond block 2 to discourage wasteful use.

Based on a detailed review of its customers' usage, the utility determines that 40 percent of its water sales are within block 1 (the indoor budget), 45 percent within block 2 (the outdoor budget), 10 percent within block 3, 4 percent within block 4, and 1 percent within block 5. This equates to annual sales by block (in thousands of gallons) as noted in Table IV.6-1.

For the example utility, the rate differentials noted in Table IV.6-1 are based on a technical (cost-of-service) analysis undertaken by the utility and represent the differences in unit production cost or alternative water supply sources. As the utility's resources become more constrained, alternative and higher cost resources are required. At the same time, customers with high peak demands should be allocated a greater proportion of the utility's peak capacity costs, thus creating a higher per-unit cost of service. With the total cost-of-service amount to be recovered ($2,720,381), estimated consumption, and rate differentials in hand, it is possible to calculate the water-budget rates as illustrated in Table IV.6-1.

SUMMARY

Water-budget rates provide water utilities with a conservation-oriented rate design that focuses on efficient water use at the individual customer level. Although more complex than other rate designs, the ability of water-budget rates to discourage inefficient water use has made this approach an attractive alternative to utilities facing significant water shortages.

REFERENCES

Mayer, P., W. Deoreo, T. Chesnutt, and L. Summers. 2008. Water Budgets and Rate Structures: Innovative Management Tools. *Journal AWWA*, 100(5):117–131.

Pechiney, D., and T. Chesnutt. 1997. *Landscape Water Conservation Programs: Evaluation of Water Based Rate Structures*. A report prepared for the Metropolitan Water District and the Municipal Water District of Orange County by A&N Technical Services, Inc.

Chapter **IV.7**

Revenue Stability— Fixed Charges and Other Considerations

To maintain financial viability, water utilities in North America need to address the rising cost of capital improvements, operations, and water resources. They also need to address year-over-year revenue volatility and long-term revenue erosion due to changes in metered demands over time. Wet weather, conservation efforts, and general economic conditions can make it difficult to accurately project metered demands. Significant deviations in the metered demands can mean revenue shortfalls or surpluses.

One of the more common means of stabilizing revenues from water rates is increasing the portion of rate revenues recovered by fixed charges through rate design. Cost-of-service rate designs typically include both a fixed and a variable charge. The fixed charge portion of a customer's bill will be the same, or fixed, for each bill regardless of the amount of water the customer uses. Unless stated otherwise, the fixed charge is the minimum bill an active customer will be charged. Variable charges, often referred to as *consumption charges*, are the rates applied based on the amount of water a customer uses. As described throughout this manual, these charges can take many forms.

GENERAL CONSIDERATIONS

Recently, water sales in many parts of North America have been declining. Reasons for this drop in sales include: more environmentally conscious customers; higher wastewater charges that are tied to water use; increased regulatory pressures that encourage programmatic conservation; installation of more efficient fixtures, particularly in new homes; and the recent economic downturn. The appropriate pricing mechanism to address changes in revenues from declining sales can vary depending on whether the declines are considered long term in nature or more temporary. Examples of long-term declines include

- conservation that results in physical changes such as xeriscaping or the installation of more-efficient fixtures,
- customer price elasticity response to water and sewer rate increases or structure changes,
- economic downturns,
- demographic changes (population decrease, decline in average household size, etc.), and
- increased efficiencies in the use of water by industries or the loss of major industries in a service area.

Examples of more temporary declines include sales affected by

- changes in metered demands and supply availability due to weather patterns (extreme wet/dry year),
- changes in overall economic conditions,
- natural disasters, and
- system interruption due to aging or inadequate infrastructure.

Utilities can address revenue erosion from long-term declines in sales through proactive long-range financial planning based on demand forecasts that account for demand declines. For example, in developing rates, utility rate studies typically base projected sales on an average/normalized sales year (three- to five-year average). This exposes the utility's revenue to risks if sales continue to decline. However, if a utility calculates its rates based on worst-case annual sales, or conservatively accounts for declining demand trends in its demand forecast, this risk can be minimized. This method produces higher rates and can result in cash flows in excess of utility needs. These funds can be used to protect against short-term revenue volatility or to smooth out future rate increases. Long-term planning will enable management to proactively adjust rate structures to achieve multiple objectives, including revenue stability.

Revenue volatility derived from temporary sales declines can be addressed through reserves accumulated in anticipation of brief revenue shortfalls. In addition, these short-term sales declines can also be recovered through temporary rate adjustments and/or surcharges. Alternative methods for addressing revenue volatility are listed at the end of this chapter.

In light of the decreased predictability and increased volatility of the variable or consumption portion of water-rate revenues, many utilities are looking to increase the portion of fixed-charge revenues. The revenues that come from fixed charges can be predicted with a high degree of certainty. This section describes some of the fixed charges available and other rate-making considerations that can be used to stabilize a utility's eroding revenue stream. Chapter IV.8 specifically discusses fire protection charges, which are also a form of fixed charges.

A cost-of-service approach to setting water rates results in the distribution of costs to each customer or customer class based on the costs that each causes. A dual set of fees—fixed and variable—is an extension of this cost-causation theory. For example, a utility incurs some costs associated with serving customers irrespective of the amount or rate of water they use. These types of costs are referred to as *customer-related costs* and typically are expenses that would be recovered through a fixed charge. These costs are usually recovered on a per-customer basis or some other nonconsumptive basis. Regardless of the level of a customer's consumption, a customer will be charged this minimum amount in each bill.

Utilities also incur costs associated with providing for a given amount of demand. As described in chapter III.1, these costs may be categorized as base-extra capacity costs, or commodity and demand costs, depending on the cost allocation method used. Regardless of the allocation method selected, a utility incurs these costs because of the amount and pattern of its customers' water demands. For various reasons, it has become common practice in the water industry to recover such costs, even those defined as fixed in traditional cost-accounting terms, through a consumption charge that varies with the customer's consumption.

Fixed and variable charges, as defined for rate design in a cost-of-service water-rate analysis, depart from standard or traditional accounting definitions of fixed and variable costs. A traditional cost-accounting definition considers fixed costs as charges that do not change in total as the volume of activity changes. In contrast, variable costs are those that do change in total as the volume of activity changes as measured in a specific time period. Notably, over the long run, a utility may be able to control fixed costs by avoiding constructing additional units of capacity resulting from water conservation/declining demands. Consequently, over the long run, fixed costs can be viewed as at least partially variable. Water utilities can use these concepts in somewhat different ways, as described in the following sections.

FIXED CHARGES

Water utilities use many different types of fixed charges in their rate designs. Three commonly used fixed charges are billing (or customer) charges, service (or meter) charges, and minimum charges.

Billing or Customer Charges

The terms *billing charge* and *customer charge* are often used interchangeably. This charge typically recovers costs such as meter reading, billing costs, and other costs that the utility incurs equally per customer or per account. This type of fixed charge can be the same for all customers or it can vary by customer class if certain customer classes have more complicated billing or customer service requirements. These costs are not a function of the amount of consumption a customer uses. An example of a billing or customer charge is $6.00 per bill.

A billing charge is relatively easy to calculate, implement, and understand. A billing charge is frequently lower than other types of fixed charges (or represents a relatively small component of a larger overall fixed charge).

Service or Meter Charges

A *service charge* (or *meter charge*) is a fixed fee that increases with meter size. It often recovers the same costs as a billing charge plus other customer-related costs that change as a function of meter size. These other costs typically include meter-related costs such as meter testing, repairs, and replacements.

Table IV.7-1, based on inside-city unit costs of service from Table III.2-5, shows an example determination of a schedule of monthly service charges. Because service charges vary by meter size, they may be more complicated to explain and require additional data to allocate costs to each meter size in a fair and equitable manner.

In some cases, utilities include other costs to provide service to a customer as a part of a service or meter charge. The argument is made that utilities make investments to provide the ability to serve, and that these costs must be recovered regardless of the amount of water used during a given period. This is sometimes referred to as a readiness-to-serve

Table IV.7-1 Fixed charges by meter size

Meter Size, in.	Billing and Collection,* $	Meters and Services,[†] $	Total Meter Charge, $
5/8	5.80	6.46	12.26
3/4	5.80	9.70	15.50
1	5.80	16.16	21.96
1½	5.80	32.32	38.12
2	5.80	51.72	57.52
3	5.80	103.44	109.24
4	5.80	161.62	167.42
6	5.80	323.25	329.05

*From Table III.2-5, rounded to nearest cent.

†Based on inside-city unit costs of service in Table III.2-5 as follows: $77.5793 per equivalent meter per year divided by 12 bills = $6.465 per equivalent meter per month. Meter equivalents based on appendix B.

charge. An approach that may be useful in establishing a cost basis for readiness-to-serve costs is referred to as the minimum system analysis. This analysis considers that there is a minimum system in place to meet minimum service requirements regardless of use. The minimum needs are defined by determining the minimum size a system would be designed to meet minimum or average service needs (e.g., 4-in. service) not considering sizing for peak-day capacity needs or fire protection. The percentage of the distribution system related to meeting the minimum system needs would be applied to distribution-related costs and would be collected in the fixed charges. Incremental system sizing related to sizing the system to meet peak-day needs and fire flow requirements may also be considered for inclusion in the fixed charges. Fire protection charges are discussed in more detail in chapter IV.8. The requirement to recover costs without regard to the volume of sales is real, but it does not necessarily suggest that fixed charges should represent a large portion of total revenue requirements, nor that the rate structure should match the cost structure of a utility. The use of a water system is reflected in both potential and average usage patterns, so a continued reliance on volumetric charges to recover fixed costs has value from an equity perspective.

The extent to which a strategy of large service charges is employed is frequently limited as a result of concerns over impacts on affordability for smaller-volume customers.

Minimum Charges and Water Allowance

A minimum charge is equal to the sum of the fixed-fee components of a water bill that must be paid regardless of metered usage. A minimum charge could consist of a billing charge, or a billing charge plus a meter charge. In some cases, a fixed fee based on an allowance for a certain amount of water consumption is included in the minimum charge. The allowance is the minimum volume of consumption for which a customer is billed regardless of whether or not the water is used. The allowance is generally set at a relatively low level to equal an amount that is typically used by most customers in a month. Some utilities use an increasingly larger water allowance for larger size meters.

The minimum charge may be viewed as a means to recover a portion of fixed costs associated with investments to which all customers should contribute, because the utility continues to incur the fixed costs regardless of whether customers consumed water during that billing period.

This charge typically recovers the same costs as the billing and service charges, plus the cost of the allotted consumption allowance, multiplied by the consumption rate.

Table IV.7-2 Fixed charges—Minimum charge

Meter Size, in.	Meter Charge, $	Water Allotment,* $	Total Minimum Charge, $
⅝	12.26	5.62	17.88
¾	15.50	5.62	21.12
1	21.96	5.62	27.53
1½	38.12	5.62	43.74
2	57.52	5.62	63.14
3	109.24	5.62	114.86
4	167.42	5.62	173.04
6	329.05	5.62	334.67

*This charge includes consumption of the first 2,000 gallons.

For example, if a utility had a service charge of $12.26 per equivalent ⅝-in. meter and a consumption charge of $2.81 per thousand gallons (based on the residential cost per thousand gallons as displayed in Table IV.2-2) and it wanted to set a minimum charge that included 2,000 gallons, the minimum charge would be $17.88 per equivalent meter ($12.26 + [2 × $2.81]). Table IV.7-2 shows how to calculate a minimum charge by meter size. This example assumes the service charges presented in Table IV.7-2 and a consumption charge of $2.81 per thousand gallons for all meter sizes.

Minimum charges generally result in the highest fixed fees of those fees discussed herein. Often they are criticized for being unfair in that they charge a customer for consumption even when the customer does not use the allotted amount of water.*

It is often assumed that a minimum charge adds to the utility's revenue stability. However, if the consumption allotment for a minimum charge is set at a low level, a utility may actually receive little benefit in terms of revenue stability. The amount of revenue generated from the consumption component of the minimum charge is revenue that, for the most part, would normally be generated from water sales using the consumption charge.

OTHER CONSIDERATIONS

Many utilities have adopted a water rate structure that is heavily weighted on volume charges. This discourages wasteful use by implementing a "the more you use, the more you pay" price signal. Relying solely on volumetric rate increases to implement conservation efforts can increase the risk of revenue erosion and increase revenue volatility. Upward adjustments to volumetric rates to recover lost revenues exacerbate declining sales and can expose the utility to affordability concerns (see chapter V.4 for discussion of utility rate affordability).

Balancing revenue stability with policy objectives like conservation is an important consideration when deciding the level of fixed charges. Because conservation rates are designed to encourage more efficient water use by charging higher rates (consumptive charges) for discretionary uses, the drop in revenues, in some cases, may be greater than the drop in water sales. For example, a 10 percent drop in sales may result in a 20 percent drop in revenues if the reduced sales come from the higher priced water. Mitigating this

---

* In some instances, legal challenges have been threatened by users of systems with usage allowances. The challenges result from the argument that the customer is charged for a certain amount of water regardless of whether the amount of water is used. Under this line of reasoning, the minimum charge can be argued to violate cost-of-service principles. To avoid legal challenges, a utility may determine that it is best suited by not including a usage allowance.

volatility through increased fixed charges may reduce the effectiveness of the conservation efforts and the level of water conservation.

Many utilities across North America are prohibited from eliminating rate structures with customer conservation pricing signals, even if they have identified a need for additional revenue stability. However, there are several established approaches that can protect utilities from the impacts of revenue swings even under the most aggressive conservation pricing strategies.

Alternative methods for addressing revenue volatility including the following:

- **Temporary pricing adjustments and surcharges.** As discussed later in chapter V.3, a surcharge is a charge separate from existing permanent rates and is usually implemented to collect a target amount of revenue. Rate surcharges can be a reactive yet effective tool for meeting short-term revenue shortfalls. Notably, these price changes tend to have a twofold effect: while gleaning additional revenue, it can also strengthen the pricing signal to conserve water if applied volumetrically.

- **Reserve funds.** Many utilities manage revenue volatility by funding special reserves that can be used to stabilize temporary revenue shortfalls. Rate stabilization funds are common and provide a source of funds to meet debt-service coverage covenants. Funding for the reserves is included in the utility cost of service and collected through rates or funded from additional funds generated in years where revenue exceeded budget expectations (e.g., dry weather year).

- **Conservative water sales projections in rate-making.** In developing rates, utility rate studies typically base project sales on an average/normalized sales year (three- to five-year average). This exposes the utility's revenue to risks as sales decline in response to both conservation-rate pricing signals and adverse weather. However, if a utility calculates its rates based on worst-case annual sales, this could minimize the risk. This method produces higher rates; thus, it has been suggested that utilities adopting the conservative approach also implement a customer "dividend" program. This program would return some of the funds that may be collected in excess of the utility's revenue requirement. Alternatively, more frequent rate analysis can be completed to adjust rates based on actual water sales if estimates were too conservative.

- **Ratchets.** This method uses the individual customer's peak monthly use to set the customer's base/fixed charges as a financial incentive for conservation (Woodcock 1995). It encourages customers to reduce their peak water use and lower their monthly bills (Eskaf et al. 2014). This alternative method can be burdensome for utility administrations. Thus, recalculation of the customer's base/fixed charge should be infrequent enough to reduce the utility's burden yet frequent enough to permit the customer to realize the benefit of managing water use. Because the increased fixed charge targets customers with high monthly demand, it helps the utility stabilize revenue while still sending the desired price signal.

SUMMARY

In designing rates, there are a number of options that can provide increased revenue stability to a utility. The option selected should be primarily determined based on the underlying cause of revenue erosion or volatility and whether that cause is long term or short term in nature. There are secondary concerns that should also be considered, such as the trade-off between affordability (which is naturally facilitated by low fixed charges) and revenue stability (which is naturally facilitated by high fixed charges). There is also a trade-off between conservation objectives and revenue stability—it is more difficult to send conservation-oriented pricing signals if fixed charges are high. These trade-offs must be carefully considered and balanced by utility staff and policymakers to achieve alignment with the policy objectives of the utility and its stakeholders.

REFERENCES

Eskaf, S., J. Hughes, M. Tiger, K. Bradshaw, and S. Leurig. 2014. Measuring and Mitigating Water Revenue Variability. Ceres and Environmental Finance Center at the University of North Carolina at Chapel Hill.

Woodcock, C. 1995. Social Rate Making: Has the Time Come? Presented at New England Water Works Association Annual Conference, September 18, 1995.

This page intentionally blank.

Chapter **IV.8**

Rates for Fire Protection Service

Fire protection service differs from other services provided by the utility. Essentially, this is a standby service that the utility makes available on demand. Although most fire hydrants and sprinkler connections are rarely used, the utility must be ready to provide adequate water quantities and pressures to meet firefighting needs at all times throughout the distribution system. Fire protection services are provided for both public (municipal fire hydrants) and private (individual property fire sprinklers) fire protection purposes. As used herein, the general term *fire protection* includes both public and private fire protection services.

GENERAL CONSIDERATIONS

Among the different viewpoints and ways that utilities address the recovery of public and private fire protection costs are the following:

- **Ignore the issue.** Mistakenly, some utilities do not recognize, acknowledge, or allocate any costs to fire protection within their cost-of-service analysis or charge any public or private fire protection rates.

- **Address only public fire protection costs.** Public fire protection costs are equitably allocated within the cost-of-service analysis, and the costs are collected via recoupment from the customers within the retail user rates and/or directly billed to a governmental agency via a hydrant charge or similar mechanism. Under this viewpoint, private fire protection costs are not allocated and are essentially ignored.

- **Address only private fire protection costs.** Private fire protection costs are equitably allocated and the costs collected via private fire protection rates billed directly to those customers with private fire protection systems. Under this viewpoint, public fire protection costs are not allocated and are essentially ignored; the costs are left to be recovered through other rates and charges.

- **Address both public and private fire protection costs.** Both public and private fire protection costs are equitably allocated within the cost of service and collected via rates reflecting the end user and service provided (i.e., allocate public and private fire protection costs and establish rates similar to the approaches previously noted for the respective service).

Section III of this manual, Cost Allocation, presents examples of the allocation of costs to general water service customers and to fire protection. These examples illustrate that cost allocation principles can be used to determine fire protection charges under a traditional cost-of-service rate philosophy. After the total revenue requirements associated with fire protection service are determined, the utility must establish an equitable method for recovering this cost from those served with fire protection services. This chapter provides guidance on developing cost-based rates that reflect the cost of fire protection for the users of the system.

Previous editions of this manual emphasized the collection of fire protection charges through the assessment of costs associated with direct fire hydrant–related costs, along with a proportionate share of costs associated with getting water to the fire hydrant system (source of supply, treatment, pumping, and transmission/distribution costs). The cost associated with public fire protection has typically been charged to a municipal government where it is recovered through the ad valorem property tax system and perhaps other tax sources (e.g., sales taxes). While that approach is still a common and generally accepted practice, limitations on property taxes have caused municipalities to seek different cost recovery methods that do not burden the general fund. An alternative and contemporary approach develops fire protection costs that can be passed on directly to customers through charges based on the respective demands for fire flow by user class or to individual retail customers. The traditional fire hydrant charge approach is still presented in this manual because it may reflect local policy preferences, may be required by state law, or it could be the preferred method stipulated by a state regulatory commission.

Traditionally, fire protection charges were assessed to the municipalities or fire districts served by the utility, and the municipal governments passed on the cost to individual taxpayers. If these fire protection charges are passed along as part of the ad valorem property tax, private sector property owners are assessed a portion of the fire protection costs based on the value of their property. This method has been justified by the rationale that the benefits of fire protection services are related to property value or that fire protection is a function or duty of general government. One issue with this method is that public sector or tax-exempt properties do not pay ad valorem taxes and are thus subsidized by tax-paying property owners. In some communities, the value of tax-exempt properties is significant, potentially ranging between 10 and 30 percent of total property values.

This chapter examines additional issues in fire protection cost allocation. It is intended to supplement the cost allocation guidelines and numerical examples provided in section III. The following sections summarize the history of fire protection rate-making and the allocation of fire protection costs between public and private fire service. Additionally, other potential rate-design concerns are addressed, such as intra-class inequities. The derivation of private fire service charges based on connection size is presented along with methods that can be used to recover public fire service costs. Lastly, considerations for the growing use of single-family, residential, private fire services are discussed.

HISTORICAL PERSPECTIVES

The concepts, policies, procedures, and practices related to fire protection service charges have evolved over the past 100-plus years. During this period, numerous papers that

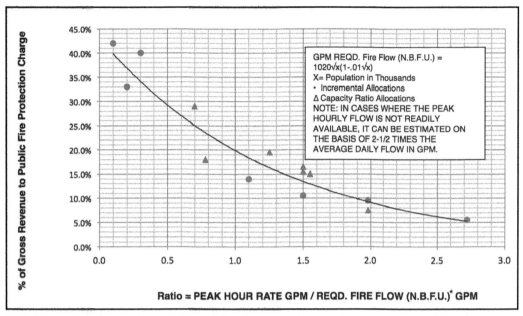

GPM REQD. Fire Flow (N.B.F.U.) =
$1020\sqrt{x}(1-.01\sqrt{x})$
X= Population in Thousands
• Incremental Allocations
Δ Capacity Ratio Allocations
NOTE: IN CASES WHERE THE PEAK
HOURLY FLOW IS NOT READILY
AVAILABLE, IT CAN BE ESTIMATED ON
THE BASIS OF 2-1/2 TIMES THE
AVERAGE DAILY FLOW IN GPM.

*N.B.F.U. stands for National Board of Fire Underwriters, now known as Insurance Services Office (ISO).

Source: *Maine Water Utilities Association*

Figure IV-8.1 Percentage of total revenue allocated as fire protection costs

present differing theories and opinions on establishing rates and charges have been published and debated. In 1888, F.L. Fuller wrote the first paper published by AWWA on the subject of fire-service rates and charges. This was followed in 1911 with a study by Metcalf, Kuichling, and Hawley proposing that costs be prorated between general water service and fire service based on the comparison of the capacity of the facilities required. Robert Nixon published a paper in 1937 that suggested an allocation between general water service and fire service based on a capacity-ratio method.

In 1955, D.A. Root and T.R. Camp determined that systems without a fire protection function should be designed to meet peak loads, and a system designed to include fire protection should be sized to meet the maximum-day demand plus required fire flow demands. The authors noted that the cost of distribution piping is not proportional to capacity, and they argued that the cost of the fire system should be equal to the incremental cost associated with fire protection.

In 1961, the Maine Water Utilities Association Committee on Fire Protection Charges published a report that included a curve that indicated the percentage of total revenue allocated as fire protection costs, based on the population served and peak-hour water demands. The curve is shown in Figure IV.8-1.

The horizontal axis is the ratio of the utility's peak-hour demand in gallons per minute divided by a fire flow rate using the following formula:

$$1{,}020 \sqrt{X} (1 - 0.01 \sqrt{X}) \text{ in Gallons per Minute}$$

where X is the population, in thousands, served by the utility.

In 1987, the Maine Public Utilities Commission adopted the use of this curve. Its regulations state that, except under extraordinary circumstances, fire protection charges will be no more than 30 percent but not less than 6 percent of gross revenues. In 1996, the Maine Public Utilities Commission adopted amendments to its regulations and clarified that the percentage of the revenue established by the curve applies to public fire protection

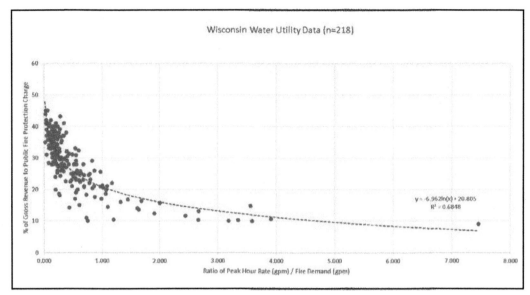

Figure IV-8.2 Maine Public Utilities Commission fire protection curve

services. The amendments also set forth procedures to determine private fire protection charges based on demand requirements. As an alternative to the use of this curve, utilities are permitted to prepare fully allocated cost-of-service studies.

The Public Service Commission of Wisconsin attempted to recreate the "Maine Curve" based on water utility data from Wisconsin. The data represents 218 municipal water utilities that completed rate cases between March 2006 and April 2015. The plot of the "percentage of gross revenue allocated to fire protection charge" versus the "ratio of the utility's peak hour demand divided by fire flow rate" is shown in Figure IV.8-2. The Wisconsin fire flow rates are highly correlated to the National Board of Fire Underwriters (NBFU) equation but may have been adjusted over the life of each utility to reflect population changes and limitations to the fire flow capacity of a given water system. The 218 data points represent water utilities that serve communities with populations ranging from 100 to 595,000 persons. The Public Service Commission regulates the rates for 583 public water utilities.

The Wisconsin data generally fits the shape of the Maine Curve between x-axis values of 0.0 to 1.5. Beyond an x-axis value of 1.5, the Wisconsin data plots higher than the Maine Curve.

Currently, the Public Service Commission of Wisconsin does not allow regulated water utilities to estimate their fire protection cost-of-service by using this curve. They must compute their fire protection cost allocation by using a rate model based on this AWWA Manual M1.

In general, the following three approaches have historically been used in allocating costs to fire protection:

1. Allocating primary cost to general water service, with incremental costs allocated to fire protection service

2. Allocating primary cost to fire protection service, with incremental costs allocated to general water service

3. Allocating costs to general water service and fire protection service on a basis proportional to the system design and usage

The first two approaches presume that the system was primarily built to provide either general water service or fire protection. A review of these methodologies and additional historical publications was published in 1982 in *Journal AWWA* (Corssmit and Green 1982). The use of each approach results in a significantly different allocation to fire protection service. Since the mid-1900s and continuing through the present, the third approach has been most widely used and accepted. Section III of this manual illustrates the use of this third method. This approach recognizes that the dual functions of water systems, to provide basic water service and to provide a readiness-to-serve capacity for fire protection, are equally important. This is the rationale used in this manual to develop cost-based rates that avoid subsidization of users. Both the base-extra capacity and the commodity-demand methods of cost allocation adhere to the principle of proportional cost allocations. In both models, the service characteristics of each customer class include fire protection demand. Fire protection demands by user class can be established in both maximum-day and maximum-hour fire flow demand units. The total quantity of water used for firefighting is minimal in comparison to other uses and is ignored in some studies. In other studies, a nominal amount of base use (between 0.5 and 1.0 percent) is assigned to fire protection because flow from fire hydrants is rarely metered.

PUBLIC VERSUS PRIVATE FIRE PROTECTION

Utilities typically provide fire protection services in two distinct ways—public and private. Public fire protection service is provided to all customers on a community-wide basis through fire hydrants located throughout the water system. Usually, the fire hydrants are owned by the utility, located on public rights-of-way, and available for use primarily by fire departments (or other authorized parties) for the purpose of extinguishing fires. Hydrants may also be used for system purposes, such as flushing or testing. Even though the hydrants are not directly controlled by the retail water users, the standby capacity to provide needed water is clearly intended for the use of the utility's retail users.

In contrast to public fire protection service, private fire protection service is provided to individual customers that receive additional fire protection services through private hydrants, standpipes, or sprinkler connections. In this instance, the costs of private fire protection can be directly allocated to the user of the private service through separate fire line charges or other methods. These private fire protection connections provide a direct service to the individual customer's property that is not available to customers without such connections; these customers receive a service from the utility that others do not receive and should pay for the cost of the additional service. A counterargument is made by some that charges for private fire protection should be limited because fires can be extinguished by private sprinkler systems very early in their development, representing a much smaller system demand.

Because utilities provide both public and private fire protection services, they may choose an approach that separates the total system fire protection into each type of service. Total fire protection costs may be split between public and private fire services based on the proportional demand potentials of each service. Costs associated with providing public fire protection may be shared by all customers either as an indirect part of their rates or directly allocated as a customer class requirement based on fire flow needs. Because the relative magnitude of the public-level fire protection costs may be significant, the indirect recovery through other water rates and charges results in a less-than-desired level of precision in allocating the cost of public fire protection.

Table IV.8-1 Fire protection cost calculation—Base-extra capacity method (test year)

Line No.	Item	Total Cost of Service	Base Demand	Extra Capacity Maximum Day	Extra Capacity Maximum Hour*	Customer Costs Meters & Services	Customer Costs Billing & Collection	Direct Fire Protection Service
	Inside City							
1	Unit Costs of Service, $/Unit		$1.7885 1,000 gal	$213.7455 1,000 gal	$67.2925 1,000 gal	$84.9268 per equiv. meters	$6.3257 per bill	$185,495
	Fire Protection Service							
2	Units of Service			840	4,200			
3	Allocated Costs of Service	$647,669		$179,546	$282,628			$185,495

*Maximum-hour demand in excess of maximum-day demand.

DETERMINING FIRE PROTECTION COSTS

Both direct and indirect fire protection costs may be addressed in comprehensive cost-of-service studies. Corresponding cost functionalization and distribution of allocated costs to customer classes are completed before the development of a rate design. The rate model discussion and corresponding tables in section III of this manual do not highlight this level of detail, but total fire protection cost of service is displayed in Table III.2-5 under the label "Fire Protection Service."

Direct Plus Indirect Costs

Tables III.2-1 through III.2-6 earlier in this manual include the direct fire protection portion of total fire protection costs using the base-extra capacity and the commodity-demand cost allocation models. Tables III.2-1, III.2-3, and III.2-5 present details following the base-extra capacity example, and Tables III.2-2, III.2-4, and III.2-6 present cost allocation details for the commodity-demand model. The customer class cost allocation tables from chapter III.2 are used in this chapter to illustrate the segregation of direct and indirect (or capacity-related) fire protection costs based on the unit costs for fire protection cost parameters. The allocation of fire protection costs, under the base-extra capacity method from section III, is presented in Table IV.8-1.

Line 1 of Table IV.8-1 presents the unit cost of service for each class service characteristic developed in line 1 of Table III.2-5. The derivation of various unit costs of service is provided in chapter III.2. The unit costs of service are multiplied by the units of service for maximum-day and maximum-hour capacity to yield total capacity-related (indirect) costs for fire protection. Direct fire protection costs are added to these costs to yield the total allocated costs of service for fire protection of $647,669. Although not shown in Table IV.8-1, a nominal amount of costs associated with public fire hydrant costs is sometimes assigned to the base category because hydrants are used for system purposes, such as pressure testing, C-value tests, and flushing of mains.

Public Versus Private Fire Service Cost Allocation

The direct fire protection costs listed in the last column of Table IV.8-1 are typically assigned directly to public fire protection. The indirect costs associated with providing maximum-day and maximum-hour capacity to fire services (public hydrants or private sprinklers) can be allocated between public and private fire service, as shown in Table IV.8-2.

Total fire service costs presented in Table IV.8-1 can be further allocated to public and private fire protection service by using the relative demands of various size hydrant

Table IV.8-2 Allocation of fire service costs to public and private fire service—
Base-extra capacity method (test year)

Line No.	Item	Number of Service	Demand Factor*	Equivalent Connections	Percentage Allocation	Allocation†	Total Fire Protection
	Public Fire Service						
1	City A	953					
2	Town B	202					
	Total Public Hydrants	1,155	111.31	128,564	71.55%	$330,689	$330,689
3	Direct Fire Protection						185,495
4	Total Public Fire Protection						516,184
	Private Fire Service						
	Size of Connection, inches						
5	1.5	4	2.90	12			
6	2.0	6	6.19	37			
7	3.0	12	17.98	216			
8	4.0	24	38.32	920			
9	6.0	80	111.31	8,905			
10	8.0	120	237.21	28,465			
11	10.0	23	426.58	9,811			
12	12.0	4	689.04	2,756			
	Subtotal	273		51,122	28.45%	131,489	131,489
13	Direct Fire Protection						0
14	Total Private Fire Protection						131,489
15	Total	1,428		179,685	100.00%	$462,174	$647,673

*Demand factors based on nominal size of connection raised to the 2.63 power.

†Includes all capacity-related costs but excludes direct fire protection costs presented in Table IV.8-1. Rounding is more precise than in Table IV.8-1.

branches and private sprinkler connections. Table IV.8-2 presents the allocation of the total fire protection costs to public and private fire service. Because a utility's fire protection costs depend on the potential demands for firefighting purposes, the non-hydrant-related fire protection costs may be allocated between public and private fire service based on the relative potential demands from each type of service.

In Table IV.8-2, the number of fire protection services (hydrants and connections by size) is shown as number of services, and the *demand factor* is shown to bring the various connection sizes into equivalence. The demand factor or relative potential of the size of service or connection is derived based on the nominal size of the cross-sectional area of the connection. Using the principles of the Hazen–Williams equation for flow through pressure conduits, the relative flow potential for various size pipes is dependent on the diameter raised to the 2.63 power. The 2.63 factor was used in Table IV.8-2 to derive the demand factors shown from the size of each connection. All public fire hydrants were assumed to have a 6-in. connection. Demand factors for each size service are then multiplied by the number of connections of each size to derive the total number of equivalent connections. Comparing the total public fire hydrant equivalents to the total public and private equivalents indicates that, in this example, 71.55 percent of the capacity-related fire protection costs should be allocated to public fire service. The percentage of costs that

Table IV.8-3 Customer class fire flow demands and unit cost—Base-extra capacity method (test year)

Line No.	Customer Class	Maximum Needed Fire Flow, gpm	Duration, minutes	Number of Customers	Equivalent Fire Service Demands, 1,000 gal
	Inside City:				
	Retail Service				
1	Residential	1,000	120	15,480	1,857,600
2	Commercial	2,000	180	1,220	439,200
3	Industrial	3,500	240	35	29,400
4	Total Inside-City Fire Protection Units			16,735	2,326,200
5	Total Fire Protection Cost				$516,184
6	Unit Cost, $/Unit				$0.2219

should be recovered through private fire-service charges (28.45 percent in this example) is derived in a similar manner.

The example presented in Table IV.8-2 for the base-extra capacity method distributes the allocated fire service costs, excluding the direct fire protection costs of $185,495 between public ($330,689) and private ($131,489) fire service based on relative demands. Total costs typically include some costs that apply only to public fire hydrants maintained by the utility. In this example, costs associated with the maintenance, depreciation, return on rate base, or associated debt service for public hydrants are deducted from the total fire service amount before allocating costs to public and private fire service. Costs applicable only to public fire hydrants are then added back to the public fire service costs to determine the total public fire service cost allocation.

Unit Costs

Table IV.8-3 shows one potential method for allocating the cost of public fire protection to various customer classes for the derivation of public fire protection flow under the base-extra capacity method. The table starts by estimating a total number of fire protection units by class of customer provided by the water system. These units represent a total potential demand from each of the customer classes. The maximum flow needed by a customer class is best determined based on utility-specific information or data, but lacking such utility-specific data, it may also be established based on generic ISO (Insurance Services Office) information and data. In many cases, the residential customers are assigned the same fire flow needs. The example lists 1,000 gpm for each account in this class. Assumed flows per account for the commercial and industrial classes in this example are 2,000 gpm and 3,500 gpm, respectively. The assigned duration for maintaining the capacity for these flows is listed in the "Duration" column. In this example, the aggregate fire flow demand of 2.3 billion gallons* is used to calculate the unit cost (in thousand gallon units).

The average unit cost of public fire protection is calculated by dividing the total public fire protection cost of $516,184 listed in Table IV.8-2 by the customer classes aggregate maximum fire flow demand. The resulting unit cost is $0.2219 per thousand gallons. As with all other examples in this manual, fire flow demands vary from system to system and need to be developed for each unique situation.

---

* This demand is, in effect, a noncoincidental fire demand that is not intended to match the coincidental demand in the examples used throughout this manual.

Table IV.8-4 Public fire protection cost distribution to customer classes—Base-extra capacity method (test year)

Line No.	Item	Total Cost of Service	Maximum Fire Flow Demand
	Inside City:		
1	Unit Cost of Service, $/Unit		$0.2219 per 1,000 gal
	Residential		
2	Units of Service		1,857,600
3	Allocated Cost of Service	$412,201	$412,201
	Commercial		
4	Units of Service		439,200
5	Allocated Cost of Service	$97,459	$97,459
	Industrial		
6	Units of Service		29,400
7	Allocated Cost of Service	$6,524	$6,524
8	Total Inside-City Allocated Cost of Service	$516,184	$516,184

Fire Service Cost Allocation to Classes

The determination of public fire flow revenue requirements by class of users is shown in Table IV.8-4. The total cost of service is distributed among user classes using the respective class fire flow demands listed in Table IV.8-3. For example, the maximum residential fire flow demand of 1,857,600 thousand gallons is multiplied by the unit cost of $0.2219 to determine the $412,201 user class cost-based revenue requirement in the base-extra capacity model.

RATE DESIGN

The final step in cost-of-service rate-making is the rate design. *Rate design* is the step in rate-making that allows the user class revenue requirements to be billed to customers. Cost-of-service rate design aims to collect total revenue requirements while minimizing rate inequities including interclass rate inequities. The interclass rate equity criterion is satisfied with the development of fire protection revenue requirements by customer class. This section includes guidelines for the development of interclass equitable fire protection rates.

Retail Users

Several choices available for public fire protection rate design are displayed in Tables IV.8-5 and IV.8-6 for the base-extra capacity cost allocation method. For example, residential customer class costs can be recovered in fixed monthly (or other billing periods) service charges, annual fixed charges per account, a volume charge per thousand gallons, or through hydrant or similar charges. Rate-design options may vary by type of customer class.

In Table IV.8-5, units of service from Table IV.8-1 are divided into total allocated costs of fire protection service by customer class from Table IV.8-4. The results indicate unit costs for fire protection per bill, per equivalent meter, and per 1,000 gallons.

Table IV.8-5 Public fire protection rate design—Base-extra capacity method (test year)

Line No.	Item	Total Cost of Service	Monthly Service Charge per Bill	Annual Charge per Equivalent Meter	Volume Charge per 1,000 gal
	Inside City:				
	Residential				
1	Allocated Cost of Service	$412,201			
2	Units of Service		1,857,600	15,652	968,000
3	Charge		$2.22	$26.34	$0.43
	Commercial				
4	Allocated Cost of Service	$97,459			
5	Units of Service		14,640	1,758	473,000
6	Charge		$6.66	$55.44	$0.21
	Industrial				
7	Allocated Cost of Service	$6,524			
8	Units of Service		420	251	1,095,000
9	Charge		$15.53	$25.99	$0.01

Table IV.8-6 Public fire protection rate design for municipalities per hydrant—Base-extra capacity method (test year)

Line No.	Item	Charge per Hydrant	Number of Hydrants	Charge per Hydrant	Annual Fire Charge
	Municipalities				
1	Allocated Cost of Service	$516,184			
2	Units of Service (Total Hydrants)	1,155			
3	Charge	$446.91			
	Allocation to Communities				
4	City A		953	$446.91	$425,905
5	Town B		202	446.91	90,276
6	Total		1,155		$516,181*

*Total does not match the sum of the displayed values because of rounding.

Municipal Users

In those instances when the rate design calls for the public system fire protection costs to be allocated to municipal customers, the fire hydrant rate design is often applied; however, in many situations, the methods from Table IV.8-5 could be used as well. Many regional utilities encounter resistance when developing public fire protection charges for customers that are municipalities. Because municipalities have little recourse other than to increase tax rates when there are increased or new public fire protection charges, they can be expected to resist such charges or to try to minimize them.

Fire hydrant charges. Table IV.8-6 provides an example of the determination of the public fire protection cost allocation through the use of fire hydrant equivalencies. The top portion of Table IV.8-6 presents the calculation of a per-hydrant charge. In this example, there are two communities served and the number of public fire hydrants in each community is determined.

After the per-hydrant charge is calculated, the annual public fire protection charge for each community can be determined. Municipalities can take several approaches to collect these costs from fire protection users. As previously discussed, the property tax method has been a common technique to collect such costs, but that method does not address equity issues resulting from non-property-tax-paying service recipients and inter-class rate-design issues.

Inch-foot charges. For purposes of allocating public fire protection costs between two or more communities, charges based on the proportional number of fire hydrants between communities do not necessarily reflect an appropriate or equitable allocation of the full costs associated with providing public fire protection. The direct cost of fire hydrants is a relatively small portion of total fire protection costs. Usually, the majority of costs are associated with providing capacity to deliver sufficient quantities of water to fire hydrants. To reflect this, an alternative to the per-hydrant charge is to combine hydrant charges and charges based on the size and length of pipe used to support the fire hydrants.

To determine the quantity of piping used to provide water to hydrants, a measure that reflects both the size and length of pipe is commonly used—*the number of inch-feet of pipe*. The total number of inch-feet of pipe in a community is determined by multiplying the length of each size pipe by its nominal diameter (e.g., 1,000 ft of 6-in. diameter pipe would equal 6,000 in.-ft). In many studies, pipe less than 6 in. in diameter is excluded from the calculation because smaller pipes provide minimal fire protection capability. A relatively small percentage of the capacity in large transmission mains is typically allocated to fire flow. For that reason, such mains are often excluded from the calculation of inch-foot of pipe. In cases where the larger transmission mains that serve several jurisdictions are included in the inch-foot calculations, they may be distributed on the basis of population or other appropriate criteria to recognize varying demand requirements.

The calculation of a combination of inch-foot and hydrant charges is shown in the lower portion of Table IV.8-7. Typically, the costs directly associated with fire hydrants as well as some portion of administrative and overhead costs are assigned to the hydrant charge. The remaining costs are assigned to the inch-foot fire protection charge. In the example from Table IV.8-2, approximately 36 percent of the total public fire protection costs are associated with direct costs for public fire hydrants. These costs are divided by the total number of public fire hydrants to derive a per-hydrant charge. The remaining capacity-related costs are associated with the delivery of water to the hydrants. These costs are divided by the total number of inch-foot of pipe in the system to derive a charge per inch-foot of pipe.

Table IV.8-7 shows the resulting calculation of hydrant and inch-foot charges for two communities. Relative to the number of hydrants, City A has proportionately more inch-feet of pipe than does Town B. As a result, the combined inch-foot hydrant charge method assigns more public fire protection costs to City A than does a charge based solely on the number of hydrants. The inch-foot hydrant charge may better reflect both greater fire demands in City A as well as the greater capacity available to provide water to hydrants for firefighting.

Private Fire Service Charges

Table IV.8-2 presented the allocation of total fire service costs to public and private fire protection. Costs associated with providing private fire service may be recovered in several ways, as described in the following sections.

Service line size. The most common method of charging for private fire service is to base the charge on the size of the customer's fire service connection. The fire service connection size is the best measure of the potential demand that can be put on the system in the case of a fire. A private fire protection charge based on service line size does not vary based on the end connection used for private fire protection (sprinklers or private hydrant).

Table IV.8-7 Public fire protection for municipalities, inch-foot hydrant charge—Base-extra capacity method (test year)

Line No.	Item	Total Cost of Service	Units of Service	Unit Cost
	Municipalities			
1	Hydrant Allocation	$185,495	1,155	$160.60
2	In.-ft Allocation	330,689	3,691,000	$0.09
3	Total	$516,184		

Line No.	Allocation to Communities	Number of Hydrants	Hydrant Charge	In.-ft of Mains	In.-ft Charge	Total Annual Fire Charge
4	City A	953	$153,053	3,150,000	$282,216	$435,269
5	Town B	202	32,442	541,000	48,470	80,911
6	Total	1,155	$185,495	3,691,000	$330,689*	$516,184*

*Total does not match the sum of the displayed values because of rounding.

Table IV.8-8 Private fire protection rate design for municipalities, per hydrant—Base-extra capacity method (test year)

Private Fire Service Allocation	$131,489	
Fire Service Equivalent Units	51,122	
Charge per Equivalent Unit	$2.5721	

Line No.	Service Size, in.	Number of Services	Demand Factor	Equivalent Connections	Annual Charge, $
1	1.5	4	2.90	12	29.89
2	2.0	6	6.19	37	95.53
3	3.0	12	17.98	216	555.02
4	4.0	24	38.32	920	2,365.51
5	6.0	80	111.31	8,905	22,904.64
6	8.0	120	237.21	28,465	73,215.59
7	10.0	23	426.58	9,811	25,236.17
8	12.0	4	689.04	2,756	7,089.28
9	Total	273		51,122	

Table IV.8-8 provides a calculation of private fire service charges based on service sizes. Presented in the table, the private fire service allocation is divided by the total number of private fire service equivalents (this number is derived in Table IV.8-7). The per-equivalent charge is then applied to the demand factor for each size service to find the private fire service charge. The demand factors are derived as in Table IV.8-2, and the equivalent connections are the product of the demand factors and the number of services by size. The annual charge per service connection is the product of the demand factor and the charge per equivalent unit.

Joint potable/fire service lines. Residential fire sprinkler systems for one- and two-family residences and some low-rise residential occupancies commonly use a joint service line for both the potable and the fire needs of the residences. In this case, it is important that the utilities avoid double counting these services. A combined service should not be counted as separate domestic and fire services, and the rate structure should take into account this combined use.

Additional considerations. In the past, another method of charging for private fire service included charges based on the number of sprinkler heads. Because most modern sprinkler systems function so that only the sprinkler heads in the vicinity of the fire operate, the number of sprinkler heads is not considered to be particularly relevant. Also, charges based on the number of sprinkler heads require an additional administrative burden of (1) initially determining the number of sprinkler heads at each location with a private fire service and (2) periodically updating or checking the number of sprinklers on each customer's property. For these reasons, the use of the number of sprinkler heads is becoming a less prevalent practice.

Chapter IV.7 discusses fixed customer service charges. These charges consist of two components: (1) a per-meter charge to recover costs associated with customer meters and service lines, and (2) a per-bill charge to recover costs associated with billing and collection. Though private fire services do not require meter readings, they should be checked periodically to ensure that unauthorized uses of water through private service lines do not occur. In many cases, it is appropriate to add an inspection, billing, and collection charge component to the private fire service charge. Some customers install their own storage facilities for firefighting purposes.

These storage facilities may be directly connected to the customer's fire protection system. In these cases, the customer places less of a peak demand on the utility's storage and distribution system. Accordingly, the utility may wish to provide a "storage" credit in the private fire protection charges for such customers.

Because the utility often must maintain the service connection to a customer's private fire service, an additional charge for this cost component may be added. The utility should be careful not to include costs associated with water meters unless the utility meters private fire services. When the fire line is metered or impact fees are collected from new customers for each meter, the utility is advised to analyze the relative costs of water service versus fire protection and determine corresponding fees that avoid overcharging the customer.

As noted within this chapter, private fire protection is essentially related to "standby" capacity. In assessing a system development charge (SDC), the utility may charge either the domestic size without private fire protection (e.g., a ¾-in. meter) or the size installed. If the utility charges the size installed (e.g., a 1½-in. SDC), the customer has, in essence, paid up-front for the standby capacity associated with the oversizing for fire protection. This should preclude the subsequent collection of private fire protection charges to recover the corresponding capital costs of providing standby capacity. When upsizing the meter is required, it is important to note that the upsizing is not in anticipation of a higher demand or usage but only to reduce pressure loss within the system, and any fire protection charges related to operation and maintenance should reflect this. If the customer is charged only for a domestic-level SDC (e.g., ¾-in. meter), some form of private fire capital cost recovery may be appropriate. If a private fire protection charge is levied, charging the customer as a 1½-in. meter on the user charges may be double-charging the customer, once for the private fire protection charge and then again within the user rates for the larger-sized meter. Currently, there is no generally accepted approach to this issue, but the utility should carefully formulate its approach to avoid any double-charging of customers.

EMERGING ISSUES

Residential Private Fire Protection

In recent years, residential sprinkler systems have become much more prevalent and there is a significant difference in the required demands for these systems and the traditional commercial-type fire sprinkler systems. Residential sprinkler systems primarily provide life-safety benefits as opposed to the property protection anticipated by a commercial fire sprinkler system. In order for utilities to develop an equitable rate structure, an understanding of these systems is necessary.

One- and two-family dwellings. NFPA (National Fire Protection Association) Standard 13D is the installation standard for residential sprinkler systems in one- and two-family homes (NFPA 2013). The goal of these systems is to improve the chance that the occupants can escape in a fire situation. These systems accomplish this by suppressing a fire within the room of fire origin, thus providing improved protection against injury and loss of life. The expenses associated with these systems are primarily the responsibility of individual homeowners. NFPA 13D states that where stored water is used as the supply, the system needs to provide 7 to 10 minutes of water with a maximum of two residential sprinklers operating. The seven-minute duration is applicable to smaller single-story houses that are less than 2,000 ft² in area. Residential sprinklers require different flows and pressures based on the area being covered and the individual sprinkler listing. A common demand for these sprinklers is 13 gpm at a minimum pressure of 7 psi. The typical maximum water usage of an NFPA 13D sprinkler system would be about 260 to 480 gallons, depending on the characteristics of the sprinklers being used. Although these systems when connected to a waterworks system are not subject to a time duration, this information does indicate the limited water demand required by the standard.

Low-rise residential occupancies. NFPA Standard 13R is the installation standard for residential sprinkler systems in low-rise residential buildings up to four stories in height and no higher than 60 ft above grade (NFPA 2012). These systems are typical of motels and multi-residential occupancies. The goal of these systems is also primarily life safety, but there is also some level of property protection as well. NFPA 13R indicates that the required water duration is 30 minutes for up to four residential sprinklers operating.

Other residential occupancies. NFPA 13 is the appropriate installation standard for residential occupancies that exceed four stories or exceed 60 ft in height (NFPA 2002). This standard provides life safety as well as a high degree of property protection. The required duration for these systems is also 30 minutes for the light hazard of a maximum of four residential sprinklers operating. Because of difference in the requirement of this standard, a residential system installed in accordance with NFPA 13 may have significantly higher water demand than an NFPA 13R system.

As residential fire sprinklers for one- and two-family dwellings increase and the traditional methods for fire protection charges do not take into consideration the specifics of these types of systems, the utilities should develop policies to ensure fair and equitable charges for these residential sprinkler systems. There is a variety of acceptable methods to provide service to NFPA 13D-type fire sprinkler systems, and the service method chosen will affect the relevant charges. These methods include

- combined domestic and fire service line with metering of only the domestic service,
- combined domestic and fire service line with both the domestic and fire flows metered,
- separate fire line provided with a meter, and
- separate fire line with no water meter.

The chosen method must be taken into account when determining appropriate fees.

It is common and preferred by NFPA 13D to be provided by a single domestic/fire line. When this configuration is required by the utility to be provided with a meter (including the fire demand), it may be necessary to upsize the domestic water meter (e.g., instead of a ¾-in. meter, a 1-in. or 1½-in. meter is installed). In this situation, several cost allocation and equity issues arise. These might be related to the SDC, the monthly meter charge for user rates, and the assessment of a private fire protection charge. Unless the utility is careful in establishing its service policy and fees around this issue, there is the potential for double-charging the customer.

A separate allocation of costs to private fire service and the resulting charges to customers with private fire service connections have become issues in some locations (Lamie and Woodcock 1996). It has been argued that private fire connections place no additional demand on the utility water system and, in fact, can reduce public system fire demands by faster, more efficient extinguishing of fires. Accordingly, it is argued, there should be no additional charges for private fire service. The basis for this is that the water system is designed to meet fire protection demands based only on the demands from public fire hydrants. In addition, customers with private sprinkler connections share in and pay their fair share of public fire service costs. Water used through private sprinkler connections is used to control or to quickly extinguish the fire before firefighters arrive. Private sprinkler connections also use significantly less water than hydrants for firefighting. Consequently, they may reduce actual fire demands, because water is typically supplied only to the area of the fire. Finally, there is the issue of the overall safety to firefighters from the benefits provided by private fire protection systems.

The alternative view is that customers with private sprinkler connections do indeed receive a service that customers without such connections do not receive. They have water provided on demand for their private fire sprinkler systems. Such customers could potentially receive savings on property insurance as a result of having sprinkler connections, although this is not the reasoning or basis behind the establishment of the private fire protection charges. In some cases, the building could not be constructed or occupied without the private fire connection, which would clearly indicate that an additional service is being provided. In addition, it may be argued that some private fire protection customers may want additional protection against a special hazard that they create or that is inherent in their business.

Those who support assessing private fire service charges contend that the community as a whole should not carry the cost of providing this service to a relatively few customers. Those who wish to take advantage of receiving additional fire service capacity in this manner should expect to pay the corresponding costs of this service.

The debate about the appropriateness of assessing charges for private fire protection and the appropriate level of such charges will continue as long as

- the benefits of private fire connections increase (by saving lives and extinguishing fires more quickly),
- more municipalities require private sprinklers for certain buildings,
- design factors for the public system fire flow needs do not decrease, and
- water service costs increase.

REFERENCES

Corssmit, C.W., and D.D. Green. 1982. Water Utility Costs and Rate Design for Fire Protection Services. *Journal AWWA*, 74(6):270–277.

Fuller, F.L. 1888. *Journal AWWA*.

Lamie, N.R., and C. Woodcock. 1996. Fire Protection Rates Refined in Maine. *Journal AWWA*, 88(10).

Maine Water Utilities Association Committee on Fire Protection Charges. 1961. *Journal of the Maine Water Utilities Association,* (March).

Metcalf, L., E. Kuichling, and W.C. Hawley. 1911. *Journal AWWA.*

NFPA (National Fire Protection Association). 2002. Standard 13. *Standard for the Installation of Sprinkler Systems.* Quincy, Mass.: NFPA.

NFPA (National Fire Protection Association). 2012. Standard 13R. *Standard for the Installation of Sprinkler Systems in Low-Rise Residential Occupancies.* Quincy, Mass.: NFPA.

NFPA (National Fire Protection Association). 2013. Standard 13D. *Standard for the Installation of Sprinkler Systems in One- and Two-Family Dwellings and Manufactured Homes.* Quincy, Mass.: NFPA.

Nixon, R. 1937. *Journal AWWA.*

Root, D.A., and T.R. Camp. 1955. *Journal AWWA.*

Section *V*

Other Rate Issues

This page intentionally blank.

Chapter **V.1**

Water Reuse Rates and Other Considerations

Water reuse has been recognized as a safe, reliable option in securing new water supplies. This "option" continues to increase in importance, particularly as water reuse projects help diversify existing water supplies and provide a drought-resistant source that matches user changes in annual demand. Reuse may also provide for a more energy-efficient option, particularly compared to the cost of pumping groundwater. Traditionally, water reuse projects have focused on nonpotable customers, including agriculture, irrigation, and industrial or commercial uses. Recently, as public perception, knowledge, and acceptance of reuse projects has improved, water systems have increasingly started to use reuse water to provide both indirect and direct potable water. However, the financial implications of introducing reuse to water and wastewater systems present unique challenges. Pricing reuse water also presents many challenges that are unique, considering generally accepted rate-setting principles.

The purpose of this chapter is to provide the tools and knowledge to assist in the development of appropriate cost-of-service rates for reuse service. These include

1. a detailed understanding of the full range of monetized and non-monetized benefits and costs of reuse projects;

2. financial planning and cash-flow considerations over the project life cycle; and

3. the rate allocation of reuse costs, which may depend significantly on the presence of subsidies, development charges, or other non-volumetric revenue streams within each customer class.

The rising costs of developing traditional new supplies coupled with a growing awareness and appreciation of the nonmonetary benefits of reuse projects increasingly allows utilities to use reuse projects to meet both their financial and physical obligations.

BACKGROUND AND TERMINOLOGY

Water reuse goes by many names: "reclaimed water," "reused water," and "recycled water." At its core, water reuse is wastewater that has been treated to a level that allows for a beneficial use. This use may include human use for either potable or nonpotable uses, or it may include water reuse for environmental augmentation in surface bodies or groundwater aquifers. Nonpotable water use for irrigation, agriculture, and industrial or commercial use requires separate distribution infrastructure, and many states require that nonpotable supplies be clearly marked, usually with signage and purple-colored pipe. Thus, nonpotable systems are sometimes referred to as "purple pipe" systems.

Potable water reuse is further divided into two categories: *indirect reuse*, which describes reclaimed water that is passed through a natural or environmental buffer before use, and *direct reuse*, in which reclaimed water is immediately introduced into existing drinking water supplies. National statistics on reuse are limited, but in 2010, planned potable reuse projects accounted for 355 mgd of supplies (NRC 2012). This excludes de facto water reuse in situations where wastewater supplies are discharged into a surface water body upstream of drinking water systems. In 2002, the US Environmental Protection Agency (USEPA) estimated that water reuse consumption was growing at a rate of 15 percent per year. More recent estimates suggest that US systems currently use only 7 to 8 percent of all available wastewater (32 billion gallons per day) for potable and nonpotable uses; therefore, use of reclaimed water is expected to increase (USEPA 2012).

Early water reuse projects were concentrated in Florida (introduced to address water quality impacts related to nutrient pollution), California, Texas, and Arizona (to address water quantity and scarcity concerns). Programs are now located throughout the United States and have been implemented in more than half of all US states. Reuse programs continue to benefit as well from extensive state and federal support, including the US Bureau of Reclamation's Title XVI Program that provides cost sharing for up to 25 percent of total project costs for projects in the Western United States and through State Revolving Fund loans.

The USEPA's 2012 *Guidelines for Water Reuse* offers a comprehensive resource for individuals or entities interested in consensus best practices and guidance related to the technical, legal, institutional, and public involvement issues surrounding reuse projects. The WateReuse Association, including its 2009 *Manual of Practice: How to Develop a Water Reuse Program*, also offers a wide-ranging perspective on the technical, social, and legal issues of water reuse. Both publications provide additional detail on financial and rate-making issues, primarily focused on funding projects and demonstrating cost-effectiveness during financial planning exercises.

WATER REUSE CONSIDERATIONS

Water Reuse and the Integrated Resource Planning Process

Water utilities are required to provide reliable service to customers today, tomorrow, and long into the future. A fundamental activity necessary to comply with this intergenerational mandate is the development of new water supply resources adequate to meet long-term demand growth. The process of identifying specific water supply projects to achieve this objective can be a complex undertaking that requires utilities to consider an array of often complicated environmental impact, regulatory, engineering, operational, and financial issues.

The complexities associated with identifying new water supply resources is magnified for utilities located in regions with a high probability of significant population growth but limited remaining undeveloped surface and/or groundwater supplies. Utilities confronted by this dilemma must consider nontraditional water supply resources to meet future demand growth. As a result, water supply resources such as large-scale water reuse and desalinization projects are increasingly being considered by utilities as an adjunct to more traditional resources, such as enhanced reservoir capacity, aquifer storage and recovery programs, and water supply diversion projects.

Integrated resource planning (IRP) is the analytical process most frequently used by large utilities to identify the optimal portfolio of water supply resources required to serve long-term demand. Economic costs include the social, environmental, and financial costs of a reuse project. The IRP process establishes a baseline level of demand that must be met by the utility based on assumptions such as future population growth, land-use patterns, economic conditions, plumbing fixture efficiencies, and customer price elasticity of demand responses. Having established this baseline, utilities can begin to identify potentially viable water supply resource options that, in addition to being capable of serving forecast long-term demand, also achieve a variety of critical strategic objectives.

The IRP process also provides an analytical framework that allows water supply resources to be evaluated in a rigorous manner via the use of traditional financial analysis techniques and nontraditional economic analysis. This type of economic analysis, often referred to as triple bottom line analysis, takes into consideration the benefits and costs associated with broad environmental, social, and economic externalities that are invariably not recognized or quantified when using traditional financial analysis techniques.

Unique Cost Characteristics of Water Reuse Projects

Traditional utility financial analysis techniques focus solely on the question: How much must rates increase to add a water resource to our existing supply portfolio? Because of their unique cost characteristics, water reuse projects often compare quite unfavorably to more traditional water supply resources when viewed solely through this one-dimensional lens. Indeed, without cross-subsidies from potable water and/or wastewater customers, the rates required to fully recover the cost of water reuse projects may be so high that it can limit customer acceptance and hinder long-term demand growth.

Unique cost characteristics of water reuse projects include the following:

- **Treatment costs.** Stringent public health regulations govern the quality of reuse water, even for outdoor irrigation applications. Compliance with water quality standards often requires large capital expenditures for upgrades to existing treatment facilities or the construction of entirely new stand-alone treatment facilities.

- **Transmission and pumping costs.** Reuse treatment facilities are frequently constructed downstream of treatment plant effluent outfalls. These treatment facilities are often a long distance and downgradient from potential reuse customers, and expensive upstream pumping and transmission costs must be incurred to serve customer demand.

- **Distribution system costs.** Water reuse service requires the construction of a distribution system that is entirely separate from the existing potable water distribution system. The installation of separate facilities can be an expensive proposition because it requires facilities to be built around existing infrastructure (roads, potable water, wastewater and natural gas mains, telecommunication lines, etc.).

- **Rate-making treatment of utility facilities.** The method of rate-setting used for developing reuse rates may affect the full-cost rate due to how capital is treated. Under the cash-basis revenue requirement methodology, rates are designed to recover the cost of debt-service payments used to finance the construction of utility

Table V.1-1 Evaluation of water supply resources

Financial Analysis	Economic Analysis
How much will the resource cost?	What is the avoided cost of other alternative resources?
How will the resource be financed?	How will the resource enhance water supply portfolio diversification?
What are the cash flows associated with implementation of the resource?	How will the resource enhance system drought resistance?
What is the net present value of revenue requirements associated with the resource?	What are benefits and costs of the resource from an environmental sustainability perspective?
How much must rates increase to pay for the resource?	What are benefits and costs of the resource from an energy use efficiency perspective?
How will the required rate increases affect customer affordability?	What are the benefits and costs of the resource from an economic development and broader societal perspective?

facilities. The utility-basis revenue requirement methodology recovers capital-related costs through a rate of return earned on the net book value of facilities coupled with annual depreciation expense. Regardless of the revenue requirement methodology used, newly constructed facilities, including reuse projects, are often more expensive than the embedded cost of existing potable water facilities.

FINANCIAL ANALYSIS VERSUS ECONOMIC ANALYSIS

A comprehensive evaluation of water supply resource alternatives undertaken as part of an IRP includes the evaluation of traditional financial metrics, economic costs and benefits, and long-term demand planning. When viewed from this broader perspective, water reuse projects may compare much more favorably with traditional water supply alternatives than would future water supply alternatives. An important consideration when evaluating the viability of a reuse project is to ensure that the IRP contain realistic demand projections. Over-forecasting can lead to an oversized system, which will cause a further financial burden to the water or wastewater utility through cross-subsidies. Table V.1-1 contrasts traditional utility financial analysis methods with broader economic analysis techniques.

Figure V.1-1 is a graphical representation of the evaluation of potential water reuse projects as developed by the WateReuse Association.

It is important to note that *both* traditional financial analysis and nontraditional economic analysis techniques are required to make fully informed decisions regarding the development of water supply resources. Although a water reuse project may be evaluated in a more favorable light using nontraditional economic analysis techniques, this does not eliminate the financial challenges utilities must confront due to the unique cost structure of water reuse projects. Cost of service and rate-design considerations for water reuse projects, including the question of subsidies provided by potable water service customers, are discussed later in this chapter.

TYPES OF WATER REUSE CUSTOMERS

A key consideration in developing a water reuse program—and by extension, developing water reuse rates—is the need and type of customers (WateReuse 2009). As described previously, reuse customers typically fall into one of three categories:

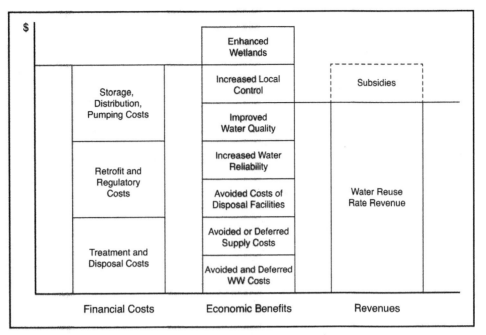

Courtesy of WateReuse Association.

Figure V.1-1 Evaluation of potential water reuse projects

1. *Nonpotable uses*, often including agriculture, irrigation, and industrial or commercial needs

2. *Indirect potable uses* that can supplement existing surface or groundwater supplies while taking advantage of environmental buffers for retention/storage, filtration and nutrient attenuation, dilution, and as a tool to increase public acceptance

3. *Direct potable uses* to complement existing supplies

Nonpotable Reuse Customers

Historically, the majority of reuse water supplies have been used for nonpotable applications. This is due, in part, to perceived and real concerns regarding customer acceptance for potable projects. Irrigation customers often include agricultural needs and municipal green spaces, such as parks and golf courses. Within the industrial and commercial sectors, large thermoelectric plants often represent the largest customers by volume.

Nonpotable reuse customers require separate distribution pipes to avoid cross-connection and contamination with potable water supplies. Distribution costs most commonly represent the single largest expense in a water reuse project. Reuse customers are less densely populated throughout the service area, which requires a greater number of distribution mains to reach fewer customers. Therefore, it is important to identify potential nonpotable reuse customers during the planning stages and, when possible, develop financial plans or long-term contracts ahead of time. Other considerations include what reuse infrastructure costs are borne by the utility versus the potential customer. Many utilities have extension agreements or requirements that require new customers to pay for a portion of infrastructure to their meters. These costs coupled with impact fees may produce a negative return on investment for the developer or end user. However, if these costs are prohibitive and as public acceptance for reuse increases, utilities are increasingly finding that indirect potable projects are now more cost-effective because of the lower distribution costs (see, for example, Friedman, Roohk, and Khoury 2014).

Indirect Potable Reuse Customers

Indirect potable reuse customers use an environmental buffer to store, treat, and transport water supplies between a wastewater discharge and a potable water intake. Environmental buffers may decrease potential contamination through natural attenuation, increased retention time, and by diluting or blending treated supplies (NRC 2012). Indirect environmental buffers include both groundwater recharge and surface water augmentation. Groundwater systems can use either an active direct injection system or a passive retention basin such as a constructed wetland. Surface water augmentation similarly may also involve retention basins or constructed wetlands or a more direct discharge to surface water supplies.

Some utilities have identified indirect potable reuse as a possible method to reduce and minimize total distribution costs. In regions with defined water rights, utilities may be able to trade reclaimed water credits with other users in the basin (NRC 2012). For other utilities, indirect potable reuse and the presence of an environmental buffer may lower total capital costs and increase public acceptance of projects. However, these projects typically require more extensive land rights and a larger project footprint, which may be difficult to obtain in more populated regions.

Direct Potable Reuse Customers

In contrast, direct potable reuse projects provide a direct connection or closed loop between wastewater discharge and public consumption. These projects may include an engineered buffer to provide additional retention time. Potable reuse projects typically have the most stringent treatment standards, which can increase project costs.[*] However, these costs can be more than offset by savings in conveyance costs and land acquisition/land management costs. Recent studies (Raucher and Tchobanoglous 2014) found that potable reuse projects are generally less expensive than other alternative (nonpotable reuse, indirect reuse, seawater and groundwater desalination, imports, and water efficiency projects) sources in California.[†] As treatment technologies continue to improve and become more cost-effective, utilities—particularly in dense, urban areas—are increasingly looking to direct potable reuse projects to minimize land acquisition and land management costs.

FINANCIAL PLANNING FOR REUSE

The financial planning process provides a "road map" of projected operating expenses, future capital improvement projects and funding, and anticipated future fund balances as well as forecasted debt obligation requirements, such as debt-service coverage. This section presents reuse-specific issues that should be considered in the financial planning process.

Utility infrastructure is expensive, and the initial cost of constructing a reuse system can be a significant obstacle. The additional infrastructure needed to provide reuse water can include additional levels of treatment, new transmission and distribution lines, pumping facilities, land and easement acquisitions, and design costs as well as costs associated with permitting and environmental compliance. Although the costs of including reuse distribution infrastructure as part of new development are typically less than reuse retrofit programs, the capital costs associated with reuse systems can be substantial.

---

[*] NRC (2012) estimated that capital costs for indirect potable reuse projects ranged from $1.14 to $18.75 per 1,000 gallons, while direct potable reuse projects ranged from $3.90 to $31 per 1,000 gallons. All values expressed in 2009 dollars.

[†] Raucher and Tchobanoglous (2014) estimated a total cost of potable reuse projects in the range of $2.52 to $6.14 per 1,000 gallons, expressed in 2014 dollars.

One option for utilities interested in providing reuse water is to connect the most economically feasible customers first. Generally, the most economically feasible reuse customers are high-volume users that use water for nonpotable purposes and are located near the reuse water source point. Examples of these types of customers could be golf courses, athletic facilities, large green spaces, and power generation facilities requiring cooling water. Connecting these customers first allows the greatest volume of reuse water distribution with the least capital investment. After the initial transmission mains are constructed to connect these customers, additional reuse customers can be added to the existing reuse transmission infrastructure. Additionally, as discussed further below, providing reuse water to high-volume users that are not currently purchasing potable water from the utility enhances the economic feasibility of providing reuse, because it will not affect potable water and/or wastewater revenues of the utility.

A utility must carefully evaluate and balance the targeted customer base with governing policies that promote water reuse. There are instances where a reuse customer may be a beneficial addition to the reuse system; however, the policies that govern reuse system rules and standards do not provide financial benefits to the customer. In addition, utilities need to have governing policies for the needs of both types of customers: the developer building the facility and the customer who will own the facility. The policies will affect these customers differently. For example, requiring a developer to pay for extending reuse infrastructure to the property while paying an impact fee is cost prohibitive, especially when potable water may be readily available. This policy may be balanced with a lower-than-potable-rate incentive to encourage use. However, the developer does not benefit from that; the end-use customer will see the savings.

Because of the high initial cost of installing reuse infrastructure, debt is an important component in the financial planning process. Infrastructure must be constructed and operational before customers can connect and revenues are generated. Utilities will often use debt as a means to offset the initial construction costs and spread these costs over future years when revenues are forecasted to be available.

Although the use of debt is the most commonly used funding option, there are other sources of available funding. Other common sources of funding include grants, special assessments, and developer-contributed assets or impact fees. Several grant programs are available for water reuse projects at the federal, state, regional, and local levels. The primary federal and state-level funding program includes the Clean Water State Revolving Fund and the Drinking Water State Revolving Fund. At the state level, grants may be available from regulatory bodies, such as local water management districts, with an interest in promoting reuse. Special assessments can also be used to fund reuse projects where these projects would benefit a specific service area of the system. Utilities may require the developer to construct reuse systems within new developments and dedicate these assets to the utility after construction. In some instances, a utility may provide loan assistance to the developer to mitigate up-front capital costs. Other special assessments may include an availability charge for all customers who have reuse service available in their area.

The addition of reuse can be beneficial to existing water and wastewater systems, serving as an alternative for effluent disposal and either "freeing" existing sources of water supply or avoiding/deferring additional water supply investment. As such, it is common for many utilities to subsidize a portion of reuse water costs from their water and/or wastewater systems, recognizing the net financial impact of reuse water to these systems.

An aspect of reuse water that all utility providers should consider in the financial planning process is the revenue impact of substituting reuse water for potable water. As reuse water is introduced, customer's consumption of potable water is replaced and potable water revenue will subsequently decline. From a financial perspective, the transition of service will not likely result in a positive financial outcome. Because of the difference in quality and to encourage reuse water usage, reuse water is often priced at a level that is much less than potable water. Consequently, a negative revenue impact can occur when reuse water is substituted for potable water. A similar impact occurs with wastewater. Wastewater is billed based on a customer's water usage, sometimes with limitations such as a cap or percentage of water usage in recognition of outdoor water use. The introduction of reuse water can result in a decline in wastewater revenue as potable water usage is reduced. It is important to understand the financial impact of introducing reuse water to mitigate the possible negative effects on water and wastewater revenue.

Although water and wastewater billed usage can be affected by the introduction of reuse water, this does not always mean that the financial results of a reuse system will be negative. In many cases, the introduction of reuse water is necessary to avoid future costs that would be greater than the cost of reuse and the resulting impact to water and wastewater revenue. This is especially true in areas where water supply is limited. Reuse water can act as an alternative source of supply as potable water sources are reserved for essential usage. In many cases, the incremental cost of adding source water can be very expensive, if an alternative source is even available. In these cases, the addition of reuse water allows systems to better use limited source water supplies and avoid significant capital costs or water supply shortages.

It is necessary to provide a word of caution with regard to reuse demand forecasts, especially when the benefits of a reuse project are anticipated to result in avoided costs. As an example, there have been cases where systems have needed to maintain supplemental potable water supply to cover reuse water needs during periods of limited reuse water supply. These periods generally occur during dry weather periods where wastewater flow is diminished because of weather-related reductions in inflow and infiltration. These dry weather events also correlate with the highest demand for reuse water for irrigation. Similarly, during wet weather periods, reuse water consumption can be inadequate to meet disposal needs, and alternative disposal options may be required. Some systems have been required to construct reuse storage to provide reuse water service during periods of high demand. Demand variability may also be a function of water rights ownership and the specific conditions when reuse water can be produced and the basin area in which it can be sold.

COST ALLOCATION OF WATER REUSE RATES

Developing rates for reuse water typically follows the same cost-causation principles used for setting potable rates. Costs are assigned to functional cost components such as treatment, pumping, storage, and transmission and distribution. The functionalized costs may be allocated further to cost components: base or average-day, maximum-day, maximum-hour, and customer. The base, maximum-day, and maximum-hour cost components may be combined into a single commodity cost component if the utility only has one class of reuse customers or where a utility does not distinguish between customer groups with different demand characteristics.

However, allocating costs and pricing reuse may vary based on the type and purpose of reuse, how costs are accounted for by the utility, public policy objectives, and how subsidies, if any, are shared between utilities.

Reuse facilities may be stand-alone or an additional treatment process on a wastewater facility. Either type of facility may be an enterprise fund separate from the water or wastewater utility funds, or costs may be commingled within water or wastewater utility funds. Setting revenue requirements and cost allocations will follow the same process for each situation; however, a stand-alone reuse enterprise fund can allow the user to develop separate revenue requirements and cost allocations independent of the water or wastewater utility revenue requirements. In this case, the principles of functionalization, allocation, and distribution of costs for potable water discussed in sections II and III would be applicable to reuse.

If water reuse costs are part of the water or wastewater utility enterprise fund, the reuse revenue requirement may be part of the total utility revenue requirement rather than a stand-alone utility. The embedded reuse costs can be specifically assigned in the cost allocation process. Additional cost components for reuse water may be required to specifically identify costs associated with reuse. Table V.1-2 illustrates allocation of operation and maintenance (O&M) costs and nonrate revenue for utilities with combined potable and reuse costs. In this example, cost components are separated into cost pools: common-to-all, common-to-potable, and common-to-reuse customers. A cost pool captures costs that are specific to a particular group of customers. The common-to-all cost components include costs that are incurred by all potable and reuse customers. Common-to-potable cost components include costs incurred only by potable customers, and common-to-reuse cost components include costs incurred only by reuse water customers. This allocation method also applies to the other revenue requirement line items such as capital costs, taxes, transfers, debt service, and change in reserves.

The common-to-reuse columns would apply to a wastewater utility cost allocation process. If the utility plans to have only one class of reuse customers, the base, maximum-day, and maximum-hour columns can be replaced with one column representing total demand costs. This cost allocation method explicitly shows which costs are attributable to potable water and reuse water. Similar to wholesale cost allocation, the units of service for the common-to-reuse would only include reuse customer demands.

Subsidies

The cost allocation method described above is based on full-cost pricing. Using this method may result in the unit cost of reuse water being higher than potable (see Line 26 in Table V.1-2). Reuse systems are typically newer compared with most potable systems whose costs benefit from significant depreciation on past treatment and distribution system investments. Conversely, reuse systems incur additional costs, such as higher per-unit pumping costs due to locations at lower elevations, influent water quality, and brine disposal requirements. Reuse water also requires a separate distribution system. Densely populated areas already benefit from a potable distribution system. Installing a new reuse distribution system alongside other utility services in built-up areas is costly.

As discussed in more detail in the other sections of this chapter, reuse water is an imperfect substitute for potable water. Customer preferences will dictate the price at which they are willing to use reuse water over potable water. The perception of lower quality and availability of reuse water generally shapes these customer preferences. As a result, reuse water must be priced at a level that will favor the use of reuse over potable in the absence of a utility charging the full cost of reuse water service. The difference between the full-cost rate of reuse and the actual rate is the subsidy to be recovered from other sources.

There are many considerations in determining which utility provides the deficit or subsidy in funding. This determination requires a closer look at the drivers behind the need for the reuse system. Is the reuse facility needed to meet certain discharge requirements regardless of whether there is an end user? If the utility is required to meet discharge regulations that require incremental treatment, such as secondary or tertiary treatment, allocating all or a portion of advanced treatment costs to wastewater is appropriate. Regulations require this treatment, and all wastewater customers contribute wastewater discharge.

Is the reuse facility needed to augment water supply or reduce current potable water usage per capita? If so, there is a logical argument that the deficit should be met by the water utility. Although that would increase the cost to all potable customers, they also

Table V.1-2 Operation and maintenance expense, allocation to cost components—Combined potable and reuse costs

Line No.	Item	Total	Common to Potable Customers				Common to Reuse Customers			Common to All Customers	
			Base	Extra Capacity		Direct Fire Protection Costs	Base	Extra Capacity		Customer	
				Maximum Day	Maximum Hour			Maximum Day	Maximum Hour	Meters & Services	Billing & Collection
1	**Source of Supply**	270,000	270,000								
	Pumping										
2	Purchase Power	832,000	699,300	77,700			50,000	5,000			
3	Other	639,000	376,350	202,650			10,000	50,000			
	Water Treatment										
4	Chemicals	463,000	363,000				100,000				
5	Other	471,000	306,150	164,850							
	Transmission and Distribution										
6	Storage	78,000	7,800		70,200						
7	Transmission Mains	156,000	101,400	54,600							
8	Distribution Mains	234,000	105,300	58,500	70,200						
9	Reuse Transmission Mains	125,000					75,000	50,000			
10	Reuse Distribution Mains	200,000					90,000	50,000	60,000		
11	Meters and Services	465,000								465,000	
12	Hydrants	39,000				39,000					
13	Other	216,000	41,040	21,600	41,040	8,640				103,680	
	Customer Accounting										
14	Meter Reading and Collections	741,000							0	741,000	
15	Uncollectable Accounts	132,000	62,040	18,480	7,920	1,320				18,480	23,760
	Administration and General										
16	Salaries	582,000	196,279	80,466	29,264	7,566	27,045	23,181	9,272	205,255	3,672
17	Employee Benefits	531,000	179,079	73,415	26,699	6,903	24,675	21,150	8,460	187,268	3,350
18	Insurance	405,000	136,586	55,995	20,364	5,265	18,820	16,131	6,452	142,832	2,555
19	Other	798,000	269,125	110,330	40,125	10,374	37,082	31,784	12,714	281,432	5,035
20	Total O&M Expense	7,377,000	3,113,449	918,586	305,812	79,069	432,621	247,246	96,899	2,144,947	38,372
21	Nonrate Revenue	(78,000)	(26,305)	(3,637)	(183)	(2)	(0)	(0)	(0)	(0)	(0)
22	*Reuse Subsidy*	0	0	0	0						
23	**Net Revenue Requirements**	7,299,000	3,087,143	914,949	305,629	79,067	432,621	247,246	96,899	2,144,947	38,372
24	Units of Service		1,000 gal	1,000 gpd	1,000 gpd		1,000 gal	1,000 gpd	1,000 gpd	Equiv. Meters	Bills
25	Total System		2,766,000	8,402	12,243		276,600	840	1,224	17,695	200,868
26	*Unit Cost*		1.12	108.90	24.96		1.56	294.27	79.15	121.22	0.19

benefit from reuse through lower alternative water supply costs. Subsidies for reuse system costs are further complicated if the water and wastewater systems are separate agencies. A wastewater utility setting reuse rates may be constrained by the maximum potable rate from their water utility provider, and may face challenges from the water provider because the introduction of reuse could affect its water revenues. Cost structures between agencies can vary significantly based on several factors, such as size, age of facilities, and governance. Consequently, the wastewater agency may be required to recover more costs from wastewater customers.

Line 22 in Table V.1-3 shows the reallocation of the subsidy to the treated water system. Importantly, subsidies can be allocated as part of the cost allocation process as shown in Line 22 of Table V.1-3 or within the rate design process. The advantage to allocating the subsidy within the cost allocation process is that the subsidy can be allocated proportionally to either all customer classes or a select group of customers. In this example, a subsidy of $356,940 (Line 22, sum of 214,825 + 102,455 + 39,660) has been reallocated to the potable volume cost components based on the distribution of reuse system costs in Lines 1 through 13. This allocation assumes that potable customers are incurring the subsidy at the same proportionate cost as if they were using the reuse system. The potable volume rate is $1.69 per 1,000 gallons while the reuse rate is $1.52 per 1,000 gallons, or 90 percent of the potable rate.*

As with any subsidy, a particular group incurs the additional cost to the benefit of another group. Practitioners need to consider who should bear the impact of the subsidy. These choices may become political and not based on a cost-of-service methodology. Reuse subsidies may only be temporary in nature as the cost of reuse and cost of potable continue to converge; however, the short-term impacts of the customers affected should be carefully evaluated. In addition to subsidies from water and wastewater, subsidies may also be recovered outside the utility through sales tax, property taxes, or other revenue sources.

Reuse as a Source of Supply

Reuse water may be used as an alternative to securing new water supplies. As new freshwater sources continue to diminish and increase in cost, reuse water is becoming a viable, cost-effective method to extend existing water supplies. Reuse as a "new" supply can also increase reliability because the source of reuse water, typically wastewater effluent, can be somewhat weather independent. In some instances, the demand for reuse water may exceed available effluent, which may require the need for additional reuse storage facilities.

Allocating reuse costs as part of a utility's source of supply is completed in a similar manner as discussed previously. The primary difference is that the utility is implicitly using reuse as an alternative to new water supplies and using cost of service to allocate such costs. This allows the water utility to use reuse water while reducing demand on potable supplies. This can benefit both reuse and potable system customers. Reduced treated demand requires less new infrastructure for growth and eliminates the search for new water supplies that are generally expensive. For reuse customers, the distribution of costs to all customers, both reuse and potable, can achieve an economically viable solution to promoting reuse. Table V.1-4 illustrates how allocating reuse costs as a source of supply affects the potable costs. Reuse costs are allocated proportionately to all potable customers.

The calculated potable volume rate under this scenario is $1.81 per 1,000 gallons while the reuse rate is $1.37 per 1,000 gallons.† The potable rate is the quotient of the sum of the maximum-day costs, maximum-hour costs, and the potable proportionate share of base costs divided by potable system demand.

However, there may be an inequity with this approach. Potable customers may not be able to take delivery of reuse water even though they are paying for it. The challenges

---

* The potable volume rate is the quotient of the sum of base, maximum-day, and maximum-hour potable costs divided by the potable annual demand. The reuse volume rate is the quotient of the sum of base, maximum-day, and maximum-hour costs divided by the reuse annual demand.

† The potable volume rate is [($1.37 × 2,766,000 + $919,053 + $307,456) ÷ 2,766,000] = $1.81 per 1,000 gallons. The reuse volume rate is 4,160,626 ÷ 3,042,600 = $1.37 per 1,000 gallons.

Table V.1-3 Operation and maintenance expense, allocation to cost components—Combined potable and reuse costs with subsidy

| Line No. | Item | Total | Common to Potable Customers | | | | Common to Reuse Customers | | | Common to All Customers | |
| | | | | Extra Capacity | | Direct Fire Protection Costs | | Extra Capacity | | Customer | |
			Base	Maximum Day	Maximum Hour		Base	Maximum Day	Maximum Hour	Meters & Services	Billing & Collection
1	**Source of Supply**	270,000	270,000								
	Pumping										
2	Purchase Power	832,000	699,300	77,700			50,000	5,000			
3	Other	639,000	376,350	202,650			10,000	50,000			
	Water Treatment										
4	Chemicals	463,000	363,000				100,000				
5	Other	471,000	306,150	164,850							
	Transmission and Distribution										
6	Storage	78,000	7,800		70,200						
7	Transmission Mains	156,000	101,400	54,600							
8	Distribution Mains	234,000	105,300	58,500	70,200						
9	Reuse Transmission Mains	125,000					75,000	50,000			
10	Reuse Distribution Mains	200,000					90,000	50,000	60,000		
11	Meters and Services	465,000								465,000	
12	Hydrants	39,000				39,000					
13	Other	216,000	41,040	21,600	41,040	8,640				103,680	
	Customer Accounting										
14	Meter Reading and Collections	741,000							0	741,000	
15	Uncollectable Accounts	132,000	62,040	18,480	7,920	1,320				18,480	23,760
	Administration and General										
16	Salaries	582,000	196,279	80,466	29,264	7,566	27,045	23,181	9,272	205,255	3,672
17	Employee Benefits	531,000	179,079	73,415	26,699	6,903	24,675	21,150	8,460	187,268	3,350
18	Insurance	405,000	136,586	55,995	20,364	5,265	18,820	16,131	6,452	142,832	2,555
19	Other	798,000	269,125	110,330	40,125	10,374	37,082	31,784	12,714	281,432	5,035
20	Total O&M Expense	7,377,000	3,113,449	918,586	305,812	79,069	432,621	247,246	96,899	2,144,947	38,372
21	Nonrate Revenue	(78,000)	(26,305)	(3,637)	(183)	(2)	(0)	(0)	(0)	(0)	(0)
22	*Reuse Subsidy*	*0*	*214,825*	*102,455*	*39,660*		*(214,825)*	*(102,455)*	*(39,660)*		
23	**Net Revenue Requirements**	7,299,000	3,301,969	1,017,404	345,289	79,067	217,795	144,791	57,239	2,144,947	38,372
24	Units of Service		1,000 gal	1,000 gpd	1,000 gpd		1,000 gal	1,000 gpd	1,000 gpd	Equiv. Meters	Bills
25	Total System		2,766,000	8,402	12,243		276,600	840	1,224	17,695	200,868
26	*Unit Cost*		*1.19*	*121.09*	*28.20*		*0.79*	*172.33*	*46.75*	*121.22*	*0.19*

associated with this issue is the incremental cost of reuse, which is now distributed to all customer classes proportionately; therefore, potable customers may not directly benefit from those incremental supplies. Stated differently, customers are paying a proportionate share of reuse costs but not receiving the benefit.

This discrepancy shows the short- and long-term issues associated with reuse as a source of supply cost. In the short term, potable customers may not benefit directly from

Table V.1-4 Operation and maintenance expense, allocation to cost components—Combined potable and reuse costs with reuse costs as source of supply

Line No.	Item	Total	Common to Potable Customers — Base	Extra Capacity Maximum Day	Extra Capacity Maximum Hour	Direct Fire Protection Costs	Common to Reuse Customers — Base	Extra Capacity Maximum Day	Extra Capacity Maximum Hour	Common to All Customers Meters & Services	Customer Billing & Collection
	Source of Supply										
1	Potable	270,000	270,000								
2	Reuse	540,000	540,000								
	Pumping										
3	Purchase Power	777,000	699,300	77,700							
4	Other	579,000	376,350	202,650							
	Water Treatment										
5	Chemicals	363,000	363,000								
6	Other	471,000	306,150	164,850							
	Transmission and Distribution										
7	Storage	78,000	7,800		70,200						
8	Transmission Mains	156,000	101,400	54,600							
9	Distribution Mains	234,000	105,300	58,500	70,200						
10	Reuse Transmission Mains	125,000	125,000								
11	Reuse Distribution Mains	200,000	200,000								
12	Meters and Services	465,000								465,000	
13	Hydrants	39,000				39,000					
14	Other	216,000	41,040	21,600	41,040	8,640				103,680	
	Customer Accounting										
15	Meter Reading and Collections	741,000							0	741,000	
16	Uncollectable Accounts	132,000	62,040	18,480	7,920	1,320				18,480	23,760
	Administration and General										
17	Salaries	582,000	250,496	81,769	29,738	7,689	0	0	0	208,578	3,731
18	Employee Benefits	531,000	228,545	74,604	27,132	7,015	0	0	0	190,300	3,404
19	Insurance	405,000	174,314	56,901	20,694	5,350	0	0	0	145,144	2,597
20	Other	798,000	343,463	112,116	40,774	10,542	0	0	0	285,988	5,116
21	Total O&M Expense	7,702,000	4,194,197	923,770	307,697	79,557	0	0	0	2,158,170	38,608
22	Nonrate Revenue	(78,000)	(33,572)	(4,717)	(241)	(3)	0	0	0	0	0
23	*Reuse Subsidy*	0									
	Net Revenue Requirements	**7,624,000**	**4,160,626**	**919,053**	**307,456**	**79,554**	**0**	**0**	**0**	**2,158,170**	**38,608**
24	Units of Service		1,000 gal	1,000 gpd	1,000 gpd		1,000 gal	1,000 gpd	1,000 gpd	Equiv. Meters	Bills
25	Total Potable System		2,766,000	8,402	12,243		276,600	840	1,224	17,695	200,868
26	Total Reuse System		276,600								
27	Total Units of Service		3,042,600	8,402	12,243						
28	*Unit Cost*		1.37	109.39	25.11		0.00	0.00	0.00	121.96	0.19

having reuse available to them. In the long term, overall source of supply costs will be lower for both potable and reuse customers, especially as new reuse customers come on line. As reuse technology and public perception continue to advance, indirect and direct reuse will blur the lines between the different types of supply, eliminating much of this issue.

Avoided Cost Considerations

Another methodology that may be used to apportion reuse costs as well as determine and distribute any subsidies is an avoided cost analysis. *Avoided cost* is the marginal cost avoided or saved by choosing one option over another to achieve the same goal. For reuse, the primary goal is to estimate potential cost savings in potable or wastewater systems that result from developing a reuse system. For determining a reuse rate, the full avoided costs that would otherwise impact the utility need to be considered and thus exclude the benefits, or potential revenues, that could be received from selecting an option. An example of using an avoided cost approach is shown here:

Amortized Avoided Capital Costs
+ Avoided O&M Costs
= Avoided Cost of Alternative
÷ Estimated Demand, 1,000 Gallons
= Reuse Volume Rate, $/1,000 Gallons

Moreover, avoided costs can be considered in establishing cost allocations for customer classes. For example, large wholesale users may have substantial onsite storage facilities that allow the utility to interrupt their services in instances of short supply and/or allow the user to receive water during non-peak periods. This would result in the utility being able to install slightly smaller transmission/distribution infrastructure and/or less storage facilities to meet system demands.

Avoided cost pricing can be used to estimate reuse costs when planning a reuse system. Oftentimes, the final costs, operating costs, number of potential customers and their demands, and connection timing are not known. However, the avoided costs associated with building a reuse system may be easier to estimate. Importantly, an avoided cost analysis used to estimate a reuse rate should only include the costs the utility would incur if the utility did not pursue the reuse project. For example, building a reuse plant may negate the need for additional water supply. The cost of that incremental water supply and associated operating costs would be included in the avoided cost analysis.

PRICING REUSE WATER

Rate structures for reuse water follow the same principles outlined in chapter IV of this manual. Because reuse water is an imperfect substitute for potable, location-constrained, and supply-limiting or wide variations in supply and demand, the pricing objectives for a particular customer class may be much different between the potable structure and the reuse structure. For example, a potable irrigation structure may be tiered or on a water budget to promote conservation; however, a reclaimed rate for irrigation may be uniform or on a declining block to promote the use of reuse water and to maintain a minimum level of production.

Reuse subsidies can also be developed as part of the pricing. In the section above, examples were provided on subsidies being embedded in the cost allocation process. Whereas this method is beneficial to utilities that use a detailed class cost-of-service approach to rate design, other utilities set the reuse rate as a percentage of potable. The percentage is typically policy based absent any cost justification. For example, if the potable irrigation rate is $4.00 per 1,000 gallons, the reuse rate may be set at 80 percent of the potable rate or $3.20 per 1,000 gallons. This method may be used when the utility has a new reuse facility without sufficient historical cost data, or a small customer base that could cause major fluctuations in cost-of-service-based rates as new customers come on line. It is important to note that setting reuse rates as a percentage of potable may significantly under-recover costs. Therefore, the utility should analyze customer class revenue projections for both potable and reuse to ensure sufficient recovery of total revenue requirements.

REFERENCES

Friedman, S.A., D.L. Roohk, and O.A. Khoury. 2014. Indirect potable reuse trumps landscape irrigation: Riverside, Calif., again evaluates how best to use its recycled water resources. *Water Environment and Technology* 26(5).

NRC (National Research Council). 2012. *Water Reuse: Potential for Expanding the Nation's Water Supply Through Reuse of Municipal Wastewater.* Washington, D.C.: National Academies Press.

Raucher, R.S., and G. Tchobanoglous. 2014. *The Opportunities and Economics of Direct Potable Reuse.* Alexandria, Va.: WateReuse Research Foundation.

USEPA (US Environmental Protection Agency). 2012. *Guidelines for Water Reuse.* Washington, D.C.: USEPA.

WateReuse Association. 2009. *Manual of Practice: How to Develop a Water Reuse Program.* Alexandria, Va.: WateReuse Association.

This page intentionally blank.

Chapter **V.2**

Standby Rates

Standby, or backup, water service provides supplemental water during an emergency to protect against an interruption in the primary source of water. Utilities may have agreements for standby or emergency service. A key consideration in providing standby service and rates is the particular and unique circumstances associated with providing that service (e.g., seasonal peak needs, year-round emergency standby). To properly develop standby water rates, a utility may need to further analyze its costs beyond the traditional cost-of-service analysis. In that case, the rates may be "unbundled" into the various components of supply, treatment, transmission, distribution storage, and so on. By unbundling the utility's rates, the various components that are relevant to the standby service can be consolidated into a standby rate.

Standby service (and the associate rate) is different from interruptible service or a capacity reservation. Interruptible service and rates allow the utility to interrupt deliveries to a customer, typically during a high peak-use period when the supplying utility's capacity or supply is constrained. In contrast, a capacity reservation is typically related to the holding capacity for a future expansion. As an example, an industrial customer may pay the utility to reserve capacity for a 2 mgd plant expansion within the next five years. At some future point, the industrial customer would expand its plant and take delivery of an additional 2 mgd of water. A reservation of capacity provides the industrial customer with an assurance that capacity will be available in the future when the customer desires to expand its facility. Absent the capacity reservation, the utility would be free to sell that capacity to another existing or potential customer.

GENERAL CONSIDERATIONS

Standby, or backup, water service is intended to meet emergency or unscheduled service outages or a reduction in supply from the primary water source. Standby service is somewhat similar in nature to fire protection service in that both types of service place random, infrequent loads on the system. In essence, the rate charged for standby service should reflect the cost of having capacity reserved and available for the customer. The customer pays for standby service, even if water is not consumed. When standby service is used, the loads may be large, and they will continue until the emergency situation or need is over.

In many cases, standby service is negotiated between the parties, and the terms of service and usage parameters are clearly defined.

A water utility may wish to acquire finished potable water from an outside source in the event of an interruption in its own operations. This could arise from a temporary lack of access to the source water supply, a compromise in the quality of source water supply, or a major breakdown in its system. In such instances, the purchasing utility receives water through its interconnections with the standby supplier, most likely another water system, and distributes that water until its own facilities are functioning normally.

Large industrial or institutional customers may also pursue arrangements for standby water service to back up their own private water supply. In locations served by adjacent water utilities, the customer may contract with a second water utility to provide backup service in the event of a service interruption from its primary supplier. The request for standby service could be prompted by the quality of service afforded by the primary provider or the need to support a continuous manufacturing process that requires an uninterrupted water supply.

The water utility providing standby service must have the necessary reserve capacity to supply the level of standby demand requested by the customer without compromising the safe yield commitment and operational integrity to its own customers. Additionally, transmission main interconnections must be in place to transfer the water on demand, and provisions should be made to prevent backflow to the emergency provider.

The provider must be careful to specify where the standby customer falls in the hierarchy of those demanding water. This is especially important when there are constraints on the utility's sources of supply, including drought, limitations on storage, or emergency conditions. If these constraints are severe enough, the utility should not consider providing backup service.

HISTORICAL PERSPECTIVES

Standby service and rates are commonly offered in the water industry between utilities. These are generally used as emergency interconnections but also in cases where a utility may not have sufficient supply to meet peak demands during the summer period. Distance to the standby capacity is clearly a constraint in this type of service, but in many suburban areas, proximity is not generally an issue. Standby service is typically a service between two utilities, but there may be a very limited number of situations where a very large industrial customer may request standby service.

ADVANTAGES AND DISADVANTAGES

The following paragraphs describe advantages and disadvantages of standby rates.

Simplicity

Because standby service will normally be offered to either another water utility or to a large, nonutility consumer of water service, the issue of simplicity and understandability is not necessarily crucial. As will be seen in the example later in this chapter, it is possible to design a simple standby rate that incorporates demand, commodity, and customer-related costs. Customer acceptability should not be a problem, as the rate will, in all likelihood, be negotiated between the supplier and the individual standby customer. Other customers should not object to the existence of this service, as the associated revenues from a properly designed standby rate will help to defray the utility's overall costs.

Equity

To ensure rate equity, a standby customer should be required to bear any direct costs incurred to provide the service interconnection as well as the maintenance of that interconnection. In providing standby service, there are generally two types of rates to fairly collect the costs associated with reserving capacity and then the use of that capacity. First, the customer is assessed a *fixed demand charge* to recover the costs of providing standby or reserved capacity. This charge is billed to the customer regardless of the amount of water consumed. Once a customer consumes water on a standby basis, a *consumption charge* is applied for all water consumed. By using both rate components of standby service, this will ensure that the standby customer is not subsidized by other customers. The commodity-demand method discussed in chapter III.1 can help determine the appropriate fixed demand charge and consumption charge.

Revenue Stability

By definition, standby service is intended to be used on a random and infrequent basis. Therefore, such service is not intended to be a major source of revenue and is not likely to have a material effect on a utility's financial sufficiency as long as the standby rate recovers any additional costs incurred to provide the service.

Conservation

By its nature, standby service is used randomly and at infrequent intervals. The standby customer will not use this service unless there is an emergency or other predefined situation that dictates the need for service. Thus, there is no incentive to use any more water than necessary during a given emergency situation.

If, however, the customer exceeds the capacity demand specified in the rate, or if the customer uses standby water service on a relatively frequent basis, the water utility can guard against the cost consequences of such behavior by building a surcharge into the rate or by placing the customer on the general service rate if it uses standby service above a specified number of times during, for example, a one-year period. Additionally, if necessary, the utility supplying the water could restrict the flow of water provided to prevent the customer from using more than the contractually specified capacity demand. Conservation and the efficient use of the water should be a part of any standby agreement. Any emergency services provided to another utility should take into account how wisely the receiving utility has used its resources before requesting assistance from the provider. In making standby service available, the providing utility may consider including provisions that require the customer to have a proactive conservation program.

Effect on Customers

The availability of standby service should have little or no effect on other customers, provided the utility has sufficient capacity to provide the backup service without compromising the water pressure or volumes available to other customers. An exception would be in situations of dire emergency where water restrictions may be enacted to ensure that sufficient water is available for the health and welfare of the communities involved. In addition, the receipt of additional revenues for standby service decreases, to some extent, the water utility's need to recover its fixed costs from firm general-service customers.

Table V.2-1 Example of standby charges

Line No.	Charge	
	Demand Charge	
1	Cost, per Mg per day of maximum day capacity (from Table III.2-4)	$293,537
2	Capacity reservation, 1 mgd or 1,000 Mg per day*	1,000
3	Annual demand cost	$293,537
4	Cost, per month	$24,461
	Meter Charge	
5	Monthly cost, per 8-in. meter (from Table IV.7-1)	$211.57
	Commodity Cost	
6	Outside-city charge, per 1,000 gal (from Table III.2-4)	$0.5783

* Mg = 1,000 gallons

EXAMPLE

A water utility agrees to provide backup service to a neighboring utility that desires to provide a greater level of service reliability to its customers. The provider utility's cost per unit of maximum-day capacity (per thousand gallons per day) is $293,537 (see Table III.2-4, line 20). The standby customer reserves the right to take up to 1 mgd. At this level of capacity reservation, the full service demand cost per year, which includes operation and maintenance, depreciation, taxes, and return, is $293,537, as shown in Table V.2-1. The equivalent cost per month is $24,461.

In this example, the standby charge for 1 mgd of standby capacity is $24,461 per month. Should the entity use water, the consumption charges would apply, which includes a monthly meter charge (Table IV.7-1) and the commodity charge. In this example, the utility has used the outside-city commodity unit cost from Table III.2-4 as the rate to establish the consumption charge.

SUMMARY

Standby water arrangements offer advantages to both the water supplier and the customer. For a water utility, standby service provides a backup source of supply to assure its customers that service is not likely to be interrupted or that any service interruption will be of shorter duration. Standby service to a large industrial customer provides assurance that its production processes can continue uninterrupted if its primary source of supply is not available. The utility providing standby service will have an additional source of revenue, whether or not it is actually called on to supply backup service. The additional revenues will help defray a portion of the standby provider's operating and capital costs.

Chapter **V.3**

Drought and Surcharge Rates

A rate surcharge is a separate charge added to existing rate structures either to collect a targeted amount of revenue or to assess an appropriate charge for particular usage characteristics outside of those covered in the basic charge for service. Surcharges are often presented separately from the existing rates and labeled for the specific purpose for which the funds will be used or the events that caused the need for the surcharge. Drought rates are a specific form of a surcharge rate.

Water utility rate surcharges are used relatively infrequently, but in certain circumstances, they can be an effective tool for meeting the utility's short-term and possibly long-term financial requirements. Surcharges are usually placed into effect for limited periods of time and may have a specific revenue target, often directed toward emergency purposes, to fund specific, one-time requirements or to establish/replenish a reserve fund. They may be subject to legal constraints.

The word *surcharge* may be used to describe a variety of different rates that are in addition to a basic rate structure. For purposes of this chapter, the term *surcharge* will apply to a temporary rate for the utility that wants to highlight the separate recovery of specific costs. Examples include situations where a utility is responding to a natural disaster, managing demand in times of drought, building up reserves in anticipation of large capital project financing or for rate stabilization funds, or paying for one-time upgrade requirements, such as water system security or compliance with new water quality regulations.

GENERAL CONSIDERATIONS

Surcharges are, by definition, an atypical charge designed to recover revenues for a specific purpose. Accordingly, the basis or need for the surcharge should be readily understood and considered valid from the perspective of the utility's governing body and the utility's customers. For utilities regulated by a public service commission, the ability to implement rate surcharges is subject to regulatory approval. Public utilities generally have more flexibility in the policy decision to establish a surcharge rate.

Some common reasons for implementing rate surcharges include the following:

- **Response to disaster.** A surcharge is an appropriate fee for supplying funds needed to financially assist a utility in recovering from a one-time natural or infrastructure disaster. In these cases, the cost to recover from a natural disaster (e.g., forest fire in a watershed, an earthquake, or a hurricane) or an infrastructure failure (e.g., major transmission main break) are not normal ongoing costs (i.e., included within the utility's revenue requirement). Normal ongoing costs would typically be recovered from the rate structure or could have been fully anticipated when establishing rates. From a customer's perspective, the need for the surcharge, if labeled appropriately, is clear, and when the funds are fully collected, the surcharge can be removed. In these cases, a surcharge provides a method for recovering the costs needed without disturbing the integrity of the existing rate design. The acceptability of surcharges as a response to natural disaster is, in part, a function of the severity of the disaster and the effective inability of typical measures, such as insurance or emergency reserve funds, to manage risks to cover the extent of the utilities' damages.

- **Rate stabilization.** Surcharges are often used to accumulate designated reserves for a rate stabilization fund. Once established, a rate stabilization fund can be drawn on to mitigate large impacts of prospective rate adjustments. The rate stabilization fund is used to meet a portion of the utility's revenue requirements. Rate stabilization may also help the utility manage through unexpected low-revenue periods. Once rate stabilization fund levels are established, the maintenance of the appropriate fund level is often managed by adjusting the necessary future increases in general rate revenue to recognize any variations in annual water sales rather than maintaining the fund level through subsequent surcharges.

- **Elevation surcharges.** For some systems, the cost of pumping due to differences in elevation and terrain within their service area can be significant. Elevation (zone) surcharges are a method to fairly reflect the additional or incremental costs associated with pumping from one elevation zone to a higher one. Elevation surcharges are generally accepted within the industry as cost based but have very limited applications. At a minimum, these surcharges typically include the incremental power costs associated with pumping from the lower zone to the higher elevation zone. The cost of infrastructure related to elevation zone pumping may also be included in the elevation zone surcharges, but some utilities may exclude this particular cost given the impact to the overall surcharge. Administratively, elevation zone surcharges may be challenging in that a utility may have multiple elevation zones.

- **Capital financing.** Surcharges may also be an effective means of accumulating funds for major capital project financing. For example, a surcharge may be put in place to prefund a major water treatment plant upgrade to address new regulatory requirements. By prefunding the capital project, the utility will help minimize the amount of its long-term borrowing and potentially minimize customer rates over the long term. It should be understood that prefunding typically does not cover 100 percent of the capital construction cost of the improvement. This approach typically funds only a portion of total project costs to avoid a significant one-time overall increase in general rates to provide the funding for the project.

- **Drought surcharges.** Drought surcharges are often used on an emergency and temporary basis to pay for costs associated with purchasing emergency water supplies during a severe drought or to support drought restrictions. When drought conditions result in the need to purchase emergency supplies, a surcharge is a logical and simple way to pass along the additional temporary cost of acquiring these high-cost water resources to the current users who require the water supply. Often, surcharges used during drought conditions are also intended to provide a price incentive for customers to reduce water demand. In both of these cases, the surcharge can be in place while the drought exists and can be removed once the drought has ended.

HISTORICAL PERSPECTIVES

Rate surcharges have been used when specific situations dictated the financial need for such charges. In the late 1980s and early 1990s during a severe drought, surcharges were used in California to cover the additional costs associated with obtaining emergency water supplies. In Pennsylvania, surcharges have been used to help investor-owned water systems accelerate the pace of needed improvements to the water delivery system. With the approval of state legislators and utility regulators, water investor-owned utilities in Pennsylvania have previously implemented a distribution system improvement charge. By allowing utilities to make incremental rate adjustments to pay for improvements, this mechanism enhances rate and revenue stability, reduces regulatory lag, and lengthens the time between formal rate cases. Less frequent rate cases reduce rate case expenses for all parties. The Rhode Island Public Utilities Commission has approved surcharges to repay one-time loans caused by revenue shortfalls. The Connecticut Public Utilities Regulatory Authority has allowed a revenue-adjustment-mechanism charge for revenue shortfalls caused by reduced demands. In addition, some utilities that historically attempted to pay for growth-related debt service via system development charge revenues discovered, as a result of slowed growth, the need to implement rate surcharges to cover the revenue shortfall between the growth-related debt-service payments and the reduced system development charge revenue.

ADVANTAGES AND DISADVANTAGES

The relative advantages and disadvantages of rate surcharges may be assessed in terms of simplicity, equity, revenue stability, conservation, effect on customers, and implementation, including the legal considerations.

Simplicity

For the most part, surcharges are simple to calculate, understand, implement, and administer. Surcharges can be applied and collected in different ways, but utilities typically strive to implement a surcharge that is easy to administer, given the typical short-term nature of this type of charge. Drought surcharges may be more complex if they follow the various stages of drought specified within a drought management plan (Stage 1, Stage 2, etc.).

Equity

The issue of equity can often be addressed by considering the specific circumstances that create the need for the surcharge and the way in which the surcharge is assessed and collected. For equity to prevail, there should be a reasonable relationship between the amount of surcharge revenue collected from each customer class and the benefits that accrue when the surcharge revenues are used. Properly designed drought surcharges should be equitable if discretionary usage is primarily targeted.

Revenue Stability

By definition, a surcharge is a temporary rate assessed to collect revenues above those generated from existing rate levels. Accordingly, surcharges generally enhance revenue adequacy by increasing the total amount of revenue generated. Surcharges may provide additional revenue, but in the case of drought surcharges, the surcharge may offset the decline in revenue and consumption. It is also important to realize that demand for water may decrease due to the increased water bills caused by surcharges, which also affects revenue stability.

Conservation

Surcharges are generally not considered a long-term conservation pricing tool because they are typically temporary in nature. The distinction between conservation pricing and surcharge pricing is that conservation pricing is usually a long-term pricing approach intended to permanently alter demand, whereas surcharge pricing is temporary and is intended to support the identified need. However, drought surcharges can be effective in reducing short-term demands, especially when designed to help manage short-term, severe drought restrictions.

Effect on Customers

The effects of surcharges on customers vary in relation to the level of the surcharge and the length of time the surcharge is in effect. It also varies depending on how it is assessed. In most cases, the relative effect on individual customers is minimal and limited in duration.

Implementation

Implementing rate surcharges should be relatively straightforward but may be limited by specific billing systems. In the planning process, the utility should strive to communicate the need for the charge to its customers and to calculate a fee that is equitable, easy to implement, and simple to administer. Generally, the perception and acceptance of surcharges by customers may vary based on the need for, or reasoning behind, the surcharge. Some level of customer resistance will likely be encountered.

DETERMINING RATE SURCHARGES

Determining rate surcharges is a fairly simple matter, but the method of collection can take many forms.

Fixed Surcharge

A fixed amount surcharge is a fixed or flat rate generally applicable to all customers (i.e., each customer's bill includes a fixed dollar amount surcharge). For example, each customer may be charged a $5 surcharge on their bill regardless of the volume of usage or the type of customer. Variations of fixed surcharges include surcharges that increase with meter or connection sizes or that vary by customer class. This may be an appropriate and equitable approach to assessing surcharges and is one that has a low-cost recovery risk.

Volumetric Surcharge

The volumetric surcharge approach is often used when the surcharge revenues are used to benefit customers in proportion to how they use water or when there is a need to reduce the amount of water used via price (i.e., drought surcharges). In this approach, only the volumetric portion of the rate has a surcharge applied to it. Depending on how the volumetric surcharge is applied, it potentially allows a utility to be more specific in the customers that the surcharge targets and in the impact on demands of different user groups. Volumetric surcharges have greater revenue risk and variability than fixed fee surcharges.

Percentage Bill

This approach simply places a fixed percentage surcharge on the total bill of the customer. The percentage bill approach is simple and straightforward and can be accomplished in two ways. First, each of the rate components of the entire rate structure may be increased equally to produce the incremental amount of revenues. This approach does not explicitly separate the surcharge from the rates. Alternatively, the bill can be computed at current rates, and then a percentage surcharge assessed in addition to that amount. This approach is more explicit in that the surcharge is clearly identified.

DETERMINING DROUGHT SURCHARGES

Drought surcharges are a specific form of rate surcharge used during a drought. A water utility typically has two overriding objectives during a drought. The first is to reduce the volume of water used by its customers to reflect the utility's potentially reduced and constrained water supply resources. This reduction is usually accomplished by a combination of actions, such as appealing to customers to voluntarily reduce water demands, placing mandatory restrictions on discretionary water uses (often outdoor uses such as irrigation and car washing), and increasing rates or adding surcharges as incentives to reduce water demands. The goal is to immediately reduce demands on water supplies made scarce by the drought. The second objective during a drought is to maintain adequate revenues to meet system revenue requirements. To the extent that the first objective (i.e., water-use reduction) is met, it is often correspondingly more difficult to meet the second objective. To deal with this situation, many utilities draw on financial reserves, reduce budgeted expenditures (although during a drought, a utility will often incur unbudgeted costs), and implement drought surcharges.

DROUGHT SURCHARGE CONSIDERATIONS

Revenue forecasting for post-drought pricing periods should anticipate the potential for long-term effects on demand patterns arising from the temporary drought conditions. Drought surcharges are intended to reduce demand immediately as a precautionary or emergency response to a temporary and severe limitation in water supplies. Once the drought or emergency has passed, drought surcharges may be removed or revised to align with longer-term pricing objectives, which may be achieved through normal rate setting. In contrast, conservation pricing is designed to permanently reduce or modify total annual demand or alter demand patterns and often is an institutionalized characteristic of a utility's rate structure. Notably, however, depending on the duration and severity of a drought and the effectiveness of the drought surcharges, permanent reductions in water usage may be induced, although this may not be the intended consequence of the drought surcharge strategy.

The approach used for drought surcharges may blend the drought surcharge with existing rates, or the drought surcharges may be a separately identified surcharge on a customer's bill. A utility's ability to select between these two approaches may be limited by its billing system and either approach can be effective, although a separately identified drought surcharge provides a clearer price signal to customers.

Types of Drought Surcharges

Surcharges are often used as an emergency and temporary fee to pay for costs associated with purchasing emergency water supplies during a severe drought or to support drought restrictions. When drought conditions result in the need to purchase emergency supplies, a surcharge is a logical and simple way to pass along the additional temporary cost of acquiring these high-cost water resources to the current users who require the water supply. Often, surcharges used during drought conditions are also intended to provide a price incentive for customers to reduce water demand. In both of these cases the surcharge can be in place while the drought exists and can be removed once the drought has ended. Excess funds are generated from surcharges imposed solely to encourage conservation, above those needed to meet potentially increased costs, and should be set aside in a reserve fund to be used for future drought-related mitigation purposes, such as development of additional sources for supply.

The following paragraphs describe the different approaches for setting drought surcharges.

General rate adjustment. One method of rate setting during a drought is to implement a drought surcharge on all commodity rates. For example, all volume rates (regardless of the rate structure) could be increased by a specific percentage estimated to yield an acceptable level of demand reduction, while still generating the required revenue requirement from the decreased consumption. Although this is a relatively simple and unsophisticated method of developing drought surcharges, customers might better accept this approach because it may be perceived as treating all customers "equally." This method of establishing rate surcharges is also relatively easy to explain to customers and implement for billing purposes. However, this method does not target those users or end uses most able to reduce water demands or most likely to respond to price changes. Finally, the drought surcharge component is not explicitly identified under this approach and may not clearly communicate the drought issue to the customer. Thus, while this approach is simple and appears to treat customers equally, its lack specificity, and transparency may ultimately make it less acceptable.

General volumetric surcharge. To better communicate the price impact to customers of using water during a drought, many utilities implement separate drought surcharges that are distinct from their established water rates. A general volumetric surcharge provides incentive for customers to reduce demand and specifically identifies on their bills the cost impacts of using water during periods of drought. Volumetric surcharges may take many forms, including ones that uniformly apply the surcharge over all consumption blocks, relate the surcharge to consumption beyond a stated level (e.g., a surcharge applied to consumption over 10,000 gallons per month), or include graduated increases in the surcharge as consumption increases (i.e., an increasing block surcharge). Although this form of drought surcharge may be effective in communicating cost impacts, it is also a relatively blunt pricing technique that does not target specific individualized customer uses (i.e., residential versus commercial) or consider whether or not specific customers have the ability to reduce their consumption (discretionary versus nondiscretionary use).

Class-based volumetric surcharges. A variation of the general volumetric surcharge approach is to establish quantity limits per customer for different classes of users and to apply a surcharge to any user exceeding the limit for that class. In essence, this is a volumetric surcharge by customer class of service. This approach requires establishing reasonable consumption targets based on the consumption characteristics for each class. Often, the target setting can be performed in a reasonable and relatively equitable manner for single-family and multiple-family residential customers, with the latter group set on a per-dwelling-unit basis. It is more difficult to set uniformly applied quantity limits for commercial and industrial customers than residential customers because of diversity in the number, types, and sizes of commercial and industrial customers. This diversity limits the extent to which volumetric surcharges may be equitably applied to commercial and industrial customers. As a result, this approach may be less effective in achieving the desired consumption reduction targets for commercial and industrial customers than those applicable to relatively homogeneous residential consumption.

Individualized volumetric surcharge. Another approach is to apply drought surcharges to users whose water demands exceed a specified percentage of their base-period water use. For example, the utility might apply a 25 percent surcharge to any customer with water use greater than 80 percent of that customer's average demand during a previous base period. This approach sets a clear water reduction target for each individual user and provides reduction incentives to all customers. An individualized approach can also recognize variations within a class, such as household size and lot size that may be important in setting target consumption levels. Agricultural and irrigation limits might be based on the type of crop or plant being watered and the acreage. While this approach places a similar reduction requirement on all customers, there remains a disadvantage of using historical usage characteristics to establish targeted levels of reduction. In those instances where a customer is already using water efficiently, the customer has less of an ability to reduce their demand and thus avoid a surcharge while a customer whose water use has been the least efficient has the greatest opportunity for avoiding the surcharges. Individualized approaches are limited to utilities that have billing systems that can set individualized consumption goals or consumption thresholds.

Targeted volumetric surcharge levels. A utility could target certain customer classes for larger surcharges than others. Such classes would include those that have more discretionary use and should be able to more easily reduce water use. This approach avoids affecting customers whose water demands are extremely inelastic or are desirable from a public health or other policy perspective. For example, a utility might place a high surcharge on residential outdoor usage and might not apply the same level of surcharges to hospitals or public schools. A major concern with this approach is that the utility may be criticized for targeting some customer groups and exempting others. There are also certain legal implications and considerations to this targeted approach. Implicit in this tactic is the ability of a utility to evaluate and make conclusions about the relative merit of one use of water over another.

Drought Surcharge Policy Issues

Drought management plan. In a drought, policymakers are faced with many decisions requiring them to balance water supply management imperatives, customer and community needs, and the potential financial consequences of drought response. When prepared in advance, a drought management plan can provide well-thought-out and comprehensive guidance in times of drought. A well-prepared drought management plan should provide clear policy direction as it relates to declaring a drought. The drought management plan will also discuss the various specific "stages" of drought and the target reductions of water use for each stage. The drought management plan provides the planning basis for, and the targeted savings from, the drought surcharges. These plans should include drought pricing and financial management strategies as well as water resource strategies.

Timing for implementation of drought surcharges. With the development of a drought management plan, the utility has a clear understanding of the various stages of drought, the actions to be taken, and the needed consumption savings. The drought management plan frequently establishes clear criteria for declaring when a utility is in a drought. Drought management plans typically classify droughts as to their severity (e.g., Stage 1 through Stage 5). Given the key information contained within the drought management plan, a utility can develop drought surcharges well in advance of a drought. The drought surcharges can be adopted and in place, ready to be implemented when a drought stage is declared by the governing body of the utility. Once the drought stage is declared, the associated drought surcharges become effective until the drought stage changes or the drought is declared to be over. By developing the drought surcharges in advance of an actual drought, and using the information contained in the drought management plan, the utility can carefully consider the various options available for establishing equitable drought surcharges and any billing system limitations.

Revenue sufficiency. Although drought pricing can help a utility manage the revenue reductions that result from reduced water sales, it is likely that the utility will need to also use its financial reserves as well as reduce and defer planned expenditures. Because the duration of a drought is not known (i.e., 1-year events versus 10-year events), utilities cannot be certain about how long their reserves will last and thus should draw on them cautiously, especially insofar as the ability to replenish them is limited during the drought.

Ideally, a well-designed drought surcharge should hold customers harmless if they comply with the desired and targeted savings levels. In other words, a customer that has a targeted Stage 1 reduction of 10 percent and reduces their consumption accordingly may pay roughly the same bill as before the drought and produce the same level of revenue because the pricing of the surcharge has been structured to recover the same level of revenue, assuming a 10 percent reduction in consumption. The difficult and challenging part of establishing drought surcharges is the uncertainty of how customers will respond and what reductions in consumption will be realized. When reductions in consumption are greater than the targeted level, the utility may have a budget shortfall. If the reductions in consumption do not occur, the utility should collect more than their revenue requirement.

Additional and/or deferred expenses. A drought response often requires additional expenses beyond the anticipated revenue requirement and may at the same time require the deferral of other anticipated expenses within the utility's revenue requirement. The additional expenses may be a function of the need to obtain additional and costly water supply, additional pumping costs, and so forth. In addition, expenses may be incurred to impose water-use restrictions in the event that the utility elects active enforcement of its rules. The utility will also likely incur additional costs associated with public outreach and communication. The drought management plan may have estimates of the unplanned expenditures for each drought stage. At the same time, capital projects may be postponed or deferred during a drought to help preserve cash flow and reserves.

Equity. Cost-of-service rate-making considerations are a recommended practice when establishing the utility's overall general rate structure. However, variance from the traditional cost-of-service principles may become necessary when implementing emergency drought surcharges, which include controlling demand and recovering total system costs. In designing drought surcharges, a utility should consider the price and demand response of various types of water uses and target those that are the most discretionary and responsive to price. This may or may not strictly relate to cost-of-service considerations.

Bill presentation and accounting issues. If the drought surcharges are intended to integrate with the other drought-related programs, it should ideally be clearly communicated to customers on their bill. This means that the drought surcharge should be presented as a separate line item on the bill. Utilities should also have a method for tracking the amount of drought surcharge revenue they receive from each customer class. This is important for accountability and transparency reasons during the drought. After the drought, this will provide valuable information for analysis purposes.

Customer acceptance. Customer acceptance and ease of implementation are important considerations in selecting a drought surcharge approach. Customers naturally expect their water reduction efforts during a drought to be recognized and perhaps rewarded, not penalized. In designing the surcharge rates, and as previously discussed, if all customers respond appropriately, consumption will decrease. The surcharge rate should, if properly designed, make the utility financially whole (i.e., lower use multiplied by the higher surcharge rate should produce revenue that equals the revenue requirement). For the customers who respond appropriately (e.g., save the reduced level of usage suggested in the drought plan), their bill should be roughly equal to what they pay under normal water conditions. Those customers that do not choose to conserve will appropriately end up with increased bills. Accordingly, to achieve the expected results of the surcharge, a vigorous educational campaign is important in explaining the drought pricing rationale and gaining its acceptance by customers.

Media relations. Working with the media during a drought is critical for providing information to customers about the severity of the drought, desired customer responses, and the need, purpose, and implications of drought pricing strategies. As it relates to drought surcharges, the utility should provide information about when the drought surcharges might go into effect, the potential magnitude of the surcharges, and their purpose. It should also explain that drought surcharges are one tool in a set of measures that the utility is using to engage the community in effective water resource management.

Removal of drought pricing. Just as it is complicated to know when to implement drought surcharges, it is just as complicated to know when the drought is over and to remove these surcharges. Caution is needed to avoid removing the drought pricing prematurely and then having to re-implement the drought surcharges. Formal action declaring the end of the drought should be the basis for the removal of the surcharges.

DROUGHT SURCHARGE EXAMPLE

In this example, the drought surcharges are triggered by the severity of the drought (Stage 1, Stage 2, etc.). For increasing levels of severity, more aggressive pricing policies are implemented as part of a comprehensive drought management plan to change customer behavior and reduce water demand. These drought surcharges are instituted when a declaration is made that a drought emergency exists. The basis around which the drought surcharges are established is related to the estimated price responsiveness and price elasticity. Assuming an average price elasticity response of –0.1 to –0.2 for a relatively large change in price, a 25 percent increase in the commodity charge would yield a demand reduction of about 2.5 percent to 5 percent, all other factors remaining constant. It is presumed that other drought responses (i.e., restrictions and public education) will complement and add to this reduction.

During a moderate Stage 1 drought, the following actions would be taken:

- Single-family rates are assessed a surcharge of 25 percent that is applied to the two upper blocks (i.e., more discretionary use). The initial block is assumed to be more "essential needs."

- The multifamily, commercial, and industrial rates under normal water conditions are converted from uniform block rates to increasing two-block rates. Block 1 remains at its current level, and block 2 is indexed to the block 2 rates for the single-family class.

- Irrigation rates are also converted to a two-block rate. Block 1 increases by 25 percent (because all outdoor irrigation use is considered discretionary), and block 2 is indexed to the block 3 rates for the single-family class.

Table V.3-1 Drought surcharge pricing example ($ per 1,000 gallons)

Customer Class	Non-Drought, Normal Water	Stage 1, Moderate Drought	Stage 2, Severe Drought	Stage 3, Critical Drought
Single-Family Residential				
Block 1	$1.00	$1.00	$1.10	$1.50
Block 2	$1.50	$1.87	$2.25	$3.00
Block 3	$2.00	$2.50	$3.00	$4.00
Multiple-Family Residential				
Block 1	$1.25	$1.25	$1.38	$1.87
Block 2	$1.25	$1.87	$2.25	$3.50
Commercial/Industrial				
Block 1	$1.30	$1.63	$1.79	$1.95
Block 2	$1.30	$1.87	$2.25	$3.50
Irrigation				
Block 1	$1.75	$2.19	$2.63	$2.89
Block 2	$1.75	$2.50	$3.00	$4.00

NOTE: For example only and based on specific assumptions.

If the drought situation worsens to a Stage 2 severe drought, a greater emphasis is given to targeting outdoor usage with higher prices:

- Block 1 rates for all customers are adjusted, but at moderate levels, particularly for single-family and multifamily customers, because their block 1 use is considered to be nondiscretionary or essential and is less sensitive to price.
- Blocks 2 and 3 rates are increased, creating a steeper pricing curve to the customers as they use more water. The single-family residential blocks 2 and 3 are increased by 50 percent of their normal water condition level. Multifamily and commercial/industrial block 2 rates are indexed to the single-family residential rate and irrigation consumption. Irrigation class usage, which is deemed the most discretionary, in block 2 is priced at the block 3 single-family residential level.

Finally, if the drought situation became critical (Stage 3), the utility would need to increase the price incentive to reduce demand. In this case, the utility might implement the following actions:

- Block 1 for all customers, except irrigation, would increase by 50 percent over its normal level.
- Single-family residential blocks 2 and 3 would increase by 100 percent over their normal levels, increasing the price curve to these customers for outdoor usage.
- Multifamily and commercial/industrial block 2 would be indexed to the midpoint between blocks 2 and 3 for single-family residential customers.
- Irrigation block 2 rates would be indexed to the block 3 single-family rates.

This example for drought rate adjustments is summarized in Table V.3-1. A utility should carefully plan the details for implementation. This phased-in approach to rate setting in a drought is designed to reduce water demand and yet maintain as much of the revenue stream for the utility as possible under various levels of water shortage.

This example, while greatly simplified, provides an overview of the basic approach and considerations that may be used in the pricing and development of drought surcharges. As the drought surcharges are analyzed and developed, consideration must be given to the overall reductions in use needed under the particular drought stage and the overall revenue impacts.

The characteristics of the utility's customer base, water supply, and constraints on resources should be evaluated in tailoring a drought surcharge approach that will best meet the utility's needs. Careful planning and effective customer communication will enhance the likelihood that drought surcharges will help secure required changes in water demand patterns and gain general community acceptance.

SUMMARY

Rate surcharges can be an effective means for financially protecting the utility during periods of severe drought or other natural disasters. Surcharges may also provide an effective means to fund specific improvements or build necessary reserves for future requirements. Although rate surcharges have limited application and may also be politically sensitive to implement and subject to legal constraints, they can help stabilize rates over the long term and provide other nonfinancial benefits, such as achieving needed reductions in consumption during drought periods.

This page intentionally blank.

Chapter **V.4**

Low-Income Affordability Programs

This chapter addresses low-income affordability programs, which are intended to help mitigate financial impacts for customers who are less able to pay for water, which is an essential service. As further defined in this chapter, affordability programs can include a range of rate and bill discounts for low-income customers, but can also include other programmatic support efforts, such as assistance with water audits or assistance in reducing water consumption. The chapter is included in this manual to provide guidance to utilities interested in developing affordability programs or in enhancing existing programs. It provides a description of the primary rate-related strategies employed to address affordability, such as percentage bill discounts. It also provides examples of some additional program elements employed by some communities, such as assistance in conducting water audits or repair programs to help customers reduce water consumption. It also provides a brief introduction to selected related policy and management topics. It does not address or provide a comprehensive survey of the nonrate issues, strategies, or research associated with low-income and affordability programs. Nor does this chapter attempt to define an affordability threshold, a specific set of charge or demographic circumstances at which the financial burden to a household is deemed excessive, or metrics for communities to use as a guideline in defining such a threshold.

Affordability programs are of increased interest in the water industry for several reasons. Recently, some states, local communities, and multinational organizations such as the United Nations (2010) have more formally recognized water as a human right. The United Nation's declaration of water as a human right has had ripple effects on the affordability of water service in the United States, especially in states like California. California's Proposition 218, an initiative-based amendment to the California Constitution enacted into law by ballot in 1996 that essentially allows utility customers an opportunity to vote against a proposed rate increase, has also drawn attention to the issue of affordability.

With increasing costs associated with regulatory mandates and aging infrastructure, water (and wastewater) rates continue to rise. Given that income level growth has stagnated (Hughes, et al. 2014) in recent years, it is possible that the price of water service will increase to the point that even more low-income households will have difficulty in paying the bills for this service when calculated based on the cost-of-service principles defined throughout this manual. While the focus of this chapter is on programs to help address affordability for low-income residential customers, it is important to recognize that increases in utility rates and charges can also have significant impacts on commercial and industrial customers, particularly customers whose processes and operations require considerable amounts of water.

While disconnection for nonpayment is a common and effective billing and financial management strategy used by utilities to address financial challenges posed by customers who do not pay their bills, it does not resolve the social or public policy questions regarding the proper response of a utility to affordability challenges. Furthermore, this approach imposes collection and shutoff costs that must be included in a utility's operating costs. In the past, many utilities used nonrate strategies to address payment concerns, but as rates move upward to reach the fully allocated cost of water, more utilities are implementing structures that consider affordability as part of their response to addressing the needs of low-income residential customers.

The overall affordability challenge facing utility managers is substantially broader than addressing the economic concerns of the low-income households previously described. As a result of the combined effect of increased regulations and the need to renew and replace aging utility assets that were built as much as a century ago, water and sewer rates have increased at rates greater than most consumer commodities during the past 10 years (Hughes, et al. 2014). Because water and wastewater service is a necessity in modern society, there is an essential threshold of water use that is required by all individuals. Issues related to a number of public policy and legal matters, as well as political or management challenges, frequently arise when considering affordability programs for a specific utility. Consequently, affordability issues are becoming more important to many utilities. Perhaps ironically, in addition to addressing utilities' social responsibilities as major economic actors in their communities, providing a method for lessening the financial impact of rate increases on low-income and fixed-income residential customers has helped utility managers secure needed rate increases from utility governing boards.

It is important to note that affordability and low-income rates and programs are a policy decision of the governing body of the utility, and, in some cases, utilities' governing boards or management take the position that it is not the role of a water utility to address society's low-income or affordability issues. That viewpoint is not shared by all utilities or policymakers, but it does highlight the range of differences of opinion on this topic. Moreover, in many states, legal constraints limit the forms and sources of funding for low-income affordability measures.

Although the focus of this manual is on water rates, this chapter makes reference both to water and wastewater rates. This is done for several reasons. Regulatory pressures on many wastewater systems since the early 2000s have resulted in substantial capital program requirements often funded through rate increases. These wastewater program financing challenges and related policy discussion on community financial capabilities have resulted in productive research and discussions related to affordability challenges. This chapter references the key affordability ideas and issues developed in that context. The combined impact of paying for both water and wastewater service may be what puts some residential customers past the point at which they can pay the bills for these essential services. This is increasingly acknowledged as an important consideration by utilities, industry associations, and regulators. The US Environmental Protection Agency's (USEPA's) release of an integrated planning framework in early 2013 acknowledges the need to consider more holistically the financial requirements imposed by the spending needs of water and wastewater systems (USEPA 2013). Also, many water utilities provide wastewater service and the two services are included on a single customer bill.

Advances in affordability programs in recent years reflect insights gained from utility case examples and technological innovations. Lessons have been learned through partnering with other local agencies to identify eligible program participants. Increasingly powerful and flexible billing systems can more readily accommodate variations in bill discount options. As detailed later in this chapter, state legislation and regulatory contexts in some situations restrict the forms of affordability programs that utilities can implement. It is important to research a utility's specific enabling legislation before embarking on the creation of an affordability program.

DEFINING AFFORDABILITY

Many different and widely varying aspects of affordability are relevant to utility managers and boards, including the ability of

- the poorest households in the service area to afford their water and wastewater bills,
- the average or median household in the service area to afford its water and wastewater bill,
- an unconnected household or business to afford the one-time connection and system development charges to connect to the water or wastewater system,
- the community to bear the total costs of providing water and wastewater infrastructure and services, and
- the community to afford these costs as measured by the USEPA or other relevant regulatory entities.

For the purposes of this chapter, affordability will be addressed primarily as the economic challenge resulting from the inability of the *poorest* segment of the customer base to fund its proportionate share of the total costs of the provision of utility services. The ability of the community as a whole, or on average, to bear the costs of service relate more to what has recently been termed *financial capability*. Such questions are of importance to utilities seeking to obtain subsidized funding, variances, or other relief during negotiations with regulatory authorities, which is not the focus of this chapter. This chapter narrowly focuses on the ability of the lowest-income residential customers to pay their recurring water and wastewater bills.

How Much Is "Unaffordable"?

It is difficult to decide on the dollar amount at which a water bill becomes "unaffordable" to a low-income or fixed-income customer. Though several groups have addressed this issue, the result at the national level is limited to "guidelines" as opposed to "definitions." Given variations in local economic conditions, compositions of the customer base, and community values, defining affordability must be done at the local level.

Sometimes, dialogue related to affordability focuses on charges as a percentage of median household income (MHI), such as thresholds used in some USEPA guidance documents related to financial capability. However, these references are to thresholds used by USEPA to assess the financial capability of water systems nationally to comply with drinking water regulations and of wastewater systems individually for complying with Clean Water Act requirements (USCM, AWWA, and WEF 2013a, 2013b). They were never intended to be used by individual utilities to assess affordability of their rates to their (low-income) customers directly. Furthermore, given that MHI only measures the income level of the household in the middle of the income distribution of the community, it does not consider the income variances within a community and ignores rates of poverty within a service area.* There are many other measures that utilities can use to assess affordability, several of which focus more on low-income customers. Instead of calculating bills as a percentage of MHI, utilities can, for example, use the income level at the poverty threshold. Determining how much a family at the poverty threshold would spend on average water and wastewater bills more accurately reflects the affordability concerns of low-income customers than percent MHI (Hughes and Leurig 2013).

Since affordability concerns differ from community to community, a local approach is needed that takes into account the community's values. For example, in North Carolina, the Orange Water and Sewer Authority has defined an affordability goal that is included in the utility's financial policy document (OWASA 2012). Each utility should determine its own method for assessing the affordability of its utility rates and charges. Given the complexity of the economic and social issues involved in these considerations, this assessment will often require the use of more than a single metric.

Utility-Specific Definitions of Affordability

Defining which customers are eligible for assistance in an affordability program is a local policy decision. Affordability cannot be defined or determined at a global level. Although recent published literature and regulatory attention has heightened awareness of the affordability issue, these efforts have not rendered a consensus definition of affordability. Because of the importance of this topic to the sustainability of water utilities, AWWA is continuing to support research and dialogue to advance understanding of the affordability issue.

Local considerations, such as the demographic characteristics of a water system's customer base, overall financial profile of the community, customer water usage patterns, and the community's overall financial strength, are some of the factors that may need to be considered when devising an affordability program. As detailed in the next section of this chapter, several utilities have found it useful for identifying customer eligibility for their affordability programs to partner with agencies already identifying households that qualify for assistance through federally supported programs.

The following guidelines and guidance documents can help utilities make a determination of what constitutes affordable service for low-income customers and what forms of relief might be appropriate to provide affordable service.

- The Safe Drinking Water Act of 1974 (S. 1547) established special assistance in communities where the average residential water bill exceeds 2 percent of MHI.

- The US Department of Agriculture has a program to provide subsidized funds for water and wastewater systems. Loans are made for projects where the residential water bills are 1.5 percent of the community's MHI. Grants are available for costs in excess of 1.5 percent.

- The 1998 Water Research Foundation (WRF) report, *Water Affordability Programs*, suggests that programs should not be based on MHI but on rates that cause water bills to exceed 2 percent of income for impoverished households (Saunders 1998). Because of the focus on impoverished households, a measure of 2 percent was selected to determine if water service costs were burdensome.

- The *Journal AWWA* article "Water Utility Options for Low-Income Assistance Programs" (Hasson 2002) illustrates how the Portland (Ore.) Water Bureau established

---

* A single-parent family with two children who makes just over minimum wage will earn less than $20,000 per year. These types of distressed families make up a portion of almost every community, regardless of the community's median income. Both a community with an MHI of $80,000 or one with an MHI of $35,000 will experience the same affordability challenge related to this type of low-income family (Hughes and Leurig 2013).

eligibility criteria for assistance, established a program in light of demographic and water usage characteristics of its customer base, and evaluated the effectiveness of the program using parameters such as level of participation, impact on delinquencies, and program costs. A *Public Works* article in 2012 provides an update to the Portland example, and describes how the rate component of Portland's program is integrated with several other affordability program elements (Matichich 2012).

- An AWWA webcast presented on October 3, 2012, showcased approaches to affordability programs used by three utilities: Cleveland Division of Water (Ohio), Orange Water and Sewer Authority (N.C.), and Cape Coral Utilities (Fla.). The webcast documented current efforts to aid low-income customers, but also identified state regulatory and statutory constraints that precluded utilities from implementing all locally desired program elements.

- The AWWA publication *Thinking Outside the Bill: A Utility Manager's Guide to Assisting Low-Income Water Customers* (2014) outlines a range of affordability programs, such as the variations on bill discounts and other program options, and identifies a framework that a community can use to assess the need for such programs.

- The USEPA publication *Compendium of Drinking Water and Wastewater Customer Assistance Programs* (2016) provides additional descriptions and definitions of the range of bill discount and other programs that utilities can use to provide assistance to low-income and other financially distressed customers. It includes several case studies of programs, including the Washington Suburban Sanitary Commission and the San Antonio Water System. An appendix to the report includes a state-by-state matrix that identifies utility systems that provide customer assistance in a number of key categories, including bill discounts, flexible terms, lifeline rates, temporary assistance, and water efficiency programs. AWWA is one of several industry associations credited by USEPA as a substantial contributor to the development of this study.

In addition, there are several documents related to assessing the community's overall financial capability to pay for water and wastewater regulations. Although these documents and guidelines refer to these assessments as "affordability" measures, they should not be confused with metrics that are used by individual utilities to determine whether their rates are affordable to low-income customers. These documents include the following:

- The USEPA guidance document *Combined Sewer Overflows—Guidance for Financial Capability Assessment and Schedule Development* (1997) outlines USEPA's framework for assessing whether a community's financial position is strong, mid-range, or weak; and, based on the financial indicators, whether the burden imposed by sewerage programs imposes a low, medium, or high burden on a residential customer with an MHI.

- The Environmental Finance Advisory Board's *Comments on EPA Document: Combined Sewer Overflows: Guidance for Financial Capability Assessment and Schedule Development* recommends that USEPA develop a residential indicator that considers actual household expenditures based on average water use, using the rate structures expected to be in effect after the combined-sewer-overflow (CSO) improvements are implemented, rather than assume that the entire cost of controls is spread evenly across households. This would also allow consideration of the effect that lifeline rates or low-income assistance programs could have on mitigating impacts (EFAB 2007).

- The National Association of Clean Water Agencies (NACWA) commissioned two studies for assessing affordability in wet weather programs and experience of utilities in negotiating program requirements with the regulatory agencies. These two documents are *Financial Capability and Affordability in Wet Weather Negotiations* (NACWA 2005) and *Principles for Assessment and Negotiation of Financial Capability: A Compilation of Resources* (NACWA 2002). One of the key lessons of these studies is that using the financial impact of utility service on the MHI family can be an inadequate measure for assessing affordability for communities that have demographic profiles with significant numbers of households with incomes well below the MHI level.

- Two recent memoranda from USEPA continue the dialogue on development to approaches for assessing overall financial capability of major utility capital programs and the affordability of resulting financial impacts on utility system customers. The January 2013 memorandum Assessing Financial Capability for Municipal Clean Water Act Requirements addresses the need to look more holistically at the combined impact of various federal, state, and local mandates when assessing the impact of new capital programs (USEPA 2013). And the November 2014 memorandum Financial Capability Assessment Framework for Municipal Clean Water Act Requirements identifies more specific examples of the demographic contexts and competing financing requirements that could impact the affordability of new utility requirements such as CSO program needs (USEPA 2014).

- Two documents and related tools that AWWA co-developed with the United States Conference of Mayors and the Water Environment Federation provide substantial additional insight into how the affordability of new capital program requirements can be assessed. *Assessing the Affordability of Federal Water Mandates: An Issue Brief* (USCM, AWWA, and WEF 2013b) and *Affordability Assessment Tool for Federal Water Mandates* (USCM, AWWA, and WEF 2013a) provide insights and tools that communities can use to assess the overall level of burden imposed by utility financial requirements.

AFFORDABILITY PROGRAMS

This section describes some of the common approaches that have been used by water utilities that have established financial assistance programs for low-income customers. It also provides examples of some additional program elements that utilities are using to provide assistance to these customers.

Common Affordability Program Elements

Generally speaking, affordability programs are intended to help mitigate the financial impacts of water bills for customers who are less able to pay for service. For the purposes of this chapter, the low-income affordability rate alternatives discussed are limited to those targeted only to customers defined by specific criteria to be low-income and who require assistance in paying their water bills. Note that lower income does not correlate to lower water use any more than lower income correlates to age, veteran status, or physical disability (programs based on these other factors do not address the issue of income and affordability directly). Water rate affordability programs can include the following components:

- **Discount on the full bill.** Some discount programs involve an across-the-board reduction or discount on the total water bill. The discount can be a set percentage for all eligible customers, can vary by income level with larger discounts for more impoverished customers,* or can be discounted for total amounts of the water bill over some set dollar level for eligible customers.

- **Discount on the variable (usage) portion.** Rather than discounting the entire bill, only the portion based on use is discounted. The fixed portion of the bill is not reduced. This method provides greater dollar discounts to customers that use greater amounts of water and therefore may be most helpful to larger families that require more water. The program can be structured to provide discounts for use only up to a certain level per month or up to a specified quantity of use per family member. The variable-usage-based discounts could reduce wasteful use by providing no discount for "excessive" consumption, but could require additional, detailed household information to be monitored with the customer database depending on specific program design.† To minimize administrative and data management requirements associated with documenting the specific number of occupants, a method that applies some principles of water-budget-based rates might be applied, where usage targets could be defined by building parameters and informed by usage histories.

- **Discount on the fixed (minimum) portion.** Another alternative is to discount all or part of the fixed portion of the bill (i.e., the meter charge, service charge, or billing charge). The consumption portion of the bill is not discounted under this approach. This method can provide the overall reductions that may help make service affordable, yet the customer remains incentivized to use water efficiently and conserve. Given the trend toward moving more of the required revenues of utilities to the fixed portion of customer bills, as addressed in chapter IV.7, this form of discount is increasingly likely to address a greater portion of a customer's overall bill.

- **Percentage of income.** A percentage of income-based low-income subsidy involves charging customers for service based on a percentage of their individual income. This can include a system where customers always pay up to a predetermined percentage of income that is considered affordable. An alternative to this is a system where a percentage of a typical bill is determined based on the income level. That percentage is then applied to all bills (similar to a discount program). If customers use more water, the bill increases; if they conserve, they save even more. This requires monitoring and verification of income, which could be a disadvantage compared with some of the other program options, depending on the administrative costs for these efforts.

- **Fixed credits.** In situations where assistance is provided to water consumers who may not be direct customers (e.g., renters living in a master-metered building), credits can be provided. If the utility provides another service directly to customers, such as electric service, credits can be provided on the electric bill. Another form of credit that has been suggested is providing some form of coupon used to make rent payments to landlords who, in turn, can use these coupons to pay a portion of the water bill for the building.‡

---

* This requires income verification by the utility or department that manages the affordability program.

† More complex rate schedules present the additional challenge of being more difficult for customer service staff to understand and effectively communicate to customers.

‡ In some communities, if a landlord does not pay the water bill, renters can make the direct payment of the water bill and are provided vouchers or proof of such payments that can be used in lieu of rent.

When considering how to employ the rate-related low-income affordability options described above, the concept of lifeline rates may be useful. The term *lifeline rates* is sometimes used for rate structures designed to provide an essential amount of water at a reduced cost to all customers, independent of income level or ability to pay. This *minimal amount of water* is typically defined as the essential needs of a residential customer (i.e., for drinking, cooking, and washing). However, lower income customers can exhibit higher water usage due to less prevalence of water-efficient fixtures and appliances, and under-maintained homes that may have plumbing leaks, and these considerations should also be incorporated into any definition of lifeline rates.

When considering the rate-related affordability program elements described above, a cost-of-service analysis provides a solid conceptual foundation and some of the needed cost information to support an analysis of the potential benefits of an affordability program. During the rate-design portion of the analysis, the rate analyst can present decision makers with affordability program options, including information that identifies the contribution of those customers providing the subsidy to support the program.

In addition to policy and financial considerations, legal and regulatory policy contexts can influence the type of affordability program that utilities can develop and the degree of subsidies that can be provided. For example, in some states, there are state-level regulations or regulatory practices that prevent the use of user charge revenues to fund affordability programs. In these situations, the funding for affordability programs may be limited to funds that can be raised through voluntary contribution programs or other nonrate revenues of the system.

The rate options described above may be implemented as part of an affordability program that includes nonrate strategies to help address a variety of customer situations negatively affecting the ability to pay for water and wastewater services. Some of the nonrate strategies currently being employed include

- arrearage forgiveness;
- leak detection assistance;
- fixture repairs;
- replacement of old plumbing fixtures with high-efficiency fixtures;
- crisis vouchers, often for a limited period of time, to help customers unable to pay their bills because of specific economic hardship, such as unemployment;
- safety net concepts;
- budget billing;
- alliances with community service organizations, sometimes including funding of accounts for use in assisting with water bills; and
- targeting of conservation outreach or other education efforts to low-income customers.

A broader package of such initiatives can be beneficial because affordability rates are typically limited in the level of assistance they can provide and are most effective when they are targeted to specific low-income customers. A program with multiple elements can provide assistance to more customers and more comprehensively address the root causes of affordability challenges.

Eligibility Verification

Participants are typically required to provide some form of verification of financial need to be eligible for discounts. Determining eligibility can be a key challenge, but income verification need not be a tedious or difficult process. Several income-based government assistance programs are already in place that water utilities can look to for partnership opportunities. Proof of eligibility in one or more of these programs often provides adequate income verification:

- AFDC (Aid to Families with Dependent Children)
- SSI (Supplemental Security Income)
- LIHEAP (Low Income Home Energy Assistance Program)
- Medicaid
- Food stamps
- Local property tax assistance
- Other utilities, including electric, natural gas, telephone, or cable television companies, offer discount programs based on income.

Water utilities' eligibility determinations may require relatively limited financial information from customers and can often rely on need assessments conducted by other such entities. In particular, many water utilities have found it useful to partner with the agencies that are responsible for qualifying participants for the LIHEAP program. The qualification for this program is state specific and based on percentages of income. The LIHEAP statute establishes 150 percent of the poverty level as the maximum income level allowed in determining LIHEAP income eligibility, except where 60 percent of state median income is higher. Income eligibility criteria for LIHEAP may not be set lower than 110 percent of the poverty level. Another appealing aspect of the LIHEAP criteria is that it provides for variations based on household size.*

Administrative Considerations

The logistical and administrative challenges that need to be addressed when establishing a new affordability program may be extensive. Programs that require accessing personal information may be practically and legally complex, and customers often face personal or cultural barriers to seeking assistance. Customer service windows and lobbies are rarely conducive to private conversations.

One example of a challenge related to rendering low-income assistance and designing an affordability-conscious rate structure relates to apartment dwellers. In many cases, master-metered apartment buildings isolate the customer from the rate structure, and even in cases of individually metered units, service is often provided in the name of the landlord. Utilities have very limited options to provide assistance to such households because they are not direct customers and the utility has no direct business relationship with them. As noted above, fixed credits have been suggested by some utilities to address the challenges in providing support to this segment of the utility's residential customer base. Industry research continues on these issues.

Some state laws may prohibit water utilities from providing discounts or other financial assistance to low-income customers directly. In these cases, water utilities may instead be able to partner with other organizations or social service agencies that work directly with low-income households. The water utility could raise the funds for the affordability program—through donations or bill roundup programs, for instance—but the other

---

* Affordability programs are generally only applied to residential accounts. The "lifeline" aspect of water and wastewater service being the primary driver, many communities do not consider commercial enterprises to be relevant to this discussion. See chapter V.5 for more information on programs for nonresidential customers.

organization or agency would handle the distribution of funds to low-income customers to be used in paying their water bills.

Although implementing affordability programs can present challenges, it can also provide significant benefits. For example, a program can help enable the utility to collect some of its sales revenue instead of shutting off customers, collecting nothing, and incurring associated costs. Another benefit is avoidance of sending field crews out to shut off customers for nonpayment, potentially avoiding considerable cost to the utility (Rothstein 2012). In addition, such programs can address public and political opposition to rate increases made on the grounds that such increases are not affordable to a segment of the utility's customer base. The existence of a customer financial assistance program can allow the utility to demonstrate customer awareness and its efforts to address this problem. This may contribute to a smoother rate adjustment process with increased customer acceptance. Furthermore, helping low-income customers pay their water bills is consistent with the principle that access to potable water is a basic human right.

Historical Precedents

Costs for other utility services, such as natural gas, electricity, and telephone, have traditionally been much higher than water service. Many of these utilities faced the issue of affordability relatively early in their histories. Nearly every state regulatory commission has addressed the issue of affordable energy bills and the ability of low-income customers to pay those bills. Low-income discounts, consumer assistance programs, budget billing, waivers of customer charges, and lifeline rates are common in the energy industry. The telecommunications industry faced the issue of affordability when the concept of universal access was introduced.

Outside North America, low-income discounts, lifeline rates, and affordable water programs are common. Overall pricing at levels below the utility's average cost with subsidies from outside the utility is not uncommon, and a variety of national and international strategies attempt to target low-income households. Within North America, an increasing number of water utilities have adopted affordability programs.

Emerging Program Approaches

In light of the increased recognition that a formulaic approach to defining affordability program eligibility may leave some residential customers with legitimate financial need and little or no assistance, utilities are increasingly creating programs that bundle several program elements. The Portland (Ore.) Water Bureau program is a good example. The City of Portland has been engaged in affordability programs for more than 20 years. As profiled in several journal articles (Hasson 2002, Matichich 2012), the City has used a combination of work groups, surveys, and pilot programs to develop and refine its affordability program. The result has been the implementation of a wide variety of methods for assisting low-income customers, which include the following:

- Bill discounts for residential customers that qualify, based on eligibility determined by the local agency charged with implementing the energy assistance program

- Conservation information programs—information on activities that households can implement to reduce water usage (and therefore, bills) is distributed through churches and other community organizations.

- Monthly statements—a monthly statement, about a third of the customer's quarterly bill, is offered to assist customers with managing their water, sewer, and stormwater quarterly bills

- Crisis vouchers to address emergency situations
- Plumbing fixture repair—financial assistance up to $2,800 for leaky toilets, faucets, and underground leaks may be available to eligible customers who own and occupy their own home.
- Safety net program that provides assistance for a limited period of time for customers faced with financial challenges arising from special circumstances that may not be recognized by standard household income criteria, based on one of the following considerations:
  - Change in employment status (e.g., a reduction in work hours, a loss of employment, or transition to a new job with a lower salary)
  - Change in family status (e.g., divorce)
  - Extraordinary medical expense (e.g., major surgery not covered by medical insurance or that imposes a very high cost for the patient's share of financial responsibility)

Affordability Program Outreach and Monitoring

Many affordability programs have gotten off to slow starts in terms of participation because customers were not aware the programs had been introduced and, in some cases, the perception on the part of customers that it would take a lot of effort to qualify. Ultimately, if and when utilities adopt a low-income assistance program, effectively getting the message out to customers about the program will be critical to its success. This can include posting the utility's customer service phone number on the website and encouraging customers to call for assistance in resolving missed payments, but in some cases might include setting up a much more aggressive communications plan. Bill stuffers and other messaging platforms, such as public meetings, community fairs, and other events, could be elements in those more comprehensive programs.

It is critically important to monitor program implementations and have effective mechanisms to communicate modifications. For example, in Detroit almost 500 of the participants in new payment plans offered following a controversy over shutoffs in 2014 have since kept their accounts current. New affordability program designs with different bill assistance features are being planned as part of efforts to help the City of Portland's retail system gain financial strength.

BUSINESS CASE FOR CREATING AFFORDABILITY PROGRAMS

Programs appropriately designed to address affordability issues could have the potential to help both the targeted customers and the utility. When customers have trouble paying utility bills, the cost to the utility is manifested in increased arrearages, late payments, disconnection notices, and service terminations. To the extent that these are charged to the nonpaying customers, their affordability problems only worsen, and full payment becomes even more problematic. To the extent that these costs cannot be recovered from payment-delinquent customers, they are imposed on the remaining paying customers of the system.

Increased nonpayment and bad debt write-off are also a concern to potential purchasers of a utility's bonds—particularly revenue bonds. As bad debt increases, costs to other ratepayers rise, creating concern about the affordability of water service to all customers. Some of the specific advantages of adopting customer financial assistance programs include

- increasing availability and access to critical (water) resources;
- reducing utility collection costs, arrearages, disconnects, and reconnects, which improves the utility's bottom line;
- increasing levels of financial sufficiency for low-income customers that help ensure their ongoing ability to pay for services; and
- helping to enhance public acceptance of water rates by making them affordable to the lowest-income customers.

Potential disadvantages of customer financial assistance programs include

- requiring a subsidy from other ratepayers or administering donation programs to raise funds;
- creating controversy over water utility participation in social programs;
- inconsistencies with water conservation goals if a discount encourages wasteful use;
- administrative and management costs of implementing and administering affordability programs; and
- possibly contradicting regulations in some states.

FUNDING FOR AFFORDABILITY PROGRAM ASSISTANCE

Sources of Funding

Funding for assistance programs can be a challenge. Some utilities use revenue generated directly from customer rates to fund an affordability program. In cases where state law may prohibit this, utilities may be limited to approaches where the customers can voluntarily use on-bill donation programs to finance the affordability program. In some cases, utility customers can select to make a recurring fixed donation to the affordability program via their bills. In many cases where revenues are used, donation efforts are still employed to supplement the revenue-financed program and fund program features that may be particularly subject to challenge. For example, donations may be used for bill assistance and revenue funding for conservation assistance.

Apart from operating revenues, some utilities have successfully obtained outside grant funding to help support their assistance programs. In cases where cell phone and Internet providers rent use of the water utility's towers or tanks, the rental income has become a discrete source of money that has replenished some assistance programs' budgets. Another potential funding source for affordability programs that is gaining some traction is service line protection programs.

Understanding the Cost Impact

Utilities initiating affordability programs or making enhancements to existing programs should do so with a clear understanding of the costs of the programs, including both the administrative costs and the costs of actual subsidies provided to low-income customers. For example, several utilities that have funded bill discount programs from their overall user charge programs have found that the subsidy payments represent somewhere between 1 and 2 percent of total user charge revenues; the actual cost will depend on the demographic characteristics of the customer base, the degree of subsidy provided, and the level of low-income customer participation, among other factors.

Although it is not possible to predict exact assumptions for these variables, especially for new affordability programs, there are some resources that can be used to help estimate the cost impacts. For example, a recent Water Research Foundation project (no. 4366) produced a "Water Utility Customer Assistance Program Cost Estimation Tool" (WRF 2014). The tool was developed to help utilities assess the costs and benefits of a customer affordability program in their service area. It was designed using the assumption that customers in need can access a fund a certain number of times per year to help them pay utility bills when necessary. The utility can adjust eligibility criteria and the amount of customer assistance per customer in a given year to determine direct program costs. An example of an affordability program for a utility in this tool is as follows:

> If a residential customer annually spends more than *2 percent* of their household income on 4 kgal/month, they are eligible to receive up to *$125* in direct assistance per year assuming that they pay the rest of their bills. Only *50 percent* of eligible customers are expected to participate. (*Items in italics are inputs to the tool.*)

Using information from the US Census Bureau and inputted water and wastewater rates, this interactive tool incorporates information about the eligibility threshold to qualify for an affordability program, annual assistance offered per customer, and percentage of customers responsible for bad debt, among other fields. By adjusting the appropriate fields, the results provide insight into design considerations and program costs.

SUMMARY AND FUTURE DIRECTION

Affordability programs may be more widely needed as the cost of water and wastewater service escalates more than other goods and services, placing additional pressure on low-income customers. Failure to address affordability issues may result in increased utility costs for collections and bad debt. Because water is a necessity, many water utilities have determined that a program to provide essential quantities to customers who cannot afford minimum levels of water service is an appropriate utility function and good customer service.

In developing affordability alternatives, utilities should begin by analyzing costs and rates from a cost-of-service study, to better understand the benefits and costs of the affordability program, and to understand the extent to which providing subsidies to low-income customers represents a deviation from strict cost-causation-based rates and charges. In all cases, the utility will still need to collect its full revenue requirements, so several policy decisions will need to be addressed to appropriately implement the affordability program.

Advances in research related to affordability by AWWA and others and refinements to affordability program options offered by utilities in recent years, as described in this chapter, reflect the increased focus on this topic and its role as an issue of keen interest to utility managers, governing bodies, and customers. Given the anticipated continued importance of addressing affordability considerations to the success of water utilities in fully addressing the needs of their customers and other stakeholders, AWWA intends to continue its proactive role in supporting research, information-sharing on successful program elements, and other efforts to advance industry knowledge and insight on this important topic.

REFERENCES

AWWA. 2012. Lessons Learned From Water Utility Affordability Programs. AWWA Webcast W1213, Oct. 3, 2012. Denver, Colo.: AWWA.

AWWA. 2014. *Thinking Outside the Bill: A Utility Manager's Guide to Assisting Low-Income Water Customers*, 2nd ed. Denver, Colo.: AWWA.

EFAB (Environmental Finance Advisory Board). 2007. *Comments on EPA Document: Combined Sewer Overflows: Guidance for Financial Capability Assessment and Schedule Development.* Washington, D.C.: USEPA EFAB.

Hasson, D.S. 2002. Water Utility Options for Low-Income Assistance Programs. *Journal AWWA*, 94(4):128–138.

Hughes, J., and S. Leurig. 2013. *Assessing Water System Revenue Risk: Considerations for Market Analysts.* Denver, Colo.: Ceres. www.ceres.org/resources/reports/assessing-water-system-revenue-risk-considerations-for-market-analysts/risk-considerations-for-market-analysts/ (accessed Jan. 21, 2015).

Hughes, J., M. Tiger, S. Eskaf, S.I. Berahzer, S. Royster, C. Boyle, D. Batten, P. Brandt, and C. Noyes. 2014. *Defining a Resilient Business Model for Water Utilities.* Denver, Colo.: Water Research Foundation.

Matichich, M. 2012. Tough Times Increase Focus on Affordability Programs. *Public Works* (October):47–52.

NACWA (National Association of Clean Water Agencies). 2002. *Principles for Assessment and Negotiation of Financial Capability: A Compilation of Resources.* White Paper. Washington, D.C.: NACWA.

NACWA (National Association of Clean Water Agencies). 2005. *Financial Capability and Affordability in Wet Weather Negotiations.* White Paper. Washington, D.C.: NACWA.

OWASA (Orange Water and Sewer Authority). 2012. *Financial Management Policy.* Chapel Hill, N.C.: OWASA. http://owasa.org/Data/Sites/1/media/about/financial%20information/financial%20management%20policy%20(01-26-2012).pdf (accessed Jan. 21, 2015).

Rothstein, E. 2012. The Business Case for Low Income Affordability Programs. In *Proceedings of the AWWA-WEF Utility Management Conference, Miami, FL, February 2012.* Denver, Colo.: AWWA.

Safe Drinking Water Act of 1974. Pub. L. 93-522. https://www.gpo.gov/fdsys/pkg/STATUTE-88/pdf/STATUTE-88-Pg1660-2.pdf

Saunders, M.F. 1998. *Water Affordability Programs.* Denver, Colo.: AwwaRF and AWWA.

United Nations. 2010. The human right to water and sanitation. General Assembly Resolution 64/292. http://www.un.org/es/comun/docs/?symbol=A/RES/64/292&lang=E (accessed Jan. 21, 2015).

USCM, AWWA, and WEF (United States Conference of Mayors, American Water Works Association, and Water Environment Federation). 2013a. *Affordability Assessment Tool for Federal Water Mandates.* Washington, D.C.: USCM. https://usmayors.org/urbanwater/media/2013/0529-report-WaterAffordability.pdf (accessed June 27, 2016).

USCM, AWWA, and WEF (United States Conference of Mayors, American Water Works Association, and Water Environment Federation). 2013b. *Assessing the Affordability of Federal Water Mandates: An Issue Brief.* Washington, D.C.: USCM. www.awwa.org/Portals/0/files/legreg/documents/affordability/Affordability-IssueBrief.pdf (accessed Jan. 21, 2015).

USEPA (United States Environmental Protection Agency). 1997. *Combined Sewer Overflows—Guidance for Financial Capability Assessment and Schedule Development.* EPA 832-B-97-004. Washington, D.C.: USEPA.

USEPA (United States Environmental Protection Agency). 2013. Assessing Financial Capability for Municipal Clean Water Act Requirements. Memorandum. Washington, D.C.: USEPA.

USEPA (United States Environmental Protection Agency). 2014. Financial Capability Assessment Framework for Municipal Clean Water Act Requirements. Memorandum. Washington, D.C.: USEPA.

USEPA (United States Environmental Protection Agency). 2016. *Compendium of Drinking Water and Wastewater Customer Assistance Programs.* Washington, D.C.: USEPA. https://www.epa.gov/waterfinancecenter/compendium-drinking-water-and-wastewater-customer-assistance-programs (accessed April 21, 2016).

WRF (Water Research Foundation). 2014. *Water Utility Customer Assistance Program Cost Estimation Tool.* Denver, Colo.: WRF. www.waterrf.org/Pages/Projects.aspx?PID=4366 (accessed Jan. 21, 2015).

This page intentionally blank.

Chapter **V.5**

Negotiated Contract and Economic Development Rates

As discussed in previous chapters, it is generally accepted rate-making practice to design and develop water rates that reflect the cost of providing service to the utility's various classes of customers. From time to time, however, it may become necessary to develop a special rate to meet specific circumstances or needs of an individual customer or group of customers; the previous chapter included such a discussion. In some cases, a utility may enter into a negotiated contract rate tailored to reflect a particular customer's special circumstances and the cost of providing service to that customer. In other situations, the circumstances may include the creation of an economic development rate for a large-volume customer that may have an overall positive economic impact on the utility's service area.

A negotiated contract rate may be appropriate in situations where specific terms and conditions must be clearly defined and agreed on between the parties to help provide terms of service and rates that may reflect the specific and unique circumstances of the customer. It is not unusual to have a negotiated contract with a large industrial or wholesale water customer. The negotiated contract should be designed to protect both parties and provide surety within the relationship. In particular, the negotiated contract will typically detail the specific methodology and considerations that will be used to establish the rates for the contract customer. Negotiated contract rates are generally designed to help ensure that the customer is provided with sufficient service and is paying a cost-based rate for that service.

In contrast to establishing a cost-based negotiated rate, an economic development rate is typically designed to attract new customers who are critical to the community's development and economic welfare by providing a subsidized rate. Economic development rates may also be used to encourage new and expanded uses of water from existing customers. The economic development rate is normally offered to select and targeted customers who provide an overall economic benefit to the community in terms of employment, local tax revenues, and community services.

While these two types of rates are different in terms of their application, they are similar in many other ways and use contracts to specify terms, conditions, and rates.

GENERAL CONSIDERATIONS

A customer-specific negotiated contract represents a deviation from the traditional practice of setting cost-of-service rates for broad classes of similar customers. As such, negotiated contract rates should only be made available to specific customers under special circumstances. For example, such contracts may consider or distinguish between contracts for short-term (emergency) service, special or unique operating circumstances, specific facility requirements, or the desire for long-term surety in the form of a long-term (e.g., 20-year) agreement. The rationale, the various specific terms, and the outcomes vary widely and should be thoroughly considered by the parties. As previously stated, such contracts are typically limited to large industrial or wholesale customers.

To be effective, an economic development water rate should be part of a comprehensive community plan. On its own, an economic development water rate is not likely to provide sufficient benefits to existing or new business and industrial customers to cause them to change their strategic decisions. However, a water utility's economic development rate, when coupled with other economic and financial advantages from the community as a whole, may be significant to the targeted customer. Economic development rates typically imply the utility is willing to sell water to a targeted customer at a rate lower than the cost of providing service to the customer. As such, some level of subsidy must exist. To be successful, the subsidy must be sufficient to entice the targeted customer and, at the same time, result in a net positive economic combined benefit to the community and the utility. If this is not the case, the cost of the subsidy may likely outweigh the community benefit. The reader is directed to the example at the end of this chapter for an illustration of an approach to determining the short-term economic cost of adding a single, significant customer.

Applicability

Negotiated contracts are applicable in situations where the utility and the large industrial customer or wholesale customer mutually desires a short- or long-term agreement for service. The objective of entering into a negotiated contract is to provide assurance of long-term service, while at the same time financially protecting the utility for any investments needed to serve the customer (i.e., stranded investment). The negotiated contract may also delineate the capital infrastructure investments to be made by the customer before service is provided. Often, the magnitude of the dollar investments needed to serve the customer, or the annual revenue impact on the utility, is an important consideration in entering into an agreement.

In the case of economic development rates, at least five criteria should be met before a water utility considers an economic development rate:

1. **A comprehensive economic development plan.** The plan should identify the financial and economic benefits that the community is willing to offer targeted customers. It should also specifically identify a funding mechanism sufficient to fully offset the amount of the subsidy.

2. **A financially sound utility.** The comprehensive economic development plan should address any threats to the financial integrity of the water utility.

3. **A long-term economic gain.** The potential long-term economic gain to the community should be greater than any short-term subsidies provided.

4. **Sound analysis.** A cost-of-service analysis should be performed that will provide policymakers with a sound analysis and basis for their decisions. This allows for the quantification of benefits provided to the targeted group (in terms of the subsidy level of the proposed rate relative to the cost of providing service) and a measurement of the benefit (or lack thereof) to the existing customer base.

5. **A provision regarding unmet performance by the customer.** The economic development rate is predicated on an expected demand for water, additional jobs to be generated in the community, and/or increased local tax revenues. If the justification on which the economic rate is based is not realized, the utility needs to have defined criteria regarding how to address this unmet performance and potentially consider recovering its costs.

Key Factors and Components of Negotiated Contract Rates

Negotiated contract rates can include a variety of different types of charges depending on the circumstances. In developing the structure of the contract rate, the objective should be to design a rate tailored to the circumstances and costs involved (i.e., facility requirements needed to serve the customer and the demand and usage characteristics of the customer). The development of the negotiated contract rate should be based on cost-of-service principles and may require a separate analysis outside of the retail rate analysis to determine an equitable and cost-based rate for the customer. Provisions of the negotiated contract may limit the demand (capacity use) of the customer, and the contract may specify the method for addressing use in excess of the contracted capacity. Additionally, the utility needs to consider incorporating language to protect itself and its customers should the contract customer cease operation prior to full recovery of any up-front or other special costs associated with the contract customer.

Examples of rate components with a negotiated contract rate could include any or all of the following.

- **Customer charge.** The customer charge is typically a fixed amount to recover metering, billing, collection, contract administration, and accounting costs related to serving the customer. In addition, investment and operating costs of any facilities specifically constructed to serve the customer can be directly recovered in the fixed-charge component. This could also include the cost of water rights acquisition, if applicable.

- **Demand charge.** A demand charge can recover capacity costs associated with providing maximum-day and maximum-hour rates of flow to the customer. Costs associated with facilities that are not required to provide service to the customer can be excluded. The demand charge can be administered as a monthly charge based on either contracted or metered maximum-day and/or maximum-hour demands. A monthly minimum charge can also be structured to recover all or a portion of the fixed demand-related costs.

- **Volume or commodity charge.** These charges could be used to recover expenses that vary directly with water use, including such items as purchased water costs, power for pumping, chemicals, sludge disposal, and all other costs not recovered through either the customer charge or the demand charge. If a demand charge is not used to recover capacity costs, such costs can also be recovered through the commodity charge.

Key Factors and Components of Economic Development Rates

The following factors should be considered when formulating an economic development rate.

Targeted customer. Economic development rates are usually thought of as applying to new customers; however, they may also apply to retaining a key customer. The idea is that a community attracts a new customer to their service area with an economic package (including lower water rates) that is beneficial to the targeted customer. In return, the community increases its tax base, employment, community services, taxes, and general welfare. Selecting the targeted customer is a complicated issue that varies from community to community. It is important to consider that if the targeted customer is providing a service or manufacturing a product that is similar to that provided by an existing customer, the community and utility may have put its existing customer at a competitive disadvantage. As a result, the gain of the new customer may be offset by the loss of, or reduced usage of, an existing customer, or the existing customer may be offered a similar rate as the new customer to avoid potential discrimination issues.

A community or a utility may also want to offer an economic development rate to new/expanded uses of water by existing customers. An existing commercial customer may expand their production and require significant increases in water. Careful consideration should be made when contemplating this option. Offering a subsidized rate under these circumstances may result in other businesses making requests for the same assistance. The community or utility should have specific criteria as to when, under what conditions, and the extent of assistance that is offered. The community should be careful to avoid creating an economic development rate that favors one customer over another in the same industry.

Cost basis of existing water rates. To properly gauge the true effects of an economic development rate, it is important that the utility's existing rates meet its financial needs. If a utility is not currently self-sufficient and is receiving transfers from the general fund, water rates are already set below full cost. Any discount of water utility rates for purposes of economic development must be considered in the context of meeting the utility's full revenue requirements, along with the community's comprehensive economic development plan.

Supply and capacity considerations. Excess source of supply and treatment capacity mean potential short-run economies of scale. If excess capacity is available, the marginal cost of adding a new customer is equal to the variable costs of water production. This additional capacity utilization minimizes the impact to existing customers and may allow the utility to serve the new customer with little or no impact to existing customers' rates. If the system requires additional capacity to serve targeted customers, additional fixed investments must be made, and the utility needs to consider the impact to existing rates and customers from the additional costs of new capacity. At the same time, assuming that any capacity addition would be in excess of that needed by the targeted customer, the utility needs to determine who will bear the burden of financing the new reserve capacity. Investing in expanded capital facilities to serve an economic development customer should be carefully considered and analyzed.

Duration. The economic development rate should have a specific duration and not be considered a permanent rate for the customer. The economic development rate should generally not be subject to extension or renewal in the absence of additional benefits to the community. The utility should either have a specific policy regarding the term of the benefit or conduct an annual review of the effectiveness and impact of the rate. In addition, it should have a structured phase-out plan. Utility managers should be aware that once an economic development rate is established and available to new customers, it may be difficult to rescind as a result of local political or policy constraints.

Performance criteria. The economic development rate may by tied to specific milestones. It may be indexed to the number of new jobs and/or volume of water consumed. If a specified performance criterion is not met, the economic development benefit in the rate could be adjusted or eliminated. An alternative is to include within the economic development rate a "take or pay" provision. This protects the utility if the water demand projected by the new customer is not met, yet it does not necessarily ensure the creation of new jobs. If infrastructure was constructed to meet the specific demand of the new entity, any agreement regarding the economic development rate should include language addressing the repayment of the investment by the utility in the event that the business ceases operation prior to the utility recovering its full cost of acquisition and installation.

Effects of the subsidy. The concept of average cost rate setting assumes that increases or decreases in the cost of providing a utility's services are shared proportionally by all customers causing the change in costs. Thus, economies or diseconomies of scale generated by the addition of new customers are shared by all existing and new customers. In the case of economic development rates, the targeted customers may benefit at the expense of existing customers. If the utility is able to set the economic development rate at a level equal to the short-run marginal cost (i.e., variable costs), assuming this is less than the average cost, existing customers should not require an adjustment to their rates for the utility to recover all of its costs. However, in this case, existing customers would not receive a direct benefit from the economic development customer because the customer is essentially covering only variable costs and not significantly contributing to the fixed costs of the utility. It is the lack of a benefit to the existing customers that is the subsidy; the subsidy is the difference between the existing rate and what the existing customers would pay if the economies of scale were shared by all customers.

Similarly, if the economic development rate is set above the short-run marginal cost (i.e., covers variable and some fixed costs), existing customers receive some financial/rate benefit from the addition of the new customer. This is because the new customer covers the variable costs incurred for service, plus sharing in the system's fixed costs. While this arrangement is clearly more beneficial to existing customers, a subsidy still exists that is equal to the portion of the fixed costs not covered by the new customer.

Finally, if the economic development rate is set below the short-run marginal cost, the new customer is not even covering the additional variable costs that it creates, and the existing customers must pay for all of the system's fixed costs, plus a portion of the new customer's variable costs. In this case, existing customers are actually financially harmed by adding a new customer.

Burden of the subsidy. Any subsidy required could be met by allocating additional costs to existing water customers, utility stockholders (for private utilities), or local tax revenues (for municipal utilities).

Revenue stability. The utility should determine any potential effects on revenue stability to ensure full recognition of the impact of the economic development rate, including changes in use by the targeted customer or the customers providing the subsidy.

HISTORICAL PERSPECTIVES

Negotiated contracts are a well-accepted standard practice within the water utility industry, and contracts have been negotiated between utilities for wholesale service for many years. The practice of negotiating contracts with large retail or industrial customers, while less common, has gained increasing importance, particularly when a large retail customer uses a significant amount of capacity in a utility system or the utility has made significant investments to serve the customer. With the increasing cost of water supply, large-volume customers are now focusing on ways to reduce their overall consumption and water costs. In addition, from the customer's perspective, as the cost of purchasing water from the utility increases, the economic feasibility of developing alternative supplies, exploring conservation measures, or otherwise bypassing the utility increases.

Economic development rates are not common in the water industry. Electric utilities, however, have historically offered economic development rates for service in order to retain existing loads or to attract new industry loads. These rates are generally referred to as *incentive rates, load retention rates, revitalization rates,* or *economic development rates.* These types of rates have historically been approved by many public service commissions. Economic development rates for water utilities may not be commonly used because fewer opportunities exist to attract large water customers that can provide a positive economic and job benefit to a community.

The method of subsidy allocation varies greatly among the various states. Because private companies are involved, local tax revenues or other local funding sources are not usually available, and the subsidy is allocated to other ratepayers or to utility stockholders.

ADVANTAGES AND DISADVANTAGES

This section examines some advantages and disadvantages of negotiated contract and economic development rates.

Simplicity

Both a negotiated contract rate and an economic development rate are fairly complex to create. Foremost, developing the cost basis for the rates and understanding the potential implications of the rate are important. Both types of rates will likely require negotiations with outside parties, which require more time and effort than other retail rates. In addition, administration of these rates may be more complex and require annual "true-ups" or other adjustments.

Equity

Negotiated contracts can promote equity as long as the negotiated rates are based on the cost of providing service to the customer involved. In developing negotiated rates, rates should recover the costs of any facilities used solely to serve the customer, recover the variable costs of treating and supplying water, and contribute toward the fixed costs of the water system. When the water utility purchases water from another utility, the unit cost of that water should be considered in setting the negotiated rate to the extent that the utility would avoid purchasing at least some of that water if it no longer served the negotiated-rate customer.

In contrast to a negotiated rate, an economic development rate provides a subsidy to the targeted customers. However, from a community-wide perspective, if the water utility subsidy strengthens the economic base of the community, the water utility inequities may be outweighed by the community-wide benefits.

Revenue Stability

A negotiated contract rate can help maintain the financial condition of a utility by retaining a revenue stream that provides continued fixed-cost recovery that might otherwise be lost.

With an economic development rate, a water utility can remain financially sufficient, and, in fact, may improve its financial position. The utility may generate additional revenue from a targeted customer that exceeds the incremental cost of providing service to that customer, thus improving overall financial sufficiency. Alternatively, where a revenue shortfall exists, the amount of shortfall must be offset by

- increases in the rates to all nonsubsidized users,
- additional funding from utility stockholders (for private companies),
- local tax revenue supplements, and
- revenue from other sources.

The utility needs to have sufficient financial resources so that it can still offer the subsidy during low-demand periods such as wet weather or drought restrictions.

Conservation

For both a negotiated contract rate and an economic development rate, water conservation is not normally a consideration in determining the appropriateness or level of the particular rate. However, in the event that conservation is an important issue for the utility, the agreement for service and the associated rate structure may specifically address the issue of conservation and efficient use. Conservation and efficient use of the water are often best addressed within the terms and conditions of the negotiated rate.

Effect on Customers

The financial effect of a negotiated contract on other customers depends on existing rates and their relation to cost. To the extent that negotiated contract rates reflect the costs of providing service, the effect on other customers is determined by the relationship between existing rates and the costs allocated to them. If the contract is with a new customer or provides additional service to an existing customer, the agreement may allow the utility to spread its fixed costs over a wider base than might be possible in the absence of the contract.

By definition, an economic development rate obviously benefits the customer who receives the subsidy but may increase the water bills of other customers. Not all existing customers enjoy the benefit of the economies of scale from adding a new customer to the system. Some existing customers will benefit from the direct and indirect employment that is generated from a successful economic development rate. The degree of the effect on an individual depends on the size of subsidy provided, size of the remaining customer base, available system capacity, system efficiency, cost levels of existing rates, and several other variables. If properly structured, the impact of an economic development water rate on customers should be measured as a component of the community's comprehensive economic development plan.

Implementation

The use of a negotiated contract between two entities to accomplish a specific project or provide a specific service is a common business practice. Careful consideration should be given when establishing the circumstances under which the utility would enter into a negotiated contract. It is vital to establish a clear and unambiguous rationale for a negotiated contract lest the utility be accused of favoring one industry over another in the same or similar type of industry and thereby placing one customer at a competitive disadvantage. A water service contract between a water utility and a large-volume customer should specify the obligations of each party, the service standards to be met, the basis for initially establishing rates and making subsequent changes to those rates, the process for resolving disputes, and the terms of the agreement. Additional provisions in the contract should potentially address any debt that was issued for the benefit of the customer and conditions under which that debt must be repaid to the utility. Establishing a contractual arrangement can be a complex process, both technically and legally. Typically, a cost-of-service study is needed, and the specific contract terms must be established. Negotiations take time and effort, and outside technical assistance may be required by both parties.

Implementation of an economic development rate could create public acceptance problems. Some customers may not understand or agree with the need to provide a subsidy to one particular customer. In economically depressed areas trying to attract new customers, this concern may be particularly acute. On the other hand, in communities where the development rate is important for the economic well-being of the area, such as where there is a single major employer, it is not uncommon for local residents to favor advantageous rates or other concessions to that employer. Long-term benefits of economic development rates and any other justifications for their application should be stressed in all cases and justified as appropriate for the local circumstances. Once the form and level of the rate have been decided, actual implementation should present less difficulty.

Operational Issues

Utility managers are generally well advised to develop a complete understanding of the operating and technical issues associated with the provision of service to any large-volume customer and a customer being considered for a negotiated contract or economic development rate. Suggested components of the analysis should include demand, peak demand, impact on overall water system capacity, water storage impact, and customer time-of-day demand and its implication on the utility's demand charge from the electrical provider.

In some instances, a particular level of water quality is required by the customer. The additional cost of infrastructure and the method in which it will be acquired (cash on hand, bonds, etc.) should be reviewed. A contingency plan should be developed by the utility should the customer unexpectedly cease operations. The contingency plan would identify the potential consequences to the financial and operational well-being of the utility. Part of this analysis will include the potential uses of the idled equipment and capacity (stranded investment).

NEGOTIATED CONTRACT RATE EXAMPLE

As an example, an industrial customer is seeking to negotiate a special contract rate with the local water utility. The customer is the utility's largest, using approximately 2 mgd (62.5 Mg/month). Under the utility's existing general service rates, the customer would pay $132,770.05 per month (including the monthly service charge plus the volume charge) or $1,593,240.60 per year (see Table V.5-1). The utility is willing to offer a negotiated contract rate because the following conditions exist: the utility has adequate capacity to meet its customer's needs and does not need to undertake any significant expansion in the near future, the customer has a viable supply alternative, and the customer has favorable load characteristics with a maximum-day demand ratio of 1.25 times average day, and on-site storage facilities ensure no discernible peak-hour demand.

To develop a rate for the customer, the utility uses the unit base cost of water ($1.7885 per thousand gallons) and the maximum-day extra-capacity unit costs ($213.7455 per thousand gallons per day) developed in its recent cost-of-service study. Based on these unit costs and the customer's ratio of maximum-day to average-day usage of 1.25, a contract rate of $1.93 per thousand gallons is established for the customer. In addition, the customer also continues to pay the $154.95 per month service charge that recovers customer-related

Table V.5-1 Example of contract rate determination

General Service Water Rate Item	Monthly Usage, 1,000 gal	Rate, $/1,000 gal	Total Monthly Cost, $
Customer Charge	One 6-in. meter	$154.95/month	$154.95
Monthly Rate Block, 1,000 gal/month			
First 15	15	$2.94	$44.10
Next 1,485	1,485	2.60	3,861.00
Over 1,500	61,000	2.11	128,710.00
Total	62,500		$132,615.10
Annual Cost—Retail Rate			$1,593,240.60
Monthly Contract Rate			
Type of Charge	Monthly Usage, 1,000 gal	Rate, $/1,000 gal	Total Monthly Cost, $
Customer Charge	One 6-in. meter	$154.95/month	$154.95
Commodity Charge, 1,000 gal	62,500	$1.93	120,625.00
Total			$120,779.95
Annual Cost—Negotiated Rate			$1,449,359.40

costs. Under the negotiated contract rate, the customer pays $120,779.95 per month, or $1,449,359.40 per year.

In this example, the utility may benefit from a long-term agreement for service with this particular industrial customer. At the same time, the customer benefits from a negotiated contract that provides surety of service, the development of a specific rate based on their unique service characteristics, and a more favorable rate than the existing retail rate.

ECONOMIC DEVELOPMENT RATE EXAMPLE

In this example, a community has developed an economic development plan and the community has decided to try to attract a large manufacturer that is evaluating where to locate its new production plant. The community's water system has ample water supply and treatment capacity to serve the new plant, and the community has developed a conceptual benefit package for the manufacturer to attract it to their community.

The community is evaluating how much of a water rate discount (subsidy) it can provide to the manufacturer. The annual revenue requirements of the water utility are $10.624 million as shown in Table V.5-2, based on Table II.1-2 of this manual. The utility has determined that in the short term these costs are primarily fixed, with the exception of some of the operation and maintenance expenses. In this example, short-term variable expenses include source-of-supply costs, power costs, and chemicals. The utility's cost-of-service analysis has allocated the portions of these costs that vary directly with water use to the commodity cost component and the remainder, such as the demand portion of power costs, to the demand cost component. A summary of this allocation is displayed in Table V.5-3, based on Table III.1-6 of this manual.

The utility's annual metered use without the new customer is 2,766,000 thousand gallons. As a result, the variable expense unit commodity cost is $0.4283 ($1,184,670 ÷ 2,766,000 thousand gallons). The manufacturer is estimated to use 50 million gallons per year resulting in an increased system-wide cost of providing water service of $21,415 ($0.4283 × 50,000 thousand gallons—Table V.5-4). In Table V.5-4, the average unit cost (rate) impact of the addition of the new industrial customer is shown.

Table V.5-2 Annual revenue requirements (in $1,000)

Line No.	Item	Cost
1	Operation and Maintenance Expenses	$6,837
2	Debt Service	2,580
3	Debt-Service Reserve	180
4	Capital Improvements	1,141
5	Other Operating Revenues	(78)
6	Nonoperating Revenues	(159)
7	Net Income From Operations	123
8	Total Revenue Requirements From Rates	$10,624

Table V.5-3 Short-term variable operation and maintenance expenses (in $1,000)

Line No.	Item	Total	Commodity	Maximum-Day Demand
1	Source of Supply	$270,000	$270,000	$0
2	Purchased Power	777,000	551,670	225,330
3	Chemicals	363,000	363,000	0
4	Total Variable Expenses	$1,410,000	$1,184,670	$225,330

Table V.5-4 Impact of the addition of a new industrial customer

Line No.	Item	Costs	1,000 gallons	$/1,000 gallons
1	Existing Customers	$7,652,790	2,766,000	$2.7667
2	New Customer	21,415	50,000	0.4283
3	Revised Total/Blended $/1,000 gallons	$7,674,204	2,816,000	$2.7252

The overall consumption-related cost of providing service to all of the utility's existing customers is currently $7,652,790, based on the summation of the total commodity ($1,586,207) and demand ($4,281,075 + $1,785,508) costs displayed in Table III.1-7 (line 6 under the Commodity-Demand Method). The current overall average cost per thousand gallons for the existing customers is therefore $2.7667 (Table V.5-4, line 1). If the cost and sales to the new manufacturer were blended with the cost and sales to existing customers, there would be an economy-of-scale benefit to all customers, resulting in a reduction of the average cost per thousand gallons from $2.7667 to $2.7252 (see Table V.5-4).

If average pricing methods are used, existing customers would save $114,846 (2,766,000 thousand gallons × [$2.7667 − $2.7252]). If rates to existing customers are not adjusted, $114,846 will be generated that can be used to subsidize the new manufacturer. The cost borne by the manufacturer would then be equal to its demand (50,000 thousand gallons) multiplied by the new system average cost per thousand gallons ($2.7252) less the subsidy ($114,846), or $21,415 ($0.4283 per thousand gallons), which approximates, with allowance for rounding, the short-run marginal cost of providing service to the new customer.

After determining the relative boundaries between the short-run marginal cost ($0.4283) of extending service to the new manufacturer and the average cost per thousand gallons ($2.7252) of serving new and existing customers, the community is in a good position to make a policy decision about how much of a subsidy to provide to the new manufacturer. The utility could extend service to the new manufacturer at a rate of

$0.4283 per thousand gallons without adversely affecting existing customers. If the new manufacturer pays more than $0.4283 per thousand gallons, some of the economies of scale will be shared with the existing customers. If the new manufacturer pays less than $0.4283, the existing customers will be required to pay an additional amount to maintain revenue neutrality.

SUMMARY

Negotiated contract rates and economic development rates are specialized and unique rates that may be developed and offered to certain large-volume or targeted customers. When used appropriately, both types of rates can provide a benefit to the utility and the customer. In most cases, these benefits center on the surety of supply and revenue, consistent terms of service, and the development of cost-based rates to the customer.

This page intentionally blank.

Chapter **V.6**

Indexed Rates

Some utilities' annual rate adjustments are primarily driven by the need to simply keep pace with the rate of inflation. Rate indexing provides an alternative to a comprehensive rate study proceeding such as a rate case for an investor-owned utility, if allowed. Indexing enables periodic adjustments to rates based on changes in a generally accepted cost or price index, such as the gross domestic product–implicit price deflator (GDP-IPD) or consumer price index (CPI). Rate indexing can help ensure that rates keep pace with overall inflation with less expense and oversight board review. Indexed rates do not ensure that rates will be adequate when costs escalate at a pace greater than inflation or when additional investments are needed to maintain or upgrade the water utility system. In recent years, the cost of water service has increased at a faster rate than the general GDP-IPD or CPI.

GENERAL CONSIDERATIONS

Rate indexing allows for regular and relatively simple rate adjustments based on overall fluctuations in costs or prices. During inflationary periods, unadjusted rates might fail to produce revenues that meet the utility's revenue requirements. The GDP-IPD or CPI has been used to calibrate rate changes based on one measure of the rate of national price inflation. Thus, a percentage increase in consumer prices can be translated into a comparable percentage change in utility rates.

Some of the state public utility commissions that regulate water utilities have used indexing as a method of greatly simplifying the rate-making process, particularly for smaller water utilities. The indexed rate adjustment substitutes for a lengthier and sometimes cumbersome regulatory review of costs and rates. Indexing is a less costly way to adjust rates, both for utilities and regulatory agencies. A generic order can be issued periodically (usually annually) to specify the allowable rate increase. Utilities typically must file appropriate forms with regulators and notify customers of the change in rates. Rate indexing can also be combined with other automatic cost-adjustment mechanisms sometimes used for such items as purchased water, energy, and taxes.

In the regulatory context, rate indexing can also be used with alternative rate-making methods (such as efficiency-oriented incentive regulation or price caps), which impose less regulatory oversight and allow greater pricing flexibility on the part of utilities.

Price indexing might be considered for smaller utilities that need to make more frequent rate adjustments to keep pace with inflation, and, for utilities of various sizes, indexing can also help bridge the years between comprehensive cost-of-service studies.

Indexing of rates is also used by nonregulated or public utilities to maintain rates that reflect changing costs. However, it is important to understand that indexing is a short-term approach to adjusting rates on an interim basis between comprehensive rate studies.

ADVANTAGES AND DISADVANTAGES

The following paragraphs summarize the advantages and disadvantages of rate indexing in terms of simplicity, equity, revenue stability, conservation, and implementation.

Simplicity

Simplicity is a key advantage of rate indexing. The simplicity of rate adjustments tied to inflation also tends to enhance customer understanding and acceptance. Simplicity of the indexing may vary based on the measure of GDP-IPD or CPI used to index the rates.

Equity

The equity of rate indexing depends on the equity of the initial rate structure, as differentials among customer and service classifications are maintained. Inequities built into initial rates are not remedied through simple indexing and may increase with a simple "across-the-board" change. Also, emergent cost-of-service differentials among classes of service are not recognized if indexed changes are uniformly applied. For example, if a cost increase is related to the need for capacity for peak demand, price increases that do not allocate costs proportionately to peak users might be considered inequitable.

Revenue Stability

Rate indexing ensures that revenues grow at the rate of inflation indicated by the selected index, neither more nor less. If costs rise below the inflation rate, revenues might be in excess of the cost of service; if costs rise at a rate above the inflation rate, revenues might be insufficient to cover the cost of service. Care should be taken to select an index that reflects changes in water utility costs.

Rate indexing is particularly problematic if historical underpricing has occurred or if significant cost increases are experienced, because revenue shortfalls will be maintained or will potentially be increased over time. Rate indexing is also insufficient to ensure adequate investment in utility infrastructure. Finally, rate indexing provides no incentive to control costs beyond what is needed to keep cost increases in line with inflation.

Conservation

Rate indexing can have mixed implications for conservation. Maintaining real water prices (i.e., inflation-adjusted prices) at a constant level means that price changes will not induce water usage changes. Price increases below the rate of inflation may actually encourage use; price increases exceeding the rate of inflation can discourage usage. If costs are increasing at a rate greater than inflation, simple indexed rates might not send an efficient, conservation-oriented price signal.

Table V.6-1 Simple rate indexing based on inflation

Year	Rate of Inflation, %	Price Increase, $/1,000 gal	Price, $/1,000 gal
Base year	2.50		
First-year adjustment	3.0	0.0750	2.57
Second-year adjustment	5.0	0.1288	2.70
Third-year adjustment	4.0	0.1082	2.81

Implementation

Changes in rates tied to the GDP-IPD or CPI can be implemented relatively easily and at a lower cost than full rate reviews. Rate-setting bodies must specify the approved indexing method and rate, and the procedures by which they are used. While indexing is a very simple method of adjusting rates, it is important to note that customers may need to be formally notified of the indexed rate change.

The ease of rate indexing might be attractive to utilities and rate regulators, but indexing should not be used to avoid an appropriate review of costs and cost allocation, particularly during periods of growing costs and changing cost profiles. Indexing could unduly postpone investments and accompanying rate adjustments needed to maintain adequate service.

EXAMPLE

A simple example of rate indexing based on the rate of inflation is provided in Table V.6-1. The price charged in the base year is simply adjusted upward by the inflation rate (as expressed in a percentage).

SUMMARY

Price (rate) indexing through the use of an inflation adjustment might be useful for reducing the cost of regulation and maintaining the revenues of water systems, but it does not ensure that additional investments in maintenance or improvement will be made. The ease of implementing an indexing rate runs the risk of postponing needed cost and rate reviews. Thus, inflation adjustments should be used with caution.

This page intentionally blank.

Chapter **V.7**

Price Elasticity

Price elasticity measures the responsiveness of use to price changes. More precisely, price elasticity of water demand measures the sensitivity of water use relative to changes in the price of water, after controlling for the influence of other factors that can also alter water demand, such as income and weather. Estimating price elasticity is an important component of water revenue forecasting and rate design. If a rate change is anticipated, the water utility should consider its effect on usage and revenues. Moreover, with the increasing popularity of conservation pricing, the principle of price elasticity is viewed as a means to modify consumer behavior to reduce water usage through conservation pricing rate structures. That is, conservation pricing relies on consumers responding to price signals and changing their consumptive behavior.

Mathematically, price elasticity is the ratio of the percentage change in use to the percentage change in price. More specifically, price elasticity, e_p, is calculated as

$$e_p = \frac{\dfrac{\text{Change in Usage}}{\text{Original Usage Level}}}{\dfrac{\text{Change in Price}}{\text{Original Price Level}}}$$

Because there is an inverse relationship between price and use, price elasticity coefficients have negative values. Given a price elasticity of –0.30, for example, a 10 percent increase in water rates would be expected to produce a 3 percent reduction in water use. When demand for a good is relatively responsive to price changes, demand is described as price-elastic; in these cases, price elasticity coefficients have absolute values exceeding 1.0 (e.g., –1.2). In contrast, when demand is relatively unresponsive to price changes, demand is described as price-inelastic; price elasticity coefficients have absolute values less than 1.0 (e.g., –0.2). Potable water is often used as an example of a good with inelastic demand.

There is also a link between price elasticity and the change in revenues resulting from a change in price. This connection is referred to as the price elasticity of revenue and described by this simple formula:

$$e_{rev} = 1 + e_p$$

where e_{rev} is the price elasticity of revenue. Hence, if one assumes a price elasticity of demand of -0.3 and a 10 percent increase in water rates, it would be reasonable to project a 7 percent increase in revenue along with the 3 percent drop on water use, all other things being equal.

GENERAL CONSIDERATIONS

Price elasticity is not always considered or used in determining the overall adjustment in rate levels needed to recover the utility's revenue requirements. In these instances, water demand is basically viewed as perfectly price-inelastic in the rates process (i.e., having price elasticity coefficients equaling zero), or in regulated environments price elasticity estimates may not be considered to be "fixed, known, and measurable"; thus, the potential for price-induced use changes are ignored. Price elasticity may be ignored when rate adjustments are relatively small and may not be all that noticeable to most ratepayers. However, because future rate changes can be more significant and the aggregate effects of small changes can compound over time, demand forecasts should account for price effects on use as an essential element in developing accurate revenue forecasts.

Price elasticity is an important tool for estimating the effect of a rate change on water use and utility revenues. The omission of price elasticity from rate analysis creates the potential for revenue shortfalls. Shortfalls can be large and unexpected for the utility if the rate structure is substantially modified to generate consumer responses (e.g., shifting from a decreasing block to an increasing block rate structure to encourage conservation) or if a large rate increase is implemented. To mitigate the potential for significant price elasticity in such instances, a consideration in shifting from such differing rate structures would be to initially move to a uniform rate over perhaps a two- to three-year period, gradually reducing the rate block differentials, and then moving to the ultimate increasing block rate structure differentials over another two- or three-year period of gradually increasing the block rate differentials. In some cases, rates may not be a major influence on water use for a variety of reasons. The price effect on usage can be small if there is little change in real water prices over time (real prices being actual prices adjusted for inflation). In addition, effects of rate changes can be dominated by the effects of other demand parameters, including temperature, rainfall, household income, and local, regional, and national economic conditions. In other words, the response of actual use to rate changes can be relatively small when compared to the use responses due to climatic, demographic, and water cultural factors.

Measuring the responsiveness of use to rate changes is further complicated by the timing or lags in consumer responses. Residential consumers may not immediately react to rate increases, or if the increases are widely publicized and controversial, they may overreact. In contrast, industrial users may immediately implement a variety of water cost reduction strategies. Finally, the conservation ethic among consumers in a specific locality can either enhance or impede use responses. The existence of a strong conservation ethic and customer education programs can produce substantial use reductions even with modest rate increases; the absence of a conservation ethic may result in only minimal changes in use.

HISTORICAL PERSPECTIVES

Numerous studies of the effects of price on water demand have been completed during the past four decades. Most of these studies focus on either municipal demand or residential demand; only a few examine commercial and industrial demand. These studies provide a general consensus or conclusions regarding the price elasticity of water service:

- When customer water demand can be divided into indoor-water and outdoor-water use, outdoor water demand is more price-elastic than indoor water usage.

- When seasonal peak demands are driven by peak levels of seasonal outdoor water use, the price elasticity of seasonal peak demand is higher than during periods when indoor water usage predominates (e.g., winter months in some climatic zones).

- In many North American climate zones, the price elasticity of single-family residential demand is highest in summer months, when outdoor water use is a larger proportion of the total residential water use.

- Price elasticity appears to vary proportionally with overall rate levels (i.e., there is more use responsiveness at higher rate levels than at lower rate levels).

- Governmental customer demand is often relatively price-inelastic.

Each user class responds differently to rate increases. A review of elasticity studies indicates that the most likely price elasticity range for long-term overall (outdoor and indoor) residential demand is –0.10 to –0.30, with price elasticity coefficients for long-term industrial and commercial demand potentially ranging up to –0.80. In other words, commercial and industrial water use may be more responsive to changes in price than residential use. A review of the water demand literature indicates that price elasticity of overall system demand can be difficult to interpret unless the weights of the individual demand sectors can be specified. In this context, price elasticity coefficients are comparable only for well-defined user classes.

Although relying on a literature review to estimate the price elasticity of water service for a specific locality is an imperfect approach, such a review can provide benchmarks or guidelines to establish reasonable price elasticity estimates. Given the general nature of municipal and residential water demand, comparing demand studies for similar service areas can be appropriate for benchmarking purposes.

Additional study results contributing to the use of price elasticity in the rate determination process are summarized as follows:

- Wastewater charges affect the price-elasticity results for water. When water and wastewater volume-related rates tend to increase at the same times, omitting the increase in the wastewater usage rates from the statistical analysis tends to understate the price elasticity of demand of overall water use, particularly when both water and wastewater charges are shown in the same bill.

- Consumers may react to average rates, which are a blending of service- and volume-related charges, and to total bills more than they do to the rate of the final block(s) of use—especially when the water bills do not highlight the marginal price or when the marginal price is quite low.

- Rate structure changes affect water use as well as price elasticities. There may be a tendency for elasticities to become larger in absolute value as rates change from declining block to uniform rates to increasing block rates.

- Each user class responds differently to rate changes. Price elasticities vary substantially across customer classes.

- The components of residential demand have different sensitivities to rate changes. Outdoor use is more sensitive to rate changes than is indoor or domestic use, both in the short term and long term.

- Water demand varies between peak and off-peak periods. Peak usage is more price sensitive than off-peak usage, because users can often shift use to the lower price period.

- Geography affects usage responses to rate changes (e.g., usage sensitivity to rate changes in the Midwest of North America tends to be less than in the Southwest of the United States, possibly due, in part, to the relative scarcity of water in the Southwest).

- Consumer education programs affect price elasticities.

- A key factor is the change in real water prices. Use is more affected by increases in real (adjusted for effects of inflation) water rates than by increases in nominal water rates (not inflation adjusted).

- Users that do not pay the water bill directly (do not see the actual water bill), such as apartment dwellers, are typically not responsive to price changes at all.

EXAMPLES

To illustrate the importance of price elasticity in rate design, two hypothetical examples are provided. The examples are based on a water utility that has replaced its two-tier declining block rate structure with a uniform volume charge rate. The example water utility has residential customers and one large industrial user.

The Residential Case

For residential customers, it is assumed that the shift from a decreasing block rate structure to a uniform rate structure involves a 30 percent overall increase in rates. Under the decreasing block rate structure, it is assumed that the residential class is generating $600,000 of annual revenues for the water utility. A demand analysis for the water utility indicates that the long-run price elasticity for the residential class is approximately −0.20. The projected result of adopting the uniform rate is a reduction in residential use of 6 percent.

Given that the residential class formerly provided $600,000 of annual revenues, the water utility cannot presume that residential revenues will increase to $780,000, as a result of a 30 percent increase. With a price elasticity factor of −0.20, residential revenues will be greater than $600,000 but will fall short of $780,000. The best forecast of revenue is an increase of 24 percent giving $744,000, because the price elasticity of revenue is 1+ the price elasticity of demand (1+ −0.2 = +0.8). If the price elasticity effect on residential usage is not incorporated in the rate-setting process, it will result in a revenue shortfall for the water utility.

The Large Industrial User Case

For the large user, it is assumed that the shift from a decreasing block tariff to a uniform rate results in a 60 percent increase in rates to this customer. Under the declining block rate structure, it is assumed that the large user generates $400,000 of annual revenues for the water utility. Assume further that the utility's research into price elasticity of similar firms in that industry, combined with discussions or local knowledge of the customer, suggest the price elasticity for the large user may be as great as −0.50.

The result of adopting the uniform rate is a use reduction of 30 percent for the large-volume customer. Given that the large-volume customer formerly provided $400,000 of annual revenues, again the water utility cannot presume that revenues from this large user will increase to $640,000, a 60 percent increase. However, the most likely revenue increase will be 30 percent, because with a price-elasticity demand of –0.5, the revenue elasticity will be +0.5. Thus revenue can be expected to increase to only $520,000. If the price elasticity effect on the use of the large user is not incorporated in the rate-setting process, it will result in a substantial revenue shortfall for the water utility.

SUMMARY

The consequences of omitting price elasticity from the rate-design process are becoming increasingly important. Evidence suggests that the price sensitivity of water use increases with the escalation in real water rates. It is difficult to provide practical benchmarks for assessing how much effort should be expended on developing price elasticity estimates for a given service area. Where it is not cost-effective for water utilities to conduct demand studies, results of existing research can be used to develop benchmarks for estimating the potential usage effects of rate changes.

This page intentionally blank.

Chapter **V.8**

Marginal Cost Pricing

Since the early 1900s, many economists have advocated marginal cost pricing of goods and services as a means of achieving optimal resource allocation and economic efficiency. These recommendations suggest that consumers and producers alike will benefit from this pricing approach and that resources in the economy will be used optimally in terms of efficiency.

As potentially available new water supplies are increasingly limited by population growth, environmental constraints, regulatory issues, and aging infrastructure, the possible use of marginal cost pricing has increased in visibility and has become a matter of debate. Also, marginal cost pricing is sometimes looked on favorably as part of a conservation pricing effort. Accordingly, utilities and customers could benefit from a more complete understanding of the issues related to this pricing approach before making decisions on possible rate structure changes.

GENERAL CONSIDERATIONS

Theoretically, *marginal cost pricing* means that the price for a product or service equals the cost of producing the next unit of supply. In a common version of marginal cost pricing, all units of the product or service are charged at a rate equal to the cost of producing the last unit of production. By definition, marginal cost pricing involves considering the cost of very small changes in supply "at the margin." For a water utility, marginal cost is the cost of producing the next unit of water.

Since at least the 1970s, advocates for marginal cost pricing have recommended that this pricing method be extended to the provision of water service. Others have supported this pricing methodology on the basis of its potential conservation incentives. To date, marginal cost pricing has not been widely implemented in actual water pricing practices.

Marginal cost pricing may provide benefits of better and more effective use of water resources. It may also change the way in which consumers and ratepayers think of water relative to other goods and services they use. On the other hand, marginal cost pricing can be more difficult to effectively implement than more traditional approaches, may present legal concerns, and may sometimes yield unanticipated adverse outcomes (see Figure V.8-1).

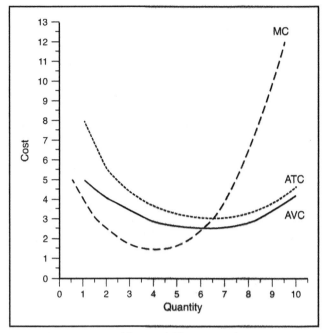

ATC = average total costs; AVC = average variable costs; MC = marginal costs

Figure V-8.1 Typical average and marginal cost curves

PRACTICAL CONSIDERATIONS

According to classical economic theory, marginal cost pricing is the best way to maximize the efficiency of water utilities. This approach encourages the consumer to make decisions on water use by analyzing the trade-offs between water use and both current and future prices. That is, when the price of water increases, it serves as a price signal to the consumer to reduce demand for water and, presumably, use the foregone expenditure in alternative economic uses that would optimize the consumer's total well-being. There are several methods to consider for determining or approximating marginal cost, and there is not a standard method of marginal cost pricing used in the water industry.

Definitions

There are several ways to define marginal costs. Four approaches are described in the following list:

1. **Classical or textbook marginal cost theory.** *Marginal cost* is defined as the total cost of providing the next unit of supply. In strict terms, this could mean calculating the total operating and capital cost of providing the next unit of supply. In the case of water supply, the next unit of supply could be 100 cubic feet or 1,000 gallons if one of those happened to be the smallest unit of metered measurement of water for that utility. This definition is the one that is closest to what is typically used in the theoretical justification for marginal cost pricing.

2. **Average increment cost approach.** The average increment cost is calculated by totaling all incremental costs (capital and operating) that will be incurred in the future to provide for estimated additional demand over a specific period, and dividing that by the incremental output over the period.

3. **Avoided cost approach.** With the avoided cost approach, the utility determines the savings of avoiding capital and operation and maintenance (O&M) costs associated with not providing one more unit of capacity, usually represented by a one-year delay in supply expansion. The marginal capital cost estimate plus the marginal operating costs associated with the new facility equals the estimated total marginal cost of the new capacity. The denominator is typically the change in demand.

4. **Long run incremental cost approach.** *Long run incremental cost* is defined as the charge equal to the cost per unit of the next capacity increment. This definition is the one most used by water utilities that have adopted some variation of marginal cost pricing.

Rate Structure

Although there are several alternatives that might fall under the banner of marginal cost pricing, three types of marginal cost pricing are most often evaluated and/or used for implementation:

1. Uniform volume rate at marginal cost
2. Increasing block rate structure with last block at marginal cost
3. Increasing block rates for which the average of all purchases equals marginal cost (lower block below marginal cost and upper block above marginal cost)

Uniform volume rate at marginal cost. A uniform volume rate is a constant unit price for all metered units of water consumed on a year-round basis and is typically expressed as dollars per thousand gallons or hundred cubic feet. This alternative suggests that all increments of water provided are priced equal to the marginal cost of the system's next unit of water. In other words, the marginal cost for one additional unit of water is the same for all water sold. Because the marginal costs are often greater than average costs, this rate structure would typically generate more revenue than the total annual revenue requirement based on average costs.

Increasing block rate structure with last block at marginal cost. Over the past few decades, there has been a trend for utilities to use increasing block rate structures in pricing water. An increasing block rate structure exists where the price for defined blocks of water usage escalates as water use increases. Taken together, the increasing block rates typically recover the average cost of a utility; however, marginal cost pricing for the last (i.e., highest usage) rate block can be considered when using this rate design.

Increasing block rate structures are considered to be conservation oriented by sending a price signal to the consumer that it is more expensive to use more water (see chapter IV.4). The higher price motivates the customer to reduce water use, which in turn may reduce system peaking, resulting in reduced capital needs and a decrease in additional water sources requirements. It is possible to complement average costs with marginal costs in water rate design both to provide efficient price signals and to match revenues with revenue requirements.

Increasing block rates when the average of purchases equals marginal cost. Another alternative in applying marginal cost pricing within increasing block rates is to set rates so that the average of all purchases equals marginal costs. In other words, the lower blocks are calculated below marginal cost and upper blocks are priced above marginal costs. Using this variation allows the utility to send a price signal that addresses economies of scale, affordability issues, and conservation at the higher use levels. This rate structure would also tend to generate total revenue in excess of the total annual revenue requirement.

Table V.8-1 Examples of three different marginal cost pricing rate schedules

1.	Average Marginal Cost		
		Service Charge	$13.00 per month
		Volume Rate	$5.00 per 1,000 gal
2.	Marginal Cost = Highest Block		
		0–4,000 gal	$3.00 per 1,000 gal
		4,001–10,000 gal	$4.00 per 1,000 gal
		Over 10,000 gal	$5.00 per 1,000 gal
3.	Marginal Cost = Average Price of Blocks		
		0–4,000 gal	$2.00 per 1,000 gal
		4,001–10,000 gal	$5.00 per 1,000 gal
		Over 10,000 gal	$6.00 per 1,000 gal

Marginal cost can be lower than required revenues for a system when the utility is achieving economies of scale. This happens when one more unit of water does not place a burden on the existing system because the capacity of the utility is not being fully utilized. Therefore, one more unit actually decreases the per-unit costs because the costs of the existing system are spread over more units of water consumed. It is possible to have some existing O&M marginal costs (e.g., chemicals and electricity) for an additional unit produced. However, O&M marginal costs tend to be less than the cost associated with capital costs or additional water sources.

Table V.8-1 illustrates these three approaches to using marginal costs and how those concepts may translate into an actual rate schedule. In all three scenarios, it is assumed that the marginal cost has been calculated to be $5.00 per 1,000 gallons.

In the third case, a simple average of the blocks shown equates to $5.00 per 1,000 gallons, but in an actual situation, a weighting of a utility's sales by block would be necessary to achieve average unit revenue equal to marginal cost.

A pure marginal cost–based rate would likely over-recover revenue if marginal costs were greater than average or historical costs and would under-recover revenue if marginal costs fell below required revenues (average costs). If a utility is close to fully using all capacity, the marginal cost may be higher than the average cost of the utility. However, utilities may implement a variation of an approach previously described to recover annual revenue requirements to minimize risks and meet utility goals. For example, a rate schedule may include a marginal price for volume water demand and a fixed amount or a base charge to be used to stabilize the revenue.

ADVANTAGES

The case for marginal cost pricing rests on the efficiency concepts of microeconomic theory, which state that scarce resources are used most efficiently if the resources are priced at their marginal cost. A corollary principle is that pricing at any level other than marginal costs results in an inefficient use of resources and that society would be better off if marginal cost prices were to be implemented at all levels of economic activity. Most professional economists acknowledge that under certain conditions regarding an economy structured around competition, marginal cost pricing is the most efficient pricing approach. Marginal cost pricing does not address other goals, such as interclass, intraclass, or intergenerational consumer rate equity, or the distribution of resources among these customers.

In addition to the efficiency rationale for marginal cost pricing, conservation benefits are frequently cited as a benefit of this pricing method. Marginal costs tend to exceed average costs for most water systems because the next increment of supply is usually more expensive than average cost of the existing supply sources. Intuitively, this is a reasonable presumption because most communities will have developed their low-cost supply options before using higher-cost supply sources. The higher rates under marginal cost pricing therefore provide a greater consumer incentive for conservation than most other pricing approaches, including the primary alternative of average cost pricing.

Proponents of marginal cost pricing acknowledge that not all of the assumed competitive market conditions prevail in the real world. However, advocates of marginal cost pricing argue that such deviations are minor with respect to the overall economy, and therefore marginal cost pricing is still a valid and useful tool for allocating resources efficiently and effectively. Also, the limitations of marginal cost pricing and any "imperfections" resulting from noncompetitive market conditions can be mitigated through other means. For example, one limitation of marginal cost pricing of water is that it may generate surplus revenues for a utility if marginal costs exceed average costs. This situation is generally undesirable for many water utilities, particularly public systems where the *political* desire to keep rates at the lowest levels consistent with safe, reliable service is strong. This issue can be resolved by strategies such as first setting all the utility's rates according to marginal costs and then lowering the initial rate block or blocks until the surplus is eliminated. However, in doing so, the "pure" marginal cost price signal is thereby "diluted." Alternatively, the entire set of rate tiers could be lowered to eliminate a surplus. In this manner the structure of relative rates is established by marginal cost pricing, but adjustments are made to eliminate the surplus. The important point is that there are often several means available to mitigate any shortcomings of marginal cost pricing.

DISADVANTAGES

Water supply, as a market commodity, is fundamentally different from other consumer markets, and even different from some other utility markets, such as electricity, telephone, and cable television. Water utilities violate virtually all of the critical conditions required for efficient allocation of resources under marginal cost pricing approaches, according to critics of this pricing method. It is asserted that these violations make marginal cost pricing problematic as a policy for municipal water utilities.

First, water utilities are *natural monopolies*, where provision of a good to the market is most socially efficient with a single supplier. They bear very high fixed costs but enjoy great economies of scale. The high fixed costs create a barrier to enter the market, for it is very expensive to build water works, and laying multiple sets of transmission and distribution lines through a service area would be both inefficient and unprofitable for more than one supplier. Among utility services, water is particularly problematic because it is heavy and expensive to transport great distances. Unlike electricity, telephone, and cable television, there is no efficient, competitive wholesale market from which local utilities can draw supply.

Detractors of marginal cost pricing also consider the conservation rationale to be a weak basis for implementing this pricing scheme. First, marginal cost is not necessarily higher than average cost, and in fact may be lower, which would suggest less conservation than traditional pricing methods, not more. Also, there may be more effective methods for achieving conservation.

Inasmuch as marginal cost prices raise some customers' water bills and lower others, they may have unintended redistributional effects. Concerns over affordability, especially for customers with large families and/or low incomes, have caused elected officials to modify marginal cost pricing schemes considerably. Ultimately, whether marginal cost pricing causes low-income or high-income customers to pay more or less is an empirical question that utilities considering marginal cost pricing should consider.

A practical difficulty with marginal cost pricing is the challenge of gaining acceptance among customers and elected officials for prices not based on costs the utility is actually incurring. Additionally, both privately and publicly owned utilities must adhere to legal pricing principles that are based on rationality and equal protection under the law. For details on these legal principles, see Corssmit 2010.

Finally, it is important to bear in mind that marginal cost pricing is aimed at only one value—socially optimal resource allocation, generally referred to as economic efficiency—among many values at stake in a rate-making decision. Policymakers considering marginal cost prices face two related decisions: (1) how important is economic efficiency relative to other values, and (2) to what degree is economic efficiency accomplished by an estimated marginal cost price?

SUMMARY

Academic economists are the traditional, but not sole, advocates of marginal cost pricing. Proponents argue that by charging all customers the marginal cost of water, gaps between water demand and supply would be eliminated. Furthermore, this form of pricing would enhance resource allocation and optimize consumer welfare. However, implementation of strict marginal cost pricing has been rare or nonexistent, although there are some examples of marginal cost pricing implementation using a less stringent incremental cost pricing variant. The potential for widespread acceptance of marginal cost pricing faces both theoretical and pragmatic obstacles.

There is nothing inherently inappropriate with using high-average or marginal cost–based rates to achieve demand-side management goals. On the contrary, such a tool can be highly effective under the right circumstances. This tool can be used under the umbrella of marginal cost pricing or apart from this concept. From a political perspective, a concern with adopting a formal marginal cost pricing approach is that the term "marginal cost" may convey a certain level of legitimacy and efficiency, to the exclusion of other objectives and values. If a utility's leaders want to adopt high marginal costs to curb demand, they should do so openly and with a clear plan for how to handle possible revenue surpluses, affordability concerns, and equity issues.

An important fact, as any other aspect of the marginal cost pricing issue, is that its use as a tool to achieve community objectives should be open and transparent. The mere term *marginal cost* should not by itself convey an aura of undeniable desirability, but rather, it should be portrayed as a concept with practical outcomes and consequences, and advantages and disadvantages. If all aspects are identified for decision makers and ratepayers, decisions can be made on the merits of the proposals. Marginal cost pricing decisions should be illuminating instead of being clouded by the terminology.

Assuming that marginal cost pricing is legally defensible and desired for application in a given utility, there are many options for utilities to incorporate marginal cost pricing in rate structures. The utility should begin by first determining the proper definition of marginal costs. The utility must consider the drivers that determine marginal costs: whether there are expensive system expansions, acquisitions of scarce water resources, or some other driver. The utility should also determine if marginal cost is lower than average cost due to oversizing or more than average cost because the lowest-cost options for supply have already been used.

In short, marginal cost pricing has been both advocated and criticized with respect to its application to pricing of all goods and services generally and with respect to water rate-making in particular. Any utility that considers this pricing approach is well advised to carefully weigh the pros and cons of this concept. The potential impacts of selecting marginal cost pricing can vary widely from those under average, embedded cost pricing or other approaches. Consequently, an informed decision-making process is very important when considering marginal cost pricing as the basis for implementing water rates.

REFERENCE

Corssmit, C.W. 2010. *Water Rates, Fees, and the Legal Environment*. Denver, Colo.: AWWA.

This page intentionally blank.

Chapter **V.9**

Miscellaneous and Special Charges

Many water utilities unbundle the costs of miscellaneous or ancillary services related to producing water by creating special service charges to cover these costs. These service charges are designed to require the customer who uses the services to pay for these costs through separate fees and charges.

Several factors are involved in establishing these miscellaneous and special charges. First, any practice that matches a customer's rate with the cost to serve that customer enhances equity. Second, by charging for a particular service, utilities can better manage demand for that service. Often, the absence of a fee for a service results in overuse of the service. Consequently, the utility incurs extra costs that must be covered through other revenue sources, most commonly through general water rates. By managing demand for a service, the utility can more effectively manage its own costs. Lastly, it should be considered whether the cost of deriving, charging, and collecting some charges is worth the additional cost of administering the charge.

As general water rates increase because of water resource limitations, development costs, new plant requirements, more stringent water quality standards, and general inflation, policymakers and utility management may view miscellaneous and special charges as a way to slow increases in general water rates.

The combination of fairness and improved efficiency make miscellaneous service charges an attractive way to minimize cost increases for the majority of customers. In essence, miscellaneous service charges are a refinement and expansion of cost-of-service pricing. Revenues generated via miscellaneous service charges (other operating revenues) are a direct reduction or credit against the total revenue requirements to be recovered from all customers (see Table II.1-2).

This chapter examines the following issues related to miscellaneous and special service charges:

- The basic legal authority for miscellaneous user fees and charges
- Factors to consider in establishing user fees and charges

- A general outline of the steps necessary to calculate fees and charges for full-cost recovery
- Common types of charges used in the water utility industry (not all charges apply to all water utility operations)

Each utility must determine what types of charges are appropriate to its operations. Through awareness of special problem areas, a utility can ensure that the benefit of a particular charge will be achieved without creating operation and management problems.

DEFINITION OF SERVICE CHARGES

Service charges, also sometimes referred to as user fees, are broadly defined as charges to the customer for a specific good or service or for the use of public facilities. The amount charged is usually based on both the cost of providing the service or facilities and the frequency and level of use. Charges for services differ from taxes. Service charges are incurred at the option of the customer and recover the specific costs of service. Taxes are assessed to all customers and may or may not be levied to recover specific costs of service. Water rates are a type of service charge and are generally the primary source of revenues for a utility's operations.

Typically, charges for miscellaneous services are used only where the

- user or customer is readily identifiable,
- unit of use and its costs can be determined with reasonable accuracy,
- utility wants to encourage or discourage certain behavior, and
- utility wants to enhance equity by minimizing subsidization of services.

Generally, as a matter of policy, the service for which a separate charge is applied is not compulsory, although, from a practical point of view, it may appear to be. The individual customer decides whether or not to use a particular service. The assumption is customers will use or consume only those goods and services they want or need, and thus the item is considered a fee or charge and not a tax.

General Principles for Establishing Charges

In deciding whether to establish various service charges, a utility should consider general policies and a philosophy for governing such charges. The following seven basic guiding principles can be used to establish charges for miscellaneous and special services:

1. Beneficiaries of a service should pay for that service.
2. Services provided for the benefit of a specific individual, group, or business should not be paid from general utility revenues.
3. Services provided to persons or entities that are not customers of the utility should not be paid from water rate revenues or other general utility revenues.
4. Services for which there are charges are generally voluntary.
5. The price of services may be used to change user behavior and demand for the good or service.
6. The level of service charges should be related to the cost of providing service.
7. The cost of administering the charge should not exceed the revenues.

EXAMPLE

An example of a situation that would justify establishing service charges is a water utility that owns and manages extensive watershed lands for the purpose of water supply development. Activity within the watershed may be regulated and controlled to ensure high water quality and to protect other environmental resources. However, utilities frequently allow recreational uses of the land for fishing, camping, hiking, biking, horseback riding, picnicking, and other activities.

Associated with recreational uses are additional costs for rangers, trail maintenance, parking and other facilities, and a host of other activities that could vary with the extent of the land's use. These costs are not related to the provision of water service to the utility's customers, and, arguably, the customer should not have to pay for them. Recreational service charges, such as day-use permits, camping fees, annual permits, and trail permits, could be developed to recover the cost of making the recreational resource available to the general public. Other charges could be arranged to offset costs, such as franchise fees with private concessionaires.

This example illustrates that a utility often provides goods or services for individuals who may not be general water service customers, or the utility provides goods and services that are separate and distinct from its primary activity.

LEGAL AUTHORITY FOR SERVICE CHARGES

The legal authority to impose various fees and charges is often included in a utility's authorizing or enabling legislation. For regulated utilities, public utility commissions may have specific requirements for the imposition of fees and charges, although these requirements are also often based on authorizing or enabling legislation. Any utility should consult its legal advisors and examine local and state regulations before implementing or changing any fee or charge program.

Generally, local governments are given wide latitude in establishing fees to pay the cost of individual services provided, although this is a power granted to local agencies as extensions of the state's governance authority. The US Supreme Court has allowed government agencies to recoup the cost-of-service delivery by charging the recipients of government services fees based on both the cost and value of the service to the recipient. The following three components are frequently found in successful programs:

1. The utility must, in exchange for payment of the fee, provide a direct benefit to a party in a way not shared by other members of society.
2. The fee must be optional, with the party given the option of not using the government service.
3. The charge must compensate the specific government entity only for the provided service. Fees received must not be collected for raising revenue beyond the cost of the provided service. The amount in excess of cost would be a tax.

SELECTING AND IMPLEMENTING SERVICE CHARGES

There are many issues and factors that should be considered in evaluating whether specific service charges should be established for miscellaneous services.

Policies Related to Service Charges

The principle of segregating costs for miscellaneous services dictates that those who use a service pay the cost of producing or supplying it. Though this principle is established in private enterprise, there may be local government activities for which it is regarded as inappropriate. Subsidies are provided for three basic reasons:

1. To permit an identified group to participate in services it might not otherwise afford
2. To provide benefits for groups beyond the immediate recipients of a service
3. To influence behavior or use of the service

Frequently, governing boards or councils have policies that address public access to important services. Ease of administration and concerns for dignity and privacy suggest subsidies may be appropriate for particular groups (e.g., public assistance recipients) through discounted fees and charges. Another type of subsidy is based on the premise that a service may provide benefits for those not qualifying as immediate recipients of the service. For example, construction inspections of developer-installed facilities not only benefit the developer but also the eventual user of those facilities. In situations where a developer constructs pipelines, storage tanks, and related facilities, the utility may not wish to charge full-cost inspection fees. It may be appropriate to spread the cost of certain services over the large base of potential beneficiaries.

The following are important questions to answer before implementing miscellaneous charges or special charges.

Are proposed charges for miscellaneous services equitable? An advantage of service charges is that they increase equity in the sharing of utility costs by directly linking costs of service to the user of that service, rather than to the general ratepayer, who may or may not use the service. However, an argument frequently made against service charges is that they create a burden on low-income individuals who may need the service but are unable to pay for it. To offset the potential regressive nature of service charges, utilities can include sliding scales, offer low-income discounts, or offer payment deferral plans.

Is the good or service readily identifiable and measurable? Goods and services should be defined in a way that (1) clearly identifies and distinguishes them from other goods or services, and (2) quantifies them so that the amount of the good or service rendered is known. In situations where there is variation in the level of service provided, the utility should consider defining more than one service. For example, a charge for an application for new water service may differ depending on the nature of the new service (new subdivision versus infill along an existing main). The various levels of review could justify different charges and planning required.

Can those who will benefit from the provision of specific services be readily identified? In considering a particular service charge, it is important to evaluate who will benefit from the particular service. The user should be the primary beneficiary of the service. When considering what fee to charge, a utility should consider the cost of the service and the extent to which the user is the beneficiary. If general water service customers also receive some benefit from the particular service, the fee may be set at something less than full cost. For example, utilities frequently provide main location services free of charge because the benefit to all customers of avoiding accidental main breaks far outweighs the benefit to the individual receiving the service.

Is the service related to the performance of the utility's primary business activity? It would not be appropriate to charge for a service if the service affects the quality of water or the integrity of water service delivery. For example, a utility would want to respond to reports of taste, odor, or color problems as quickly as possible to determine the cause and take corrective action. A utility would not want to discourage customer reports of this nature by charging for the cost of investigations. This type of service call benefits all water system users, not just those registering the complaint. Pressure tests, restoration of water service due to breaks in the utility's facilities, leak-detection programs, and similar activities that affect service and safety for all customers are normally associated with furnishing water service and are financed with general revenues.

What is the full cost of providing the good or service? The key to establishing a service charge is determining the cost of providing the service. The basic steps to determining the cost of service are outlined later in this chapter. Cost analyses should include both direct and indirect costs. Even if a decision is made not to charge the full cost of a service, it is useful to know the full cost so that decision makers are fully informed about the consequences of their decisions.

What costs are incurred in administering the levy, collection, and accounting of charges for miscellaneous services? If the cost to administer a service charge greatly exceeds the cost of providing the service, then the need for the service should be questioned. Frequently, the cost associated with documenting service provision, receiving cash, recording transactions, and establishing adequate controls exceeds the actual cost of providing the service. In these instances, a utility should consider whether a charge is appropriate. An example of a service for which fees may not be practical is charging for the use of a photocopy machine. Often, a customer needs a single copy of a document or record, and it may not be practical to charge (e.g., $0.50 per page) for the convenience of using a copy machine. When customer use of copy machines is very frequent, machines with a self-pay mechanism (credit card or cash) might be justified.

How will the charge or fee for a good or service affect the demand for the service? The degree to which demand is affected by the fee level is referred to as the price elasticity of demand. Demand for some services, such as a design review for distribution facilities constructed by a developer, is likely to be inelastic and the fee usually is a negligible portion of the overall cost of development. In contrast, fees for recreation services may be highly price-elastic, particularly if alternative recreational opportunities exist nearby; the pricing of miscellaneous services may serve to encourage or discourage the use of particular services. Though service charges are usually limited to the full cost-of-service provision, lower-than-cost prices are common in some situations. For example, the utility may wish to discourage return check charges by setting the charges at full cost. Many states, however, place limits on the amount that can be charged for returned checks.

Are there legislative, legal, or regulatory constraints under which the utility is required to operate? A utility considering implementing new service charges should evaluate any legal or regulatory constraints that may affect its decision. Laws vary from state to state, and investor-owned utilities (and in some states, municipal utilities) are subject to the rules and procedures established by public utility commissions. Typically, state public utility commissions require that the schedule of service charges be approved before it is implemented.

Clearly, a system of charges for miscellaneous services can offer many advantages to utilities as well as to customers through the enhanced equity of the service charges. This is evidenced by the large number of utilities currently using them as well as the growing number of types of fees in use.

COST BASIS AND RATIONALE

Determining cost and estimating the demand for a service are key functions in the proper implementation of service charges. Cost and activity data are essential to

- measure the cost of service,
- plan the expenditures associated with the service,
- evaluate the cost/benefit ratio of the service charge, and
- project revenues from the service.

It is impossible to accurately price the service if utility managers are unable to accurately measure the total cost of providing it. Without proper pricing, funding may be more or less than the amount necessary to provide the service. Furthermore, without adequate documentation of costs, service charges may be subject to challenge.

DETERMINING THE COST OF PROVIDING SERVICE

If a utility does not have the accounting capabilities necessary to develop cost data for each activity, a time-and-material study can be used to determine the average cost for various activities. These standard time-and-material studies can be the basis for developing fees. Where the cost differential between activities does not warrant a separate fee, groups of activities may be combined and a standard rate can be charged. To the extent that the utility can simplify its system of charges within the possible constraint of cost-based charges, it can reduce the costs of administering its miscellaneous charge system.

The following steps can be used to determine the full cost of specific services. The specific analyses for a particular service may vary somewhat. This outline is offered as guidance only; additional judgment will be required on the part of the utility.

Step 1. Define the Service to Be Provided

The first step in determining the cost of a service is to clearly define the service being provided. This may seem obvious; however, a complete statement of the service facilitates the cost analysis and exposes possible capital, direct, and indirect costs. In defining the service, the utility should first describe the specific activities involved by identifying who the users of the service are, why the service is needed, how it is measured, and how it is controlled. In many situations, what initially appears to be a single service is actually various related services. For example, accepting an application for water service will entail different activities for a new subdivision requiring an extension of service than it will for service within an existing service area.

The next two steps are necessary to determine the cost of services that require the use of facilities and infrastructure. Examples of services that may require the use of facilities and infrastructure, and therefore appropriately include capital costs, include standby service arrangements.

Step 2. Identify Capital Investments Made to Provide the Service

Once the specific service is clearly defined, it should be apparent whether or not capital costs may be appropriately included in a special charge or miscellaneous fee. In general, a service that requires the use of facilities or operating equipment recorded in a utility's fixed asset or operating equipment accounts should be considered to include capital costs. Care should be taken to ensure that those facilities and/or equipment are clearly identified as being necessary to the provision of the service. A careful review of how the service interrelates with a utility's day-to-day operations will help identify the use of facilities and equipment that may not otherwise be readily apparent.

Determine an appropriate allocation of capital costs. To avoid adverse rate impacts to utility customers that have not requested a special service, an equitable allocation of capital costs to a party requesting a special service should first be considered by the utility as far as how capital costs are currently recovered from existing utility customers. For example, a special charge for capital-intensive standby service provided to a particular customer will only be an equitable charge if the capital costs necessary to provide the standby service are included in the charge. Otherwise, the capital costs will be recovered from other revenue sources and, therefore, other customers who may not receive the benefit of the service. Appropriate capital cost recovery and allocation methods that apply to general rate-setting principles can often be applied to special charges and are discussed in detail elsewhere in this manual.

Step 3. Estimate Direct Labor Costs

Employee wages and benefits may represent a significant portion of the cost of providing services. It is the salary cost of those who directly supply the service that is used as a building block to allocate the indirect costs of supplying the service. Therefore, it is critical to accurately estimate the true and full cost of labor that goes into service delivery. At this point in the calculation, only the efforts of those who directly supply the service should be considered. Supervision, clerical support, and other similar positions are better classified as indirect costs.

Accounting records can be used as a checklist to ensure that all costs associated with a project are reflected in the cost analysis for a particular fee or charge. Historical costs must be adjusted to reflect any changes in labor rates or benefit costs; for example, such costs can give valuable information about normal labor usage levels. Historical costs can also indicate when costs for various activities differ significantly, so that separate fees may be designed.

Work activity can also be measured through interviews, detailed work logs or time sheets, or direct observation. The average amount of time required to perform a service should be determined by evaluating activity levels over a period of time. However, variations in overall workloads should also be taken into consideration. If the time required to perform a specific service varies greatly, it may be necessary to review how the service is defined and whether more than one service is being provided.

Labor costs should include full costs of salaries and benefits, including year-end accruals for unused sick and vacation time, if applicable. Total annual wages and benefits should be divided by the number of productive hours in a year, which have been adjusted for vacation, holidays, sick leave, training, meetings, breaks, and other downtime to determine a productive hourly rate for labor. Wage increases that occur mid-year should also be factored into cost calculations. The productive hourly rate may be used for invoicing of services rendered outside of those services whose cost is recovered through rates.

Step 4. Determine Other Direct Costs

In addition to labor costs, many services result in either the consumption of materials or the use of equipment or vehicles. Again, accounting records may help to identify material unit costs and, possibly, usage levels for each service rendered. Often, when materials are directly used in the provision of a service, it is possible to measure the amounts expended. Similar to labor costs, averaging techniques may be used to determine typical materials usage quantities.

Field services may require the use of vehicles and equipment. If the utility has internal service funds established for the use of vehicles and equipment, standard charge rates should be available. Internal service funds are fiscal and accounting entities created to account for resources used in providing centralized service within an organization. A motor pool is a good example: the cost allocations and overhead assignments for each vehicle and piece of equipment are in the internal service fund. These allocations will result in standard internal charge rates for each item. Another good source for information is utility work orders. They are particularly useful in determining the "standard" travel time associated with service calls.

Other direct costs to be considered in developing service charges are external costs, which are those costs the utility incurs for providing a good or service. For example, a bank's charge for insufficient funds should be included in the determination of a return check charge.

Step 5. Determine Indirect (Overhead) Costs

Indirect costs related to specific goods or services are determined by considering the level of central service support that can be allocated to specific departments and functions. Indirect costs typically include a distribution of costs associated with items such as purchasing, building maintenance, electricity, telephone charges, supervision, and clerical support. Formulas can be established to quantify the relationship between indirect support services and the applicable service-charge-supported program.

The use of a cost allocation plan is one way to determine indirect costs. These plans are frequently prepared in compliance with federal standards (Office of Management and Budget [OMB] Circular A-87, 2004) or other requirements so that the utility can qualify for maximum cost reimbursement in performing state or federal programs or grants and loans.

Several approaches can be used to prepare a central service cost allocation plan that, under given circumstances, complies with the OMB Circular A-87 and local government cost allocation needs. The following are some of the basic approaches.

Single tariff/consolidated rate method or multiple rate approach. This methodology is regarded as an acceptable cost allocation methodology within OMB Circular A-87. The essential problem with each method (to a lesser extent, the multiple rate approach) is that central service costs are accounted for in cost pools and distributed in a manner such that actual costs allocated may not reflect the services received. Also, direct billing systems are difficult to accommodate with this type of rate methodology. Generally, rate methods are not acceptable in the context of more sophisticated accounting systems.

Single step-down approach. This approach is occasionally used in the preparation of some basic plans. In this methodology, a central service department allocates only to a central service department below it on a hierarchical list. The allocations, to some degree, can be controlled to selected departments and so recoveries may be maximized. However, some distortions may exist between costs and services received. Many local governments appear to be equally interested in cost recovery and accounting information, so this method has not been widely used.

Cross-allocation approach. Some state controllers have, over a period of years, suggested a cross-allocation methodology for use by some jurisdictions. This methodology consists of two steps. In the first step, central service departments allocate to other central services and to the operating departments. In the second step, the residual in the central service departments is allocated to operation departments. The resulting allocations generally reflect the cost of services rendered. This methodology can be used to manually prepare a cost allocation plan, but the resulting plan can be extremely difficult to modify.

Step down–double allocation approach. In this methodology there are two steps. In the first step, the central service departments allocate to other central service areas and to operating departments (as in the cross-allocation approach). In the second step, the central service departments allocate to other central service areas below them on a hierarchical list and to the operating departments. It can be argued that this methodology theoretically provides the most accurate allocations of any of the methods described. It is commonly used and accepted, cost-effective and flexible, and allows for convenient updates.

In the absence of a complete cost allocation plan, utilities can develop indirect cost estimates using individually developed indirect cost rates. These estimates are developed by examining the level of overhead activities associated with each direct cost activity. For example, staff members who perform a given service will be supervised by a manager; occupy office space; use phone, facsimile, and copy machines; and rely on other central services, such as accounting, purchasing, and the motor pool.

Determine indirect costs. To determine the cost of providing a good or service, all direct and indirect costs associated with the good or service are added together. A final unit cost is determined by dividing the total cost by the number of service units rendered. The procedures for calculating unit costs used as the basis for charging for a particular good or service vary with each utility and may depend on the particular good or service involved.

Annual review of miscellaneous charges and related costs. Charges for miscellaneous services should be considered within the annual budget process, with revenues balanced against costs and included in the complete revenue analysis. The annual review makes the legal review of service charges easier, because all existing fees and charges can be acted on by the governing board or council in a single action. In addition, the annual review provides a regular mechanism to examine any cost changes or even the specific time-and-material requirements for performing services.

Fee policies can be considered in a broader context than a single fee program when all service charges and fees are reviewed at one time. In addition, utility attorneys will have little difficulty demonstrating the legitimacy of any fee or charge, and fee schedules are kept current with economic realities.

EXAMPLE SERVICE CHARGES

The procedures for calculating unit costs used as the basis for charging for a particular activity will vary with each utility. One method is to make a time study of labor requirements, material needs, vehicle and other equipment uses, and other costs to determine the resource requirements for the average task using statistical procedures. As an alternative, when the utility's operating and accounting records permit, actual historical costs for the operations can be determined. These costs are adjusted for price changes or changes in operating requirements for labor, materials, or equipment used. Each method should include all appropriate overhead costs.

Under a time-study procedure, the utility (1) identifies those operations needed to complete the required service and those required to be done by the customer or applicant, and (2) studies the time required to perform its tasks. Material and equipment requirements and the average time needed to travel to and from the job site are added to these requirements. These units of labor, materials, and equipment reflect the utility's current prices, including appropriate overheads. Normally, unit costs are rounded to provide a fixed-fee schedule for various service sizes. For job conditions that are not typical, an actual-cost price based on appropriate applicable labor rates and materials charges may be used when the resulting projected costs differ from the average by a substantial amount.

A variety of miscellaneous charges in the water utility industry include collection and delinquency charges, turn-off and turn-on charges, various application fees, tapping charges, meter installation charge, and jobbing and merchandise sales. When special charges are used, the utility should coordinate these rates and charges with its customer-service section. Procedures must be developed to ensure that the customer has advance warning about requests for services that will trigger a charge. Billing procedures must be in place to properly account for special charges. Bill inserts and other forms of customer notification are effective tools for keeping customers informed. As with all utility operations, a well-developed employee-training program is a solid foundation on which good public relations can be built. Customer service personnel must have all necessary information available so they can explain the intent and circumstances to which each charge applies. Information preparedness will minimize the perception that these charges are punitive and will enhance the utility's effort to promote customer support.

A summary of several service charges follows. This list is intended to illustrate the broad range of potential fees, but it is not exhaustive. The specific application of service charges depends on the specific nature of a utility's operations. For example, some utilities have separate charges for turning off and turning on water service following a period of delinquent payments. Other utilities find it more convenient to charge once for both turning off the service and the subsequent expected service turn-on.

Field Service Charges

The more common types of field service charges and fees relate to activities associated with water turn-off (or turn-on), meter setting or removal, special meter readings, meter testing, and temporary hydrant meter settings. Each type of charge has its place in the fee-setting process for certain operational conditions. These charges are used only when there is a customer group that can be identified, the activity produces significant costs that are not common to all customers, and costs can be identified and related to the units of activity. Some of the common types of field service charges include the following.

Turn-off and turn-on fees. A utility may charge to turn off or turn on water service. Typically, this activity occurs under one of two conditions. First, service may be discontinued when a customer vacates the premises and no one moves in immediately. This differs from a simple change in account status, which is more common and may not require water service turn-off. The second occurrence is associated with the failure to pay water bills. After a specified delinquency period, many water utilities turn off water service until past-due payments are made or a payment plan is arranged. Frequently, when this occurs, a separate turn-off and turn-on charge is imposed.

In the first example, followup turn-on charges are common because they are easy to administer and collect. Turn-off charges are unusual, because utilities have found it important that the customer report when service is to be discontinued. This enables the utility to remove the meter or take other necessary actions to avoid waste or illegal usage. When a utility employs turn-off charges, emergency turnoffs are normally exempted.

The turn-on charge can be imposed for a new service turn-on, seasonal turn-on, and other situations where the service is temporarily discontinued or when delinquent accounts have been shut off. The utility may add a surcharge for turning on service at night, after office hours, or when requested in a short period of time. A surcharge would compensate for shift-pay differential or for the need to dispatch employees outside of a normal schedule. Many utilities incorporate all routine turn-on activities into one turn-on charge when the cost differential between various activities does not justify separate fees or when the cost of administering a complex fee structure is greater than the benefit. In some instances where a customer's service is disconnected because of nonpayment, the costs of the turn-off may be incorporated into the turn-on charge due to the impracticality of collecting a turn-off charge from disconnected customers.

Employee travel time to the customer's premises, actual labor costs involved in operation of the shutoff valve, use of equipment and a vehicle, and appropriate overhead costs associated with the activity must be included in the cost of turn-on or turn-off activities.

Field collection charge. Occasionally, utility service personnel are permitted to collect delinquent water bills at the customer's premises, especially if such payments are not in cash. When a delinquent payment is made to the service person that goes to the customer's premises to shut off the water, the service fee can be reduced because the cost is less than the normal turn-off fee, provided suspension of service actions did not commence. This type of collection policy can significantly reduce the number of turn-offs, decrease the work load for office and field services personnel, and improve customer relations. The customer benefits from uninterrupted service and a smaller service charge, and avoids the inconvenience of traveling to the utility office to pay the delinquent bill. Such a policy also eliminates the need to impose a collection fee, except in the most difficult cases.

Some large urban utilities have reconsidered the benefits of on-premises collection because of problems that sometimes occur when collectors or field personnel confront delinquent customers who are unwilling to pay. Though bill collection by field personnel may prevent the need to shut off a service, utilities should consider the environments to which field personnel are dispatched. Some utilities have discontinued seeking payments from customers because of concerns for personal safety and damage to vehicles and equipment. Utilities have increasingly become apprehensive with the potential liability associated with field collections. This occurs more often when customers insist they paid more than what was reflected on their account. To avoid any potential dispute and additional customer service issues, some utilities have prohibited their personnel from accepting any payments in the field. As a concession, some utilities will encourage the customer to contact the customer service office and pay by credit or debit card to avoid the turn-off.

Repair of damaged facilities charge. On occasion, a customer will operate a service and, in the process, make the stop box inoperative. In this case, the utility should

- instruct the customer to take corrective action within a prescribed period of time, or
- send a field-service crew to clean out or dig up the stop box so that the service can be shut off during repair. Normally, a uniform fee plus a surcharge is imposed, but only when it is necessary to dig up or replace the stop box.

Routine clean-outs and dig-ups of stop boxes or meter pits are sometimes undertaken without a separate charge to the customer. This occurs where the special service is not a result of illegal customer activity and is justified because utilities have found that quick access to these boxes benefits the system as a whole.

It is not uncommon for utility property, such as a fire hydrant, to be damaged by automobile accidents. Some municipal entities have passed ordinances permitting the recovery of the repair cost from the person responsible for the damage. This has enabled the utility to seek recovery of the cost through the insurance carrier of the responsible party.

Special or final meter reading fee. A fee may be charged when customers request a special meter reading or ask that a meter be reread even though, in the opinion of the utility, no reading is warranted. The charge is designed to recover the higher-than-normal cost of this reading. For example, a customer may believe that the meter reading is in error and request that it be read again. To prevent abuse of this service, a utility may charge for a second reading under certain conditions. If a substantial reading discrepancy is found or if the individual customer seldom demands this service, it is common practice for the utility not to impose a charge. The definition of *an excessive number of requests* varies with each utility, but one standard might be that no more than one such request is made during a calendar year. A meter-reading charge is usually a fixed fee based on historical costs for performing special readings. A final-bill reading is a common type of special reading. This may occur when a home or business is sold, leased, or vacated, or when a new owner or tenant occupies the premises. Service personnel rather than meter readers usually record final readings because the request for a specific day or time seldom coincides with the scheduled day of the specific meter route. The final meter-reading charge can take the form of a uniform fee added to the final billing statement. The charge recovers the meter reading cost plus additional clerical costs for issuing a final statement.

Meter resetting fee. A charge may be made to a customer for resetting a meter when the meter has been removed at the request of the customer. Normally, this charge will vary with the size of the meter. It may be combined with a turn-on charge when both meter set and service turn-on are performed at the same time.

Meter installation charge. A charge may be made to those customers desiring an additional water meter. Typically, this is for an irrigation meter or sewer deduct meter. The fee is for the installation of the meter on the customer's side of the service line and does not require an additional tap.

Appointment charge. In certain instances, a customer may request a field-service call at a *specified time* during the working day. In such cases, a field-appointment charge is often made for the added cost of making a service call at a specific time. The cost could include the added travel time because of the disruption to the field representative's normal scheduled work activity.

To promote effective customer service, many utilities try to schedule service calls within a window of time, for example, between 8:00 a.m. and 11:00 a.m. This approach is more convenient for the customer than a completely open-ended service call and is more manageable for the utility to schedule. This type of approach may eliminate the need for a field appointment charge, unless the customer insists on a specific time for the appointment.

Meter testing charge. Water bill complaints that are not resolved by telephone may necessitate that a meter be reread or that the customer's service line or water-using appliances be inspected for leaks. If the matter is not resolved to the customer's satisfaction, the meter may be removed and tested at the request of the customer. If the field service representative suspects that the meter has become inaccurate, a test may be ordered at the utility's expense. If a meter is removed and bench tested at the request of the customer and it is found to be accurate, the utility may impose a fixed fee that reflects the average removal and testing costs for that particular meter size or type. As an alternative, some utilities may require the customer to make a deposit to cover the actual cost of the test. If the meter meets the utility's standards, the deposit is used to pay the cost. If the meter tests outside these standards, the deposit is returned to the customer. Some utilities will not render a testing fee if the meter accuracy is outside of acceptable limits. With investor-owned utilities, the requirements of the regulatory agency will be reflected in the procedures that are followed.

Determination of financial responsibility for meters that test outside the prescribed accuracy range depends on the maintenance and replacement policy of the individual utility. Many times, any back billing or refunds from overbilling are limited to no more than 90 days prior to the test. Payment for replacement of the meter also depends on individual utility policies; some utilities require the meter to be replaced by the customer, and others replace the meter at the utility's expense.

Backflow-prevention testing. Periodic backflow-prevention testing is required by many utilities to ensure the integrity of the water system. Sometimes, when a utility tests a customer's backflow-prevention devices, a charge for the test is assessed. The amount charged may depend on the type of backflow device and the number checked at each site. For example, a utility may charge $25 for the first device checked and $15 for each additional device checked at the same time.

When utilities require backflow testing on residential sprinkling systems, it is not uncommon to incorporate the cost of the test into the base charge. This enables the utility to recover its costs while promoting the backflow inspection as a "free service." From a practical standpoint, it is also easier than trying to collect a separate fee from the homeowner for the backflow inspection or having to force compliance by the homeowner to have a third party inspect the backflow preventer and provide certification of its operability or repair if found to be nonoperable.

Pressure testing. If a customer requests that the water pressure at a service be tested, a utility can dispatch a field crew to perform this check. Concerns about water pressure can result from either too high or too low pressure, which adversely affect the water service. Pressure testing may also involve examining a customer's pressure-reducing valve.

Fire flow test. Occasionally, customers may request verification of fire flow capabilities at a given location. This may be because of fire insurance ratings or related concerns about the adequacy of the system to provide a specified level of fire protection.

Hydrant maintenance. Hydrant maintenance is frequently performed by the utility but charged to the general fund or fire fund. The most common means of charging for the maintenance is through a flat per-hydrant fee that is paid annually.

Water audits. Commercial, industrial, and residential water audits performed by utility personnel are becoming an increasingly common service among water utilities. Water audits help customers identify ways of conserving water, either by changing water-using fixtures and processes or by operational changes. There is seldom a charge for a water audit because it is intended to provide conservation that ultimately benefits all customers, and utilities want to encourage participation in water audit programs. Nevertheless, this service does have a cost, and it may be useful for the utility to know what the cost of the service is, particularly when evaluating the cost-effectiveness of water conservation programs.

In areas where water audits are in high demand, it may be desirable to establish a small, nominal charge to deter those customers who are not serious about implementing audit recommendations. Alternatively, utilities could rebate audit charges if customers implement certain recommendations within a specified period of time. Charges for water audits are generally considered only when demand for the service exceeds the utility's ability to provide the service.

Temporary hydrant meters. Water uses from public fire hydrants, for purposes not related to fire fighting, such as street washing, dust control, filling tank trucks, or construction, are usually allowed, provided a special permit is obtained from the water utility. It is important to note that when a hydrant meter is used, a backflow preventer should be required. In some instances, utilities have permitted a contractor to purchase an approved hydrant meter and backflow preventer because of the frequency in which it is used by the contractor. This avoids frequent trips to customer service or the meter shop. Amounts charged for the hydrant permit can include the office and field costs to administer and monitor the metered or unmetered connection and the cost of water used. Many water utilities prefer to carefully control and meter these limited activities and initially charge a uniform fee that provides for a minimum water-use allowance. Metered water use in excess of the base allowance becomes subject to the general retail water rates, in addition to the fire hydrant permit cost. A separate and refundable deposit for rental of the meter and hydrant wrench normally is set at an amount sufficient to ensure their safe return. Inspections are usually required to ensure that use of the hydrant meets all utility operating standards, and the cost of inspection is normally included in the fee.

Office Service Charges

Some of the more common types of office service charges include the cost of setting up a new account or transferring an existing account, the cost of collecting delinquent accounts, or checks returned by the bank for insufficient funds. Some of these activities include initial efforts that may require followup work.

New account or transfer charge. Depending on the level of activity and overall costs, a new applicant may be charged an initial administrative fee for the average cost incidental to opening a new account or transferring an existing account. Such fees directly reimburse the utility for the cost of additional utility services that may be performed before the new or existing service becomes active or is reactivated. These fees reflect the status of the service connection. If the service connection is already established, the transfer fee can be designed to recover office-related costs for completing the application form, determining the applicant's credit rating or water-use-related deposit, collection of any unpaid water bills or assessments, and any other activities preliminary to instituting water service. Most government-owned utilities do not require a credit investigation because the water charges are usually considered under the applicable state or local laws as a lien against the property. When water-suspension policies require that the water be disconnected and where the stop box or water meter is already installed on the customer's premises, any additional office and field costs for initiating the turn-on order can also be incorporated into this charge.

An account fee for new construction can incorporate additional office expenses incurred for administering any special capital cost payments. The fee can also be used to cover the cost of administering and monitoring construction of the new service line during the construction phase.

An administrative fee can be used to recoup the added cost of processing a new water-service cancellation, which results in a refund of any capital cost payments or other deposits (water main extension, tapping fee, or connection charges) previously paid when a water service was issued. This fee can be deducted from the refund and the net balance returned to the applicant.

Whether one fee is used for all activities or separate fees are developed depends on the amount of activity and the cost differential among fees. Efficiency in the administration of a fee program must be considered when determining each fee.

Collection-related charges. The following service fees pertain principally to the collection and billing functions of the water utility. Because most charges relate to the collection of delinquent water bills, each charge should be reviewed periodically to determine whether the utility's overall collection program is providing optimum collection and billing control.

A *late-payment charge* can be an incentive for prompt payment. This charge recognizes the time value of money and other added costs. It is common practice for a water utility to designate a period during which a bill must be paid to avoid late payment charges. Utilities typically use 15 to 30 days, sometimes with a grace period to allow for mail delivery problems, before imposing a late payment charge. If water bills remain delinquent following subsequent billing with late-payment charges, it may become necessary to initiate collection procedures. Typically, a utility will coordinate office and field work to find an efficient balance between the length of time accounts are allowed to be delinquent and the amount of effort (number of collections) required to collect payments. Some utilities are opposed to the characterization of this charge as a late payment charge because it implies a penalty payment. Instead, to encourage timely payment of the utility invoice, they offer a discount if the customer pays the bill by a date certain.

A *returned-check charge* is made when a check is not honored by the customer's bank, regardless of the reason. This charge reflects the added cost to the utility for processing a returned check. A utility should ascertain the legal limits on returned check charges within its jurisdiction. In addition to including any bank charges for insufficient funds, the fee may also include added costs for processing the returned check, issuing a new bill, and telephone or letter notices to the customer. When a customer has a sustained record of returned checks, the utility may require a deposit account until a good credit rating is reestablished. When checks are not made good within a prescribed period, the utility may initiate service shutoff because the account is delinquent. With investor-owned utilities, regulatory agency requirements must be reflected in policies, procedures, and charges; usually, all policies are required to be filed with the regulatory agency.

With the addition of electronic payment options such as debit and credit cards that may be used for automatic monthly debits for the utility bill, financial institutions have begun charging fees to utilities for accounts that do not have sufficient funds on hand for the debit. A separate charge may be needed in the fee schedule other than a returned check charge to recover the cost incurred by the utility.

Some utilities are authorized to issue a *lien certificate* following reasonable attempts to collect past-due payments for water service. Certain documentation and, usually, a fee payable to the assessor's office are required when placing such liens. A charge for obtaining the lien can be developed and included in the lien certificate.

Some utilities provide individual water bills to tenants of a master-metered complex, such as an apartment building. Typically, this *multiple tenant billing* is performed at the request of a landlord and accomplished by dividing the total water bill by the number of dwelling units. This procedure requires the utility to maintain information about each tenant. In addition, it is the landlord (owner) who is ultimately responsible for payment of the total water bill. Utilities providing this service charge a fee for each separate dwelling unit billed; usually this fee is charged to the landlord. This billing method, however, is not used by many utilities because of its cumbersome administration.

Account status at property sale. In some locations, a title or escrow company will verify the account status when a property is sold. This action is taken because any delinquent payments may not result in recorded liens against a property until after a sale is completed. A review of account status at the request of a customer, usually over the phone, is a standard service for which no charge is made; however, a third-party request requiring written verification of account status is sometimes subject to a charge.

Another option is to make the information available electronically to the title or escrow company. This permits the customer service staff previously dedicated to this function to be allocated to more productive tasks.

Meeting agendas and related materials. The public meetings of a utility's governing body (board of directors, city council, etc.) should include proper notification, information packets, and a formal agenda. It is common for a number of interested individuals or groups to request copies of these materials on a routine basis. Often, utilities maintain a list of individuals and groups who routinely receive meeting agendas; a much smaller group may receive the entire information packet. Meeting agendas may be distributed free of charge to anyone requesting a copy and are available at all public meetings. Some utilities, however, impose a regular subscription service charge to defray the costs of copying and distributing agendas on an ongoing basis. By charging a nominal fee, only those individuals or groups with a serious, ongoing interest in a utility's activities will subscribe.

Generally, meeting materials, or board packets, are not widely distributed on a regular basis because of the high cost of distribution, although a subscription service similar to that used for agendas is possible. Usually, materials are made available for public review through the utility's website. Some systems post the agenda and meeting minutes, while others choose to add the entire agenda packet as an additional selection.

Before a utility implements any charges for public information documents, a review of applicable laws should be undertaken. In some states, charges for public information are limited to the direct cost of providing copies.

Public documents. Utilities frequently receive requests for recent studies and reports, public information materials, financial reports or budgets, or design standards. The utility should have a clear policy governing the distribution of such documents, and, if charges are to be imposed, a specific price for each document with ordering instructions (perhaps through the customer service counter) should be established. Prices for such documents may be limited to production costs, although an allowance for the administrative cost of stocking and selling documents could be included. Single copies of many materials, such as water conservation pamphlets, may be distributed free of charge. However, for multiple copies for subsequent distribution (e.g., water conservation materials to be distributed to 1,000 schoolchildren), the utility should consider charging a nominal fee to cover costs.

Construction plans, drawings, and maps. Developers, other utilities, cities, and other entities occasionally request plans, drawings, or maps of existing water facilities. Like other public documents, these items should be made available. Many utilities charge a fee for each copy. Charges may vary for prints, paper sepias, or Mylar sepias. Charges for these prints should include copying and administrative costs. Some utilities sell Mylar plans only to other government agencies.

Consultation services. Some utilities impose hourly rates for consultation services rendered by staff to persons other than customers and for special engineering, professional, and legal services. Hourly rates should be fully loaded rates, including fringe benefits and applicable overhead charges.

Service Application, Engineering, and Inspection Fees

Many types of water service application, engineering, and inspection fees are used in the water utility industry. Some fees are designed to recover only direct costs associated with certain customer activities. Others are designed to recover both direct overhead costs of processing the application and some indirect costs incurred when determining the background data required to process new applications for service. For example, if the utility must expend funds for an engineering study to ensure that expansion into a new area can be undertaken, a portion of this cost might be added to new-service application fees. As an alternative, these costs may be included in system development charges.

Because processing an application incurs costs even if no construction work is performed, the utility is justified in requiring that applicants who have preliminary inquiries pay the costs associated with the planning or design work. Otherwise, if no construction is undertaken, costs must be absorbed either by other applicants who do commit for work or by general water service customers. A nominal preliminary application fee can help deter unnecessary inquiries and pay costs when such inquiries do not result in construction.

The amount of application fees will vary and, as with all service charges, should be based on a cost analysis of those activities required to process the application. Direct administrative costs for personnel handling the application, engineering services used, field service needed, and other related activities should be determined and a fee structure developed based on the level of activity.

A description of some of the more common types of application and inspection fees follows.

Main inspection, filing, and contract fees. When preparing a main-extension agreement, a fee may be charged for filing the application, developing the contract, and for field inspection and engineering record reviews. The flat fee is paid when the application is received. The fee should specify the number of plan reviews and field inspections that are included before additional fees may be charged. In instances where the contractor has performed inadequately, subsequent inspections may be required before the project is acceptable to the utility. In these instances, the utility should recover the additional review and/or inspection costs through additional fees. The fee is applied to the cost of the work when the contract for an extension is signed. If no work is undertaken, the application fee is retained by the utility to defray costs of administration. Some utilities require a nonrefundable, flat filing fee from each applicant.

Administrative fee for service-connection inspection. Where a new service line stub-in is connected to the distribution system before service is required, the utility may charge a fee to defray the cost of administering and monitoring the new connection. After water service begins, the account can be transferred to permanent status.

Cross-connection inspection. A periodic inspection fee is used to recover costs associated with high-risk installations to ensure that no cross-connection has occurred. The utility adds this fee to its overall cross-connection control program, including adequate records of installations, regulations, and periodic inspections sufficient to ensure that infractions will be promptly corrected to avoid possible system contamination. When residential inspections are required, such as for irrigation systems, some utilities prefer to add the cost of the inspection to the base charged for residential accounts rather than invoice the customer separately.

Engineering design fee. Where substantial engineering design and study are required to provide new facilities, the cost of the extraordinary engineering service may be charged to the applicant in addition to the administrative fee. This can be charged either as a flat fee or on an actual-cost basis, with a deposit of the estimated cost required before the work is undertaken. Often, an extension of service requires engineering work to determine what additional facilities (mains, distribution storage, pumping, etc.) will be needed. Frequently, such facilities must be designed and plans and contracts prepared. Any extraordinary costs benefiting only the individual applicant or developer should be assessed against the property owner.

When facilities are constructed, these extraordinary costs may be capitalized as part of the total construction cost of the extension of service. The amount received becomes part of the customer-contributed capital for the project. When work is not undertaken, as when a project is abandoned, the funds received are accounted for in accordance with the utility's system of accounts. Expenses incurred are charged against revenues. With a sound cost-estimating program, revenue and expenses should be equal, and costs will not be borne by the utility and its general service customers. If overall system planning is necessary to develop an area in the utility's system, a planning fee may be assessed against the developer of the area for which plans are designed.

Contract Work and Merchandise Sales

A service charge is assessed when the utility performs work on a customer's premises, such as repairs, replacement, and improvements, or sells equipment to the customer or the plumber who will install the equipment. Some utilities provide financing to the customer for such services and allow the customer to pay the cost over a period of time. The utility may charge for these services at a higher rate of interest than it pays and still provide financing to the customer at a cost less than commercial interest rates. In some instances, utilities offer services or merchandise at reduced cost or at no interest to encourage customers to install water-saving devices, such as ultra low-volume (ULV) toilets. Deferred payment programs should be instituted only where adequate protection against bad checks or nonpayment can be designed into the system, for example, where the utility can place a lien on the property to ensure collection.

Through contract work and merchandise sales, a utility may be in competition with plumbers or suppliers. This is a policy consideration that must be taken into account when determining what services the utility will provide. Where there is little competition among contractors, the utility can ensure that a fair and competitive price is developed and that the customer receives the best service possible. By setting installation standards and acting as an alternative contractor to do the work, the utility can provide benefits to the customer. In performing services for private parties, or working on a customer's property, a utility should consider legal and liability issues associated with these activities.

For many services, special fee schedules can be developed. Alternatively, the utility may charge individual customers on the basis of actual cost. In either case, the utility needs to determine standard rates for use of vehicles and equipment, along with labor costs, to determine fees. If the average cost of an installation does not vary too greatly from extremes (high or low), a fee schedule may be used.

Some of the areas in which a utility might undertake contract work and merchandise sales are described in the following sections.

Service line repairs. Normally, the maintenance of service lines beyond the water meter is the customer's responsibility. A utility could charge fees if a customer requests a service line repair. Telephone companies provide similar fee-based services.

Leak detection. Though leak detection of the utility's system is a responsibility of the utility, detecting leaks on a customer's property may be a sought-after service. Leak detection assistance may result from sudden and unexplained increases in water usage. The utility may offer this service free of charge. The utility has an incentive to reduce leaks within the home, plus the free service can be a good public relations tool, particularly when the utility wants to promote conservation.

Service tap installation. Most utilities have a fee schedule for installing taps into the main when connecting to customer service lines. The fee is collected when a customer or customer's plumber applies for a tap. The fee is based on the size of the tap needed to make the service connection. When large taps are required or special costs are involved, such as a large tap in a reinforced concrete main, the utility may require that payment to reflect the added costs. If so, at the time of application the customer is charged according to the fee schedule. Included in these charges are costs for any permanent repairs to the pavement, which normally would be completed at a later date.

Meter installation. In large developments, it is common for developers to install water meters and meter boxes at new service connections. For individual or smaller developments, the utility may be requested to install the water meter for a new service. This may be combined with the service tap installation. If the utility installs the water meter, a connection fee is charged. This fee includes the cost of the meter, meter box, and related materials, plus labor. Fee schedules are developed for common meter sizes, although for large meters, many utilities charge the actual cost of installation.

Meter size change or relocation. When a customer with an existing service and meter, such as a 1-in. service line with a ⅝-in. or ¾-in. meter, wants the meter changed to a larger size or relocated, the customer may be required to pay the increased cost of the meter and the cost of installation or relocation. This may be a special situation in which customers, for their convenience, want a larger meter installed but where the utility does not deem the change necessary. If the meter size is increased and the previous system development charge had been based on the meter size, an additional system development fee may be applicable, subject to state regulations. If an additional system development fee is charged, generally the difference between the existing fee for the old meter size and the new meter size is charged. In instances where the customer's use pattern has increased and a larger service line has been installed at the customer's expense, and where such use requires a larger meter, the customer would pay on the basis of the regular rates of the utility. If, as is the case for many utilities, there is a charge for the meter and its installation, this policy forms the basis for the charge. A meter size change fee may discourage changes where, in the judgment of the utility, such a change is not necessary.

Some utilities receive requests to downsize water meters, frequently to lower the monthly or bimonthly service charge, because charges often are based on meter size. A charge for meter size change could recover the costs associated with the change.

Main location services. Utilities are frequently asked to locate water mains for other utilities or in conjunction with nearby construction activity. Main location services are an example of a service for which a charge should not be assessed. A utility should encourage other utilities and construction contractors to determine the location of water facilities before construction begins. This minimizes the chance of main breaks and related damage and repair expense. It also helps ensure continued and reliable water service to all customers. For these reasons, main location services usually are provided free of charge.

Main relocation services. Occasionally, a utility's water mains need to be relocated to make room for other utilities or infrastructure improvements. When relocations are required, they are typically paid for by the party requiring the relocation, usually another public agency or utility. These services are paid for on an actual cost basis, rather than through uniform fees or charges. The exception to this is for water mains currently in state or city rights-of-way that require relocation because of a state or city project. In these instances, the cost has generally been absorbed by the utility. The relocation of water mains can be very expensive. It would behoove utilities when financially feasible to acquire easements for the installation and maintenance of their water mains rather than rely on state or city rights-of-way.

Remote meter reading device installation. For the convenience of the customer, some utilities provide an outside remote meter-reading device in areas where a meter is normally installed inside the premises. When this is a special service and not available to all customers, a charge may be made.

Backflow-prevention device installation. Some water services require the installation of backflow-prevention devices. Usually, these are the responsibility of the customer to install and maintain, but a utility may wish to provide this service.

Miscellaneous work. Often, a developer will provide a development map with elevations that are subsequently changed. Consequently, it will be necessary to raise, lower, or even move mains, fire hydrants, meter boxes, service lines, or backflow-prevention devices. The developer normally pays for these relocation costs, which are the result of the builder's actions. The utility usually requires advance payment for the work and withholds service to the property until the facilities meet with the utility's operating and construction standards. A deposit from the developer is usually required. After the actual cost is determined, the final bill is adjusted.

Sale of water meters and meter boxes. In instances where developers install water meters for new service connections, the utility may wish to sell the meters to be installed. This ensures uniformity and decreases future maintenance and repair costs. Also, with the growing use of remote meter reading devices or automatic reading equipment, it is important to ensure that water meters are compatible with meter reading equipment.

Sale of ULV toilets and other conservation devices. With increased emphasis on water conservation, many utilities have instituted programs to encourage customers to install water-saving fixtures and devices. Low-cost items, such as leak detection kits, low-flow showerheads, or toilet tank dams, are frequently given away. Other water conservation devices and fixtures, such as ULV toilets, automated irrigation timers, and irrigation supplies, are sometimes sold to customers at cost or near cost. Increasingly, cash rebates are given for installation of ULV toilets. Another way to make the purchase of conservation devices more appealing is to offer low- or no-interest loans and allow the payment over an extended period of time. Utilities should provide for adequate protection against nonpayment of loans by having the authority to place liens on property or through some other mechanism. Some utilities install ULV toilets, other devices and fixtures, and then bill the customer an amount equal to the reduction in the customer's charge for water (and wastewater, if appropriate) until the installation cost is repaid.

SUMMARY

The discussion of charges for miscellaneous and special services provides general guidance for appropriately determining such service charges. In developing these types of charges, each utility should base its decisions and cost analyses on explicit policies and costing procedures. The utility should also carefully analyze its operations to identify what services should be subject to charges and what activities are involved in performing each service.

Each utility operation is unique to a certain extent. For that reason, an appropriate combination of charges should be developed based on the individual utility's needs and goals. For dynamic utility operations, these needs will change over time. In selecting a charge, the size of the customer base affected and the ability to identify individual users of the particular service are important factors.

The significance of the revenue/cost/use pattern is also an important consideration. Administrative costs can be an important part of any rate-setting process, thus the utility must be sure that revenue generated by the activity and related costs are sufficient to justify processing the miscellaneous and special charges. Finally, costs must be identified and related to a unit of use so that an appropriate charge or fee can be developed. The utility will achieve greater equity and better efficiency to the extent that a utility has special service charges as part of its overall revenue strategy.

REFERENCE

OMB (Office of Management and Budget). 2004. *Cost Principles for State, Local, and Indian Tribal Governments*. OMB Circular A-87 Revised. Washington, D.C.: OMB.

Section VI

Outside Customer Rates

This page intentionally blank.

Chapter **VI.1**

Overview of Outside Customer Rates

Public water utilities often provide service to retail and/or wholesale customers located outside of their jurisdictional boundaries. These arrangements may enable mutually beneficial efficiencies in service delivery and realization of economies of scale.

The guidance provided in this section relies on the same concepts and approaches discussed in sections II through V. Using cost-based principles and methodologies to set rates is the most proven and accepted way to achieve equitable rates, and is a defensible basis for establishing rates across respective customer classes. This section includes three chapters: (1) this overview chapter that discusses many of the basic considerations when contemplating rates for retail and wholesale service to customers located outside of the primary public utility legal boundaries (referred to as outside customers); (2) a chapter that looks specifically at rate-making considerations for outside retail customers; and (3) a final chapter that discusses issues related to wholesale customers.

This section offers technical guidance for the development of cost-based rates to serve outside retail and wholesale customers that may assist in limiting costly regulatory and/or legal rate reviews and may enhance public and stakeholder acceptance. The principles apply in the situation where a public water utility is providing services outside its jurisdictional or service area boundaries, and may also apply to an investor-owned or private utility. Oftentimes, customers who are outside the utility's jurisdictional boundary and/or service area boundary are referred to as "non-owner" entities because (1) they do not have the legal responsibilities to own and operate the system within regulatory specifications; (2) they do not have the direct responsibility to repay any debts incurred by the utility nor any other fiduciary responsibilities; (3) they do not have any legal liabilities related to system performance; and (4) they generally do not have any legal standing in the governance of the utility. For these reasons, this section often refers to outside customers as nonowners.

BENEFITS OF PROVIDING OUTSIDE CUSTOMER SERVICE

When a public water utility agrees to provide service to customers outside its jurisdictional or service area boundaries, it takes on additional risks, but in return may obtain many direct and indirect benefits for all system users:

- As discussed in prior sections, the utility often receives a reasonable (fair) return on its investment for the delivery of services to such nonowner customers.
- Economies of scale may be realized and the costs of advance construction of capacity (to serve both customers located inside and outside of the service area) may be distributed across a broader population of users. Providing service to outside retail and/or wholesale customers is one way to increase the use of otherwise unused or available system capacity. Such economies of scale almost always result in lower average unit costs for all customers.
- To the extent that local governments act as a hub for economic development in suburban and rural areas that are served by the public utility of such government, allowing the public utilities to earn a fair and reasonable return by permitting them to charge a higher rate to outside nonowner customers may support orderly economic development in these areas.

NATURE OF THE RELATIONSHIP

A publicly owned utility may be considered to be the property of the respective government's residents who, as owner-customers, bear both the risks and the responsibilities of utility ownership. As the utility's owners, customers located inside the public utility's jurisdictional boundaries cannot simply "walk away" from the utility. Furthermore, the utility has a responsibility to develop and maintain the system to serve all of its customers, both inside and, if such agreements exist, outside its boundaries. In contrast, outside customers are nonowner customers, and as such enjoy many of the benefits of the utility system with lower risk than that of the owners. As nonowners, these customers may have the ability to allow for the competition of service with an option to look to other entities to provide water service for them. Alternatively, a nonowner utility may have the option to develop its own water supply and system. Both of these can increase the risk of providing long-term service to the inside customers.

An important advantage for the owners of the system is that they are in a position to choose what the nature of the relationship will be with nonowner customers. Indeed, the owners may choose not to provide outside customer services at all. If outside customer services are provided, however, the owners may need to address the following issues:

- **Sharing the costs of "used and useful" assets.** Service to outside customers can take many different forms, particularly as it relates to the facilities needed to serve the outside customer. In many cases, the outside customers may not require or benefit from the entire water system, but only certain portions of it. When wholesale customers do not use or benefit from the owner's distribution system (i.e., smaller distribution pipes), they should not be expected to pay for that part of the system. In addition, outside service might be provided at different terms or levels of service. For example, providing raw (nonpotable) water service to customers located outside of the public utility's boundaries avoids the use of and costs associated with potable water treatment facilities. Care should be taken to understand what parts of the system are truly "used and useful" for the outside customer services being considered. In some cases, outside customers should be expected to pay the proportionate costs of the parts of the system used to provide them with services, but not for those components that are not used to deliver services to them. In other cases, the wholesale customer uses or benefits from most or all of the system, and should be expected to pay the proportionate cost of that use or benefit.

- **Governance.** The governing body of the owner utility (e.g., a city council, commission, board of trustees, board of directors) is considered the regulator of the utility and possesses the legal authority to act on behalf of all customers in making most, if not all, of the operational decisions affecting the utility. The legal authority to set and adjust rates is just one example. While the legal residents located within the boundaries of the local government have the ability to elect or appoint representatives to the governing body, the customers located outside of the local government's jurisdiction do not. When contemplating a service agreement for outside customer services, both parties should consider the political and legal dynamics involved.

- **Raising capital.** One of the responsibilities for the owner of the utility system is the responsibility to raise capital, as needed, to acquire and sustain the system assets. Both the owner and nonowner parties should consider how this will be accomplished in the long run and how outside customers will be expected to make capital contributions to a system that, ultimately, they do not own.

In some instances, as a matter of policy or based on contract negotiations, a public water utility might choose to waive the distinction between inside and outside customers. These arrangements might be considered metropolitan or regional in nature. In such a case, differences in costs between inside and outside customers are not recognized in cost allocation and rate-making, essentially placing outside customers on par with inside customers. This may result in the inside customers (i.e., owners) providing some subsidy to the outside customers (i.e., nonowners) when considering the above inherent differences between the two. Such a choice would be a policy decision of the utility's governing body.

Alternatively, the local government providing outside service may choose to offer services on terms like an investor-owned utility. A government-owned utility, which in most cases is not regulated by a public utility commission, usually determines its total revenue requirements on a cash-needs basis. However, as noted in section II, when that utility serves outside of its legal boundaries to nonowner customers, it is often appropriate to develop (or restate) the revenue requirements for the outside retail or wholesale customers on a utility basis, which provides for an appropriate (fair) return to the owners based on the value of the assets devoted to serving the nonowner customer groups. When properly established, the rate of return under the utility-basis approach is considered fair to both the owner (inside) customers and the nonowner (outside) customers. It compensates the owners for the risks incurred in providing services outside its jurisdictional boundaries, while at the same time protecting outside customers from excessive rates and fees.

Yet another option is for the local government to serve customers located outside of its jurisdictional limits under the terms of a negotiated contract rate, or using a stated rate differential (i.e., a multiplier of inside customer rates used to establish outside customer rates). If a stated rate differential is used, the owner utility should be able to provide documented cost justification for the rate and to investigate whether there are any laws that may apply to rate differentials, if that approach is taken. It should be noted that some jurisdictions have specific laws or guidelines regulating the rates public entities may charge customers located outside their jurisdictional limits.

Table VI.1-1 Comparison of the cash-needs and utility-basis revenue requirements

Cash-Needs Approach	Utility-Basis Approach
+ Operation and Maintenance Expenses	+ Operation and Maintenance Expenses
+ Taxes/Transfer Payments	+ Taxes/Transfer Payments
+ Debt Service	+ Net Depreciation Expense
+ Capital Improvements Funded From Rates	+ Return on Investment (Rate Base)
= Total Revenue Requirements	= Total Revenue Requirements

OUTSIDE-CUSTOMER RATE METHODOLOGIES

As was noted in section II, there are two generally accepted methods for the determination of the revenue requirements to establish rates. These two methods include the cash-needs approach and the utility-basis approach. Summarized in Table VI.1-1 is a simple comparison of these two methods.

In the situation where a utility serves retail or wholesale customers outside of its jurisdictional boundaries (e.g., for a city, the city limits), these two methods may be used in the establishment of the rates for service. In many instances, a third approach to the determination of revenue requirements is employed that is a hybrid of the cash-needs and utility-basis methodologies. This approach combines certain cost identification or allocation attributes of both methodologies in the development of the outside customer rates. The hybrid approach is discussed in more detail in the following sections.

For purposes of establishing outside-customer service rates, there are relative advantages and disadvantages of each of these approaches.

Cash-Needs Approach

The cash-needs approach is often used to set rates for inside and outside retail customers as well as wholesale customers. Its relative advantages for outside customer rate setting are similar to the advantages cited in section II and include

- conformity with public agency budgeting procedures (and accounting standards);
- compliance with rate covenants and flow of fund provisions typically included in a bond resolution/ordinance, indenture of trust, or loan agreement authorizing the issuance of debt by the public utility for capital funding;
- relative transparency, limited data requirements, and administrative simplicity;
- matching of revenue recovery and cash requirements; and
- easier to explain to the governing councils/commissions and boards of supervisors (regulators).

In many cases, the cash-needs approach involves not as much technical complexity and therefore costs relatively less for associated rate studies, record maintenance, and rate-updating procedures. At the same time, given the straightforward nature and relatively less complicated calculations of outside customer rates, it may facilitate better understanding and acceptance by outside customers. This may make the rate approval process, if not subject to state or provincial regulatory review, less subject to challenge and contention.

Utility-Basis Approach

The utility-basis approach is often used to set rates for outside customers, and in some jurisdictions, this approach is required. The relative advantages of the utility-basis approach for outside-customer rate setting include the following:

- Recognition of business and other risks
- Measure of protection for nonowner customers against potentially inefficient capital financing choices or inequitable interclass rate-setting practices of the owner
- Stabilization of periodic rate changes where significant fluctuations in revenue-funded or debt-financed capital improvements may impose year-to-year volatility in cash-needs-based rates
- Justification of the differential in rates charged to customers located inside and outside the jurisdictional limits of the local government. (Customers inside the limits allocate and recover certain costs associated with business risks arising from service delivery to nonowner customers, often resulting in lower utility bills for comparable inside owner customers.)
- Accord with several jurisdictions' public service or utility commission requirements

Hybrid Approach

The hybrid approach for outside-customer retail and wholesale rate development combines the cash-needs and utility-basis approach methods. This is the most common methodology when there is a difference in the rates charged for inside and outside service. There are two variations of the hybrid approach: *the utility basis with cash residual* and *the utility basis with rates of return differential*. These two methods will typically arrive at the same resulting rates.

The utility basis with cash residual begins by establishing the total combined revenue requirements for the utility (for all customers served, regardless of location) using the cash-needs approach. Revenue requirements for those customers located outside the jurisdictional boundaries of the utility are then determined using the utility basis reflecting operation and maintenance (O&M) expense, depreciation expense, and a fair rate of return on rate base allocable to these customers. Because the utility must meet all of its cash-needs revenue requirements, the utility-basis revenue requirement allocable to outside customers is then deducted from the total system revenue requirement, with the residual recovered from customers inside the utility's jurisdictional boundaries.

The utility basis with rates of return differential also begins by establishing the total combined revenue requirements for the utility using the cash-needs approach. Rather than simply deriving the inside customer rate based on the residual cash needs, an imputed (or resulting) rate of return can be derived for the inside customer rates to meet the cash needs. As with the cash residual approach, outside customers are charged a fair rate of return to recognize the risks of serving them and, if applicable, a return on investment to the owners. Resulting revenue requirements allocated to the outside customers then offset a portion of the total cash-needs-based revenue requirement, with the resulting rate of return charged to inside customers recovering the overall required system return. The two approaches end up with the same rates. The utility basis with rates of return differential adds the additional step of deriving the imputed rate of return. This is the methodology used in the example cost-of-service allocations presented in section III. Under this methodology, the resulting rate revenues collected in total should recover the "cash needs" revenue requirement of the utility.

The basis for the hybrid approach is that given their owner status and attendant risks and responsibilities, the owners of the utility are entitled to a reasonable and fair return from nonowner customers for their investment and delivery of services. This return is a cost component included in the utility-basis revenue requirements, and for outside customers, this return is charged within their revenue requirement in addition to their proportionate share of the O&M expenses, taxes, and depreciation expenses incurred to deliver services.

In many ways, a hybrid approach gleans the most important relative advantages of the cash- and utility-needs approaches. It enables recognition of an appropriate and fair return on investment allocable to nonowner customers, if applicable, while preserving consistency with public agency budgeting practices. As with the utility-basis approach, this method involves determination of an acceptable and fair rate of return for outside-customer service delivery. It requires maintenance of adequate asset records for valuation of the associated rate base.

Factors that affect the selection of the approach to determining revenue requirements include the ownership of the utility (public agency versus investor-owned), regulatory jurisdiction regarding the utility rates, consistency with budgeting procedures, contractual requirements, stakeholder acceptance, data availability, and whether the utility provides retail or wholesale service to its customers who are located outside the jurisdictional boundaries.

Outside Customer Contributions

In the development of the revenue requirements under the utility-basis or hybrid approach, consideration of any property or cash contributions made by the outside customers (referred to as contributions in aid of construction, or CIAC) is appropriate because the receipt of contributed capital directly reduces the owner utility's overall cost of investment. Such considerations are appropriate but more pronounced under the utility-basis or hybrid approach. In those cases, the rate base determined for the outside customer(s) is directly reduced by the amount of the contributions made. Oftentimes such contributions directly credit the specific outside customers who made the contributions and are amortized over time if appropriate. Thus, when calculating the outside-customer rate base in subsequent periods, the amortization of CIAC offsets, to some degree, the depreciation expense on the allocated rate base while the net remaining CIAC offsets the book value of those assets. Not only does this naturally result in a lower rate base for the outside customer, but also a reduced depreciation expense. In cases where non-depreciable property is contributed, however, there is no amortization of the contribution; the contributed capital would, in these cases, remain as a permanent reduction to the non-depreciable plant.

Ongoing Investment and Outside Customers

Another issue facing utilities providing services to outside customers is the issue of raising capital to fund ongoing investment in the system. To sustain the system, utilities are constantly making new capital investments to repair and replace the assets upgrade, or acquire new ones altogether. Because outside customers frequently do not use the entire system, an appropriate amount of discretion is necessary to ensure that such customers provide for only the portion of the system used and useful to them. There are many ways to satisfy this need within the cost-of-service principles described in this manual. The following are general approaches.

- *Invest-and-recover approach:* A relatively simple approach, if not more burdensome for the providing utility, is for the providing utility to raise the funds and financing to pay for all system improvements and subsequently recover the proportionate cost of the investment through the rates charged to outside customers.

The providing utility should account for new investments made in the system as part of the outside-customer's rate base to the extent that such investments are for used and useful assets.

- *Invest-and-contribute approach:* A second approach is to require the outside customer—in the service agreement, preferably—to contribute capital to offset all or part of their proportionate share of the system improvements at the time the investments are required. Under this approach, the outside customer would provide a contribution—normally in cash—as payment used to finance a portion of the individual projects. The contributions made would then be treated as CIAC, as described previously, in the determination of revenue requirements.

- *Fund management approach:* A third general approach is to include some form of annualized payment specifically identified for the purpose of offsetting future costs of system improvements as they arise. The annual payment could be included in the outside-customer's revenue requirements and charged as part of the customer's rate, or it could simply be an annual cash payment from the customer, or any combination of these. Under this approach, it is often useful to create a specific fund where the payments are deposited and from which the outside customer's share of system improvement costs are withdrawn. Although this approach may have conceptual appeal, in practice it is difficult to time investments such that the deposited funds are always adequate to meet the needs. As such, the initial capitalization of the fund is often important to determine early on, as is some method of true-up to ensure the fund remains adequately capitalized over time. As with any capital contributed by outside customers, the payments made under this approach should appropriately be treated as CIAC, as described previously.

Levels of Service and Outside-Customer Revenue Requirements

The levels of service provided to outside retail and wholesale customers, and the associated revenue requirements, may differ from inside-retail service, and it is important to understand these different levels of service to equitably allocate system facilities and costs.

Public water utilities can enter into a variety of arrangements for providing service to outside retail or wholesale customers. Generally, there are three common types of outside retail and wholesale services provided by a utility, each with its own unique consumption and cost-of-service characteristics. These service forms include (1) *firm commitment contracts* whereby the owner utility agrees to provide water to the outside retail or wholesale customers with the same level of service it provides to its own customers; (2) *surplus water contracts* whereby the owner utility agrees to sell water to an outside retail service area or to wholesale customers only if it has surplus water available; and (3) *emergency reciprocal contracts* whereby an owner utility and an adjacent utility that is located outside the legal limits of the owner utility providing service agree to provide each other with wholesale supplies during emergency periods or provide one another levels of service that place different demands and usage characteristics on a system.

As well as understanding the types of services being provided (a utility could provide all three types of service to another utility), it is also important to understand the plant facilities needed to provide the requested type of service and the associated costs of operation, maintenance, and replacement of such facilities. For example, certain dedicated facilities (e.g., transmission line) may be built to serve a specific outside retail or wholesale customer. The cost allocation methodology for outside retail or wholesale customer rate setting must fairly consider who built and paid for that dedicated facility. At the same time, depending on the service arrangement, outside retail or wholesale customers may not be allocated certain utility facility costs associated with typical inside-jurisdiction service (e.g., smaller distribution mains that are directly installed to serve only the customers located inside the jurisdictional limits of the local government).

Properly designed rates should recover the cost, as nearly as practicable, of providing service to a customer or a class of customers and minimize cross-subsidies among customer classes. In summary, the cost-of-service evaluation should take into consideration the specific conditions of service, particular type and level of service provided, and the specific circumstances associated with the transaction, such as the receipt of utility plant contributions by the public utility providing the service.

Risks Associated With Outside Customer Service

Justification for earning a fair rate of return is, in part, based on differences in risk to provide service to inside and outside retail and wholesale customers. This section provides a brief introduction to the issue of risk. Further details on the general principles of rate of return and risk can be found in chapter II.5.

If a local government or public water utility elects (or is compelled) to provide service to outside customers, it may assume some of the characteristics of an investor-owned utility. The providing utility must bear the risks and responsibilities of utility ownership. With limited exceptions and depending on the service agreement terms in the case of wholesale service, the service may not be unilaterally withdrawn, perhaps requiring essentially a permanent investment (both initial and ongoing capital and operating resources) by the providing utility to service outside customers. A utility providing service outside its jurisdictional boundaries may incur substantial risks in making this investment. These risks reflect the degree of uncertainty of recovering cost, incurring unforeseen liabilities, and securing capital on favorable terms and are often identified under one or more of the following four general categories:

1. Business risk
2. Interest rate risk
3. Financial risk
4. Liquidity risk

Risk implies uncertainty as to both the amounts and timing of expected revenue or income and financial resources to fund utility revenue requirements. The following list summarizes these risks.

- **Business risk.** This risk category relates to the uncertainty and consequences of events that result in the inability of the utility to earn sufficient revenues to meet its financial obligations and earn a reasonable return on investment. It is perhaps the single most important risk factor and is commonly cited by court authorities. In most cases, public water utilities providing outside-customer retail and/or wholesale services are ultimately responsible for paying all operating expenses and capital costs incurred by the utility and must maintain compliance with all regulations imposed on the utility. They bear the risk of tort liability and civil penalties related to system operations and construction activities. They also bear the risk of unexpected operational issues and the requirement to maintain service at a level as defined in the service agreement with the outside customer. Unexpected expenses, changes in regulations (local, state or provincial, and federal), or changes in service demographics that may result in insufficient revenues may impact fund balances and financial performance of the utility providing outside customer service. The utility may also incur specific debt obligations and direct O&M costs solely to serve outside customers, and such costs could continue even if the outside customers elect to reduce or discontinue service. This business risk can be somewhat mitigated if the providing utility has a strong agreement with the wholesale customer to provide the utility service outside of the providing utility's legal boundaries (service exclusivity, term of service and ability to extend term if bonds are issued for future capital expenditures benefitting the outside customers, delineation of capacity reservation or entitlement, rate-setting methodology, ability to receive property and cash contributions to finance capital expenditures, etc.).

- **Interest rate risk.** This is the risk that investors undertake when they are required to make long-term investments to expand or maintain capital facilities and the future interest rates are unknown. Interest rate risk is the risk that the value of an investment will change because of the change in the absolute level of interest rates. Interest rate risk generally affects the value of bonds (which is a primary source of external capital for public utilities) more directly than stocks (which is a significant source of capital for investor-owned utilities). Interest rate risk is a major risk to all bondholders. An investor who makes a long-term investment with a fixed interest rate will suffer a loss if interest rates rise and will realize a gain if interest rates fall in terms of opportunity cost. For water utilities, this risk can be at least partially avoided by the issuance of fixed interest rate bonds or other debt instruments with call provisions to finance their investment in assets used to serve customers outside their boundaries (to allow for the refinancing of the debt at lower interest rates). If short-term or variable interest rate debt is used, the water utility will likely bear some interest rate risk.

- **Financial risk.** This is the risk that a public utility will not have adequate cash flow to meet its financial obligations. As noted previously, owners may be required to make long-term investments in facilities to provide service to customers located outside their boundaries. By extending service outside the jurisdictional boundaries, the providing utility will typically require a significant commitment of funds to finance the utility plant facilities necessary to provide service to such outside customers. For public utilities, this up-front capital investment is normally financed by long-term debt. With higher levels of debt, the local government may be more heavily leveraged due to the cash-flow claims associated with repayment of debt obligations (i.e., principal and interest payments), resulting in an increased amount of fixed costs. This higher fixed cost increases the risk that a local government may not have adequate cash flow to meet its financial obligations and may dampen the ability to issue future debt due to increased capital financing requirements (e.g., higher financial risk may result in a credit agency rating downgrade, which would increase the cost of borrowing or the requirement to fund a debt-service reserve fund from bond proceeds as a hedge against nonpayment of the debt payments). Some forms of long-term debt also have debt ceilings limiting the amount of future debt that can be issued. Committing debt capacity to finance water system infrastructure serving outside customers may thereby decrease the local government's ability to issue future bonds for other utility and nonutility purposes by the primary service provider. Finally, if the amount of long-term debt is increased, the proportional amount of equity in the capital structure may result in a corresponding total rate of return being reduced (generally the cost of equity has a higher rate of return than the cost to borrow). This increases the financial risk of the system as a whole and could result in an increase to the local government's cost of capital.

- **Liquidity risk.** This reflects the investors' ability to convert their investment into cash or other marketable securities without a significant loss of principal such that the proceeds can be spent or reinvested. Liquidity represents the ability to fund assets and meet obligations as they become due. Liquidity is essential to local governments to compensate for expected and unexpected balance sheet fluctuations (e.g., changes in cash flow affecting financial position) and to provide funds for capital expansion or reinvestment. Liquidity risk is the risk of not being able to obtain funds at a reasonable price within a reasonable time period to meet obligations as they become due. As previously noted, when a local government finances the cost to construct infrastructure in order to extend service to outside customers, its funds will effectively be permanently committed to this investment, imposing liquidity risk.

Although each of these risks may prevail for an individual public water utility providing service outside its jurisdictional boundaries, perhaps the most difficult aspect for the determination of the rates for outside customer service is the assessment and quantification of the relative significance of these risk factors for purposes of assigning or determining a rate of return. Considerations include the following:

- The potential exists for outside customers to terminate (or fail to renew) their service contracts and either go elsewhere for service or build their own water supply and treatment plant. This could result in the owner utility operating and maintaining assets that have been upsized to serve such outside customers. This risk can be quantified by estimating the probability of termination, and multiplying this probability by the amount of un-recouped (stranded) invested capital.

- Outside-customer service contracts may insulate the owner from the consequences of selected risk factors discussed above by requiring a contribution toward the cost of facilities constructed to serve the respective outside customer as a condition of service, or by having provisions to enable the future recovery of un-recouped capital investments and unforeseen prior period expenses if a discontinuance of service occurs.

- The use of risk-mitigating financial instruments (e.g., insurance, reserves) and the inclusion of their associated expenses in revenue requirements allocable to outside customers may reduce certain risks.

- The extent of development of infrastructure for services to outside customers both increases and reduces selected risks. For example, water transmission main networking to deliver outside service may provide enhanced reliability for inside customers as well as outside customers. On the other hand, transmission of water to potentially more remote areas, where land-use development practices are not within the local government's jurisdiction, may engender higher risks of water quality degradation or pipeline failures.

For individual utilities, these considerations may have greater or lesser bearing. For example, in some cases, the potential for customers located outside the jurisdictional boundaries of the local government providing the service to discontinue or reduce services is quite pronounced while in other cases outside customers have no viable alternatives. In any event, inherent in the determination of fair rate of return is the assessment of these risks along with recognition that prudent utility enterprise management and sound business judgment may effectively mandate some return on investment.

Rate of Return Determination

As previously discussed, the rate of return and associated return component of revenue requirements (whether on a hybrid or utility basis) is intended, in part, to recognize the inherent risk factors involved in constructing and replacing infrastructure and delivering water services to outside customers. A significant amount of effort may be required by the inside and outside customer parties to achieve a mutually agreeable rate of return and to establish valuation of the rate base. As discussed in section II, *rate base* is defined as the net utility investment, less allowances for nonused and useful plant and unamortized contributions in aid of construction that is in service for a particular service area or customer class. Differences of viewpoints may need to be reconciled on appropriate compensation for enterprise operations and the significance of the owner's risk factors considered in determining rates of return. Appropriate procedures need to be defined for the determination and identification of historical construction costs and applicable depreciation rates allocable to the outside-customer service class. These mutually agreed-on methods should be documented in the outside-customer service agreement so that periodic updates to accurately reflect potential fluctuations and changes in cost and operations can be quantified.

If the utility-basis approach is used, calculation of an acceptable rate of return for owner and nonowner customers must be undertaken. As described in section II.5, a weighted average cost of capital analysis is the generally accepted method. The analysis considers the utility's weighted cost of debt and equity. In most cases, the utility's actual proportion of capital funded with debt and with equity is used to calculate the weighted average cost of capital. However, in some cases, the capital structure of the owning utility may be so unusual that an imputed capital debt/equity structure should be substituted.

The first component of the weighted average cost of capital is the proportion of invested capital funded with debt multiplied by the average weighted interest rate of all the outstanding debt. This can be determined from the utility's outstanding debt-service schedules. The second component is the proportion of the invested capital funded with equity multiplied by the cost of equity. This is the most difficult component of the cost of capital to calculate because there is generally no direct measure cost of equity for a local government utility.

Four potential methods to determine the second component (the return on equity) of the weighted cost of capital analysis and the rate of return are as follows:

1. Review rates of return on equity that may have been approved or published by a regional public service commission in recent rate hearings for investor-owned utilities. Differences between those investor-owned utilities and the publicly owned utilities must be considered, such as the profit requirement for investor-owned utilities, the difference between tax free and taxable borrowing, and differences in risk characteristics.

2. Establish the cost of equity using a discounted cash-flow analysis or other method that may have been approved or published by a public service commission in the utility's region.

3. Use a risk-free rate of return, such as long-term US Treasury Bond yields, and then add an appropriate risk premium negotiated by the contracting parties. This could include adding a defined equity risk premium and/or other premiums to the risk-free rate based on published information.

4. Use a multiplier on top of an embedded debt interest rate.

In the utility-basis approach, the specific return component is calculated by multiplying the rate base allocated to the outside customer class by the rate of return determined for that outside customer class. The definition and calculation of rate base is discussed in section II. Stated another way, the calculation is based on the value of the owners' assets that are used and useful in providing service to nonowners multiplied by the weighted average cost of capital (rate of return) for the utility. Differences in the weighted average cost of capital applicable to inside-customer versus outside-customer service provide a mechanism to determine a rate differential between the respective customer classes or service types.

Outside-Customer Retail and Wholesale Classifications

Fundamentally, the structuring of customer classes for outside service is a reflection of several rate-making decisions. In the event that a utility elects (or is required) to address outside retail or wholesale customer services separately to either recognize cost-of-service differentials or advance public policies (or both), separate rate classifications are likely required. Similarly, policy objectives or differences in service characteristics across outside customer groups may necessitate further disaggregation of the outside-customer retail rate classes (outside residential, commercial, etc.), but also across multiple wholesale customers (e.g., wholesale customer A, wholesale customer B).

As with inside-customer retail service, determining the appropriate outside-customer classification structure is a matter of balancing multiple objectives. Greater disaggregation of customer classes imposes greater administrative, customer service, and stakeholder engagement requirements (as discussed further below), yet may advance equity and public policy considerations.

Reasons for grouping customers into separate classifications include similarities in service characteristics, use of common facilities, ownership status, and to further public policy or economic pricing objectives. For wholesale customers, the nature of this type of service (sales for resale) alone justifies inclusion of this service as a separate class of customer. Because most wholesale customers do not use the providing utility's smaller distribution main system and perhaps other facilities, a separate classification and rate schedule is typically warranted. For outside retail customers, however, usage characteristics may (or may not) be similar to inside-retail users, and a separate classification may be used to recognize the differences in status. Therefore, customer classification for utilities providing service to customers located both inside and outside their jurisdictional limits can add a significant degree of complexity. For example, Table VI.1-2 provides rate classes for a hypothetical utility providing differing levels of service to a diverse mix of inside and outside retail and wholesale customers, each with their own unique water consumption and usage characteristics. Note that the rate classes shown in Table VI.1-2 are associated only with the provision of treated potable water service. Utilities may also have multiple rate classes for raw and recycled water service.

Perhaps the most important issues and questions that arise when developing rate classes for outside customer situations are the following:

- Is it necessary to calculate separate inside and outside service area revenue requirements? To earn a fair return on the investment to serve outside retail or wholesale customers, if applicable, the cost-of-service analysis may require this separation of customer classes of service. Some wholesale contracts specify the method to determine the rate of return, and this rate of return may be different from the rate of return for other outside retail customers. In many cases, the outside-retail customer rate classes "mirror" the utility's inside-retail customer rate classes.

- Does the utility provide differing levels of service to inside and outside customers? Public water utilities can provide a variety of service solutions to customers located outside of its legal jurisdiction depending on their contractual obligations to outside jurisdictions, such as suburban areas. If a public water utility provides

Table VI.1-2 Treated-water customer rate classes for a hypothetical public water utility*

Inside-Retail Customers	Outside Retail Customers		Outside Wholesale Customers
	Full Service	Limited Service	
Single Family	Single Family	Single Family	Wholesale Customer A
Multifamily	Multifamily	Multifamily	Wholesale Customer B
Commercial	Commercial		
Metered Irrigation	Metered Irrigation		

*This hypothetical utility provides treated water to customers located inside and outside its jurisdictional boundaries.

significantly different levels of service to outside customers, it may be necessary to develop separate outside customer classes for each level of service.

- Do outside customers exhibit significantly different usage characteristics or otherwise impose appreciably different costs to deliver services warranting their segregation into separate classes (following the general prescriptions for customer classification)? Given significantly different demands for service, a public water utility may establish customer classes for outside users that generally correspond to those used for inside users (e.g., single-family, multifamily, commercial).

In summary, care should be taken in developing and establishing the customer classes. For administrative purposes, it may be desirable to have as few classes of service as possible while still recognizing the issues previously discussed and the objective of equitable, cost-based rates for outside retail and wholesale customers. Chapters VI.2 and VI.3 provide a more detailed description of customer classification and cost allocation approaches for outside retail and wholesale customers, respectively.

IMPLEMENTATION AND ADMINISTRATION CONSIDERATIONS

The implementation and administration of outside customer rates can create a variety of accounting, data management, and financial reporting issues not generally encountered when a utility solely provides service within its jurisdictional boundaries or service areas.

Accounting Requirements

Public water utilities providing service to outside customers face accounting and record-keeping issues of greater complexity than those utilities that only provide service within their jurisdictional boundaries or service areas. This is especially true if the utility-basis method is used to calculate revenue requirements because this method involves the application of a differential rate of return on different components of the utility's rate base. According to either method, outside-customer service rates may reflect allocations of specifically assignable costs that, in turn, may require the accounting system to provide information regarding the geographic location of specific fixed assets and identification of customers that use or benefit from the asset. The accounting system must also have the ability to track grants, system development charges, and other contributions in aid of construction associated with specific assets because they reduce the total value of the rate base.

Financial and Operational Reporting

Because outside customers are not a constituency of the public water utility's rate-setting body, interested stakeholders may require financial and operational data to gauge the appropriateness of the outside customer rates to which they are subject. Detailed and transparent financial and operational reports can reduce the possibility of future controversy or litigation. Such reports can also build trust in the outside customer rate-making process and make it easier to implement future outside-customer rate increases or rate-design changes.

The reporting requirements of a public water utility providing service outside its boundaries should reflect the data required for the cost-of-service and rate-making methods being applied. It is often useful, particularly in instances of wholesale service, for service agreements to include or reference the detailed rate calculations that identify the source data and variables that must be incorporated into rate calculations. The amount and detail of information provided to interested stakeholders may vary by situation, and may include, but are not necessarily limited, to the following:

- Calculations of respective rate base values
- Depreciation expenses
- Contribution amounts and amortization of contributions
- Imputed and/or explicit rates of return

Regulatory Reporting Requirements

Public utility commissions or similar regulatory agencies impose a variety of ongoing reporting requirements on the utilities that they regulate. They also require substantial evidentiary support for proposed rate increases in the form of detailed revenue requirement calculations and cost-of-service studies. In cases where a public utility commission does have regulatory authority over a public water utility, the reporting requirements they must comply with are generally similar to those of their investor-owned counterparts. In addition to the financial and operational reports previously described, regulators may require utilities that are governed by a public utility commission to submit any of the following:

- Annual reports presented in accordance with a mandated uniform system of accounts. Such annual reports often provide a variety of operational and statistical data in addition to traditional financial statements such as balance sheets and income statements.
- Annual and/or quarterly reports detailing purchased water costs, especially if a utility is required to impose an explicit rate surcharge on customer bills for such costs.
- Annual and/or quarterly reports detailing the extra revenues that must be recovered from customers to compensate the utility for revenues lost due to water conservation programs. Such reports often involve the imposition of an explicit rate surcharge on customer bills for those costs if a utility is subject to a so-called lost revenue adjustment or revenue decoupling mechanism.
- Annual updates of the utility's integrated resource plan (if required).
- Comprehensive integrated resource plans (usually filed with public utility commissions every three to five years, if required) that include long-range demand forecasts, along with a detailed discussion of the portfolio of supply and demand-side management resources projected to meet the demand.

Demand Management Issues

The demands placed on the customer information system of a public water utility providing service outside its jurisdictional boundaries or service area can often be significant. This is especially true if the unique characteristics of inside and outside customers require the customer information system to produce multiple bill frequency reports to support class-specific rate designs. Some of the data management issues potentially encountered by public water utilities providing outside service include the need to

- collect and analyze information regarding both inside and outside customers, such as the number and size of service connections, lot sizes, irrigable area, number of residents or dwelling units, type of commercial establishments, and so on;
- bill, store, and analyze water consumption and revenue information for multiple inside- and outside-retail customer rate classes, as well as multiple wholesale customer rate classes; and
- bill multiple inside- and outside-retail customer rate classes according to a variety of rate designs. For example, a utility providing outside service could bill its different outside customer classes using a uniform rate design as well as seasonal, inclining, or declining block rate structures.

Reviews and Updates

Prudent financial management practices dictate that all public water utilities, regardless of their size or complexity, should prepare demand forecasts, operating budgets, and revenue requirement calculations on an annual or biannual basis. These respective analyses will assist the utility in assessing whether it should perform a cost-of-service study to calculate updated outside customer rates.

In general, in situations of limited demand growth and stable operating expenses, debt service, and capital expenditures, a detailed cost-of-service or rate-design analysis may not be warranted on an annual or biannual basis. Updates of system revenue requirements and distributions of costs to customer classes in the same proportions as in prior years (i.e., based on detailed prior cost studies) may suffice. However, utilities that experience significant year-to-year changes in their customer base, demands, operating expenses, debt service, and capital expenditures will likely need to revisit their allocations of revenue responsibilities to customer classes to preserve cost-of-service relationships or intended policy-based rate relationships. The benefits of performing regular rate reviews and implementing updated inside and outside customer rates include

- adequate revenue recovery that helps to ensure the cash flow and financial stability of the utility,
- accurate class-specific revenue requirement recovery for both inside and outside customers,
- water rates that send price signals to customers reflecting the most up-to-date cost of service, and
- enhanced transparency and trust in the outside customer rate-making process on the part of interested stakeholders.

STAKEHOLDER INVOLVEMENT AND PUBLIC COMMUNICATIONS

The process of developing and implementing outside customer rates is subject to a variety of political and public policy pressures not often encountered when service is restricted to customers within a common jurisdictional boundary. Outside customer rates that deviate significantly from similarly situated users within jurisdictional boundaries may become controversial and draw the scrutiny of a variety of interested stakeholders. In this context, the potential to build positive relations with outside customers (and avoid costly and contentious litigation) is generally enhanced when public water utilities have reasonable, documented, and well-communicated rationales for their outside customer rate-making practices.

Although these imperatives are generally true, stakeholder engagement and public communications related to outside customer service present many unique opportunities and challenges. In particular, outside-customer rate setting requires effective stakeholder engagement and public communications to ensure understanding of why outside customers are segregated into separate customer classes. In so doing, it is important to directly address customer concerns of why rates are different between geographic boundaries when the physical requirements of delivering water service across such boundaries may appear to be negligible or nonexistent. For wholesale service, there is often the need to distinguish as to what extent ratepayers' bills are driven by wholesale rate components and what share of ratepayer revenues recover wholesale customers' service delivery costs.

Finally, all parties involved in delivery of services to outside customers should be fully cognizant of the legal framework within which rate-setting practices are adjudicated. This framework is best defined by the provisions contained in outside-customer service contracts, state or provincial and/or any applicable federal legal standards, and observing applicable legal precedent established through case law. In addition, many utilities are subject to regulation by public service or utility commissions, many of which have guidelines for calculating rates.

The opportunities and challenges may suggest several stakeholder engagement and communication activities targeted to outside customers. For example, many utilities have had particular success in establishing Stakeholder Advisory Committees to oversee rate-setting practices. Outside customer representation on these committees may help ensure that outside customer concerns are given a voice in such committees' deliberations. Further, utilities may meet separately with outside customer groups or representatives to address particular concerns and ensure understanding of rate-making practices. In any event, given that outside customers are not a constituency of public water utilities' elected or appointed officials, these utilities carry added responsibility to clearly and effectively communicate the basis of their outside customer rates.

SUMMARY

Public water utilities' provision of services outside their jurisdictions has the potential to realize significant benefits for all parties. Outside customers may avoid having to develop (all or major portions of) expensive water system infrastructure required to meet their service needs. Public water utilities may achieve economies of scale benefiting all customer groups and earn fair returns for their delivery of services beyond their jurisdictional boundaries. In calculating outside-customer water rates, there are different, generally accepted methods for determining the cost of providing outside service and the associated revenue requirements, each with relative advantages and disadvantages. The determination of appropriate bases and rates of return for delivery of outside services is largely a reflection of each utility's assessment of its risks and public policies. When appropriate, a public water utility may elect to segregate its outside customers into separate customer classes to enable class-specific cost allocation and rate setting. Finally, similar to inside customers, there are a variety of alternative rate designs that may be used to recover the allocated outside-customer revenue responsibilities and advance public policies. These outside customer rate-setting practices carry several additional stakeholder engagement and implementation requirements to ensure that all parties understand the direct and indirect costs associated with providing services outside of jurisdictional boundaries and the benefits received due to the provision of such services.

Chapter **VI.2**

Outside Retail Rates

Public water utilities often provide retail service to customers located outside of the utility's jurisdictional boundaries. Outside retail customers typically use all of the functions of the water system, including the distribution system and meter, and customer-service functions. Outside retail customers differ from wholesale customers who tend to have limited points of delivery from the owning utility's supply and/or transmission system and do not significantly use distribution, meter, or customer-service functions. Establishment of a service arrangement with outside retail customers may enable mutually beneficial efficiencies in service delivery and realization of economies of scale.

This chapter discusses rate-setting considerations for retail customers who are located outside of a public water utility's jurisdictional boundaries, and offers technical guidance for the development of cost-based rates to serve outside retail customers that may assist in withstanding regulatory and/or legal review and may enhance public and stakeholder acceptance.

BENEFITS OF PROVIDING OUTSIDE RETAIL SERVICE

When a utility agrees to serve outside customers on a retail basis, it takes on additional risks and responsibilities in providing such service, and in return may obtain a number of direct and indirect benefits. Such benefits include

- receiving a fair rate of return for the risk of serving outside customers;
- realizing economies of scale by constructing and operating larger facilities—potentially lowering the average cost of service system-wide;
- avoiding or eliminating multiple system redundancy in terms of the cost of administering, managing, operating, and maintaining separate treatment and conveyance infrastructure and back office operations; and
- potentially allowing the ability to better manage water resources on a more holistic, watershed-wide basis.

OUTSIDE RETAIL RATE METHODOLOGIES

Generally accepted methods for establishing revenue requirements, including the cash-needs approach, the utility-basis approach, and the hybrid approach, along with the rate differential approach, may be used in the situation where a utility serves outside customers on a retail basis. Please refer to section II and chapter VI.1 for a more detailed discussion of these approaches.

Rate Differential Approach

For many years, some utilities have simply applied a multiplier to the retail rate schedule for inside customers to establish the rates applicable to outside customers (e.g., inside customer rate × 1.5 multiplier = outside customer rate). By definition, the use of arbitrary multipliers to determine outside customer rates does not conform to cost-based rate-making practices. However, it is possible to establish a rate differential based on cost-based principles and cost allocations that fairly reflect the relationship between the parties. The application of multipliers in determining outside customer rates is therefore not, in and of itself, indicative of the use of a non-cost-based rate-setting approach. However, in many cases, cost-based principles are not used to establish these multipliers, which leaves the utility potentially open to a legal challenge over the cost justification for outside customer rates.

Justifications often cited for using a "multiplier" approach to establish rate differentials between inside and outside customers are historical precedent, simplicity, and cost savings. From a public policy perspective, such rate differentials may encourage or incentivize annexation or advance other public policy objectives. These rate differentials may easily conform to local government budgeting practice, convey a mutually acceptable benefit to utility system owners by outside customers, and avoid requirements for extensive record keeping and rate calculations. However, several jurisdictions have adopted legislation that limits rate differentials applicable to outside customers without a cost-of-service justification and that precedent and simplified rate-making, as well as unclear contract terms, do not insulate parties from possible legal challenges.

Utilities can minimize the potential risk for legal challenges and improve the defensibility of their outside rate differential by periodically completing a cost-of-service analysis using the utility-basis or hybrid approach to validate the multiplier that is being used to establish the rates for outside customers. This periodic validation of the multiplier provides a balance between the simplicity and cost savings associated with this approach and the rigor and technical complexity of the utility-basis or hybrid approach. It also helps to demonstrate the cost justification for the multiplier that is employed.

Table VI.2-1 provides an example of how a rate multiplier would be calculated for an outside customer class, where the providing utility is a city. The cost of service for inside and outside customers is first calculated, for example, as shown in Tables III.2-5 and III.2-6 under the base-extra capacity method and commodity-demand methods, respectively. This information can then be used to calculate an average unit rate for each customer class by dividing the total cost of service by the annual billed usage, as shown in Table VI.2-1. The average rate for outside customer classes can then be compared to the average rate for the corresponding inside customer classes, and a rate multiplier can be calculated. As shown in Table VI.2-1, the average rate for the outside residential customer class is approximately 1.16 times and 1.18 times the average rate for the inside residential class under the base-extra capacity method and commodity-demand method, respectively. This method of calculating the multiplier for outside retail customers typically results in multipliers in the range of 1.0 to 2.0.

Table VI.2-1 Calculating outside-customer rate multipliers

Line No.	Customer Class	Total Cost of Service*	Base Units of Service, 1,000 gal	Average Unit Rate, $/1,000 gal	Multiplier (4) / (1) (9) / (6)
Base-Extra Capacity Method					
Inside City:					
1	Residential	$5,011,889	968,000	$5.18	
2	Commercial	1,399,435	473,000	2.96	
3	Industrial	2,302,435	1,095,000	2.10	
Outside City:					
4	Residential	569,369	95,000	5.99	1.16
5	Wholesale	716,801	230,000	3.12	0.60
Commodity-Demand Method					
Inside City:					
6	Residential	5,117,409	968,000	5.29	
7	Commercial	1,382,580	473,000	2.92	
8	Industrial	2,111,837	1,095,000	1.93	
Outside City:					
9	Residential	592,156	95,000	6.23	1.18
10	Wholesale	$727,048	230,000	$3.16	0.60

*Total cost of service by customer class from Tables III.2-5 and III.2-6.

Levels of Service and Outside-Customer Revenue Requirements

The level of service provided to outside retail customers is often the same as that provided to inside retail customers. However, in establishing rates for outside retail customers, it is important to understand the facilities, and associated cost of owning and operating such facilities, that are needed to provide this level of retail service. To serve outside retail customers, certain dedicated facilities (e.g., transmission lines, pumping facilities) may be needed, and the cost allocation methodology must fairly consider who built and paid for the dedicated facilities. For example, outside customers may be located in a different pressure zone than inside customers due to the service area's topography, and therefore require more, or less, extensive pumping and storage facilities to provide the same level of service. Properly designed rates should, as nearly as is practicable, recover the cost and compensation for risks of providing service to a customer, or a class of customers, inside and outside of the jurisdictional limits, with minimal cross-subsidizing among customer classes.

Cost Allocation for Outside Retail Customers

Although the revenue requirement methodologies discussed above will, in general, be applicable in determining the cost of serving outside retail customers, some additional cost allocation issues may arise when a utility's outside customers are segregated into separate customer classes.

The primary cost allocation issues associated with separately classified outside customers are estimating water demands, determining applicable outside and inside jurisdictional limit costs, distance and elevation, and peaking factors.

Estimating water demands. Developing customer water demand estimates requires a comprehensive understanding of historical customer consumption characteristics. This can impose additional requirements on public water utilities providing outside retail service if for no other reason than it requires them to complete detailed analyses of the consumption characteristics of both their inside and outside customers. Notably, outside retail customer demand patterns may be significantly different from those of inside retail classes for many reasons. In particular, land-use characteristics of outside service areas may differ from the retail service area within the utility's jurisdictional limits, reflecting differences in degree of urbanization or composition of the commercial base. Residential demand patterns may even vary dramatically because of differences in density of housing stock, lot sizes, and relative levels of affluence. When outside retail classes of service are segregated within the cost of service, the importance of accurately and fairly recognizing any differences in water demands (average and peak use) between customers inside and outside jurisdictional limits is magnified.

Determining applicable outside and inside costs. An important element of determining outside retail customer costs is understanding and recognizing the facilities needed to serve these customers. The facilities needed to serve outside retail customers may vary based on the level of service for the delivery of water, along with the geographic location of the outside retail customers. In addition, specific investments in facilities dedicated to serving these outside retail customers may need to be made. Recognizing the facilities serving these customers while equitably and fairly distributing the associated costs within the cost-of-service analysis is often challenging. Further, outside retail customer classes present several important cost allocation considerations related to fire protection and non-revenue water. Non-revenue water for the retail system would include water that is not billed and is generally due to a variety of events, including water distribution line loss (e.g., water main breaks), customer service line leaks, water used for firefighting and line flushing, internal utility water use such as for the cleaning of lift or pumping stations, and under-registration of retail meters. All customers, including outside retail customers, should be assigned a pro rata share or allocation of the costs associated with non-revenue water.

Distance and elevation. Distance and elevation of the outside retail customers relative to the source of supply may be a factor in establishing rate differentials, but does not necessarily dictate a cost-of-service differential or the need for a different rate. In situations where such physical characteristics are pronounced, a differential rate may be warranted. For example, if the outside retail customers are located far away or elevated from the source of supply, increased costs due to additional pumping over longer distances or higher elevations, or higher capacity factors may be judged to be significant enough to warrant separate treatment for cost recovery. Such rate differentials, if necessary, may also be applicable to customers inside jurisdictional limits (e.g., elevation surcharges). However, some unique situations or circumstances may occur in which the outside retail customers are located near the source of supply or treatment plant. This case may suggest that a limited amount of infrastructure is needed to deliver water to the customers; therefore, the costs allocated to the outside retail customers would be lower. In many instances, source of supply and treatment facilities may actually be located outside of the utility's jurisdictional limits.

Peaking factors. Properly developed cost-based rates are designed to reflect the equitable allocation of costs assigned to utility functions based on relative contributions to system total volumetric demands (consumption) and peak-use events (e.g., maximum day and/or peak hour). In general, individual outside retail customer classes may simply be included in this cost allocation procedure and receive their proportionate share of system costs. In this respect, there is no procedural distinction between inside and outside retail users for allocation of costs to service characteristics. However, peaking factors will have to be determined or estimated for all outside-retail customer classes to appropriately make allocations of costs to customer classes.

In many cases, outside-retail customer classes are a mirror image of similar customer classifications of retail users within the jurisdictional limits of the utility. In other cases, outside-retail customer classes may be different than inside customer classes because of the makeup and characteristics of customers in each respective portion of the utility service area. Customers within a common utility service area are often segregated into inside and outside residential and nonresidential classes of service. In this circumstance, examination of the respective peaking factors calculated for inside as compared to outside users may inform and provide a check on the validity of peaking factor assignments. Similar demand characteristics between similarly situated customer groups may affirm that the rate class distinctions are solely to capture ownership cost differences. Significant differences between inside- and outside-customer peaking factor assignments may signal inaccuracies in billing data or calculation procedures—or may reflect true differences in demand characteristics that further support class segregation. For example, instances of higher outside-residential peaking factors than inside customers may give pause, but also may simply reflect demand pattern differences due to larger lot sizes and irrigation demands among suburban residential users. Tables III.2-1 and III.2-2 provide an example of possible differences in peaking factors for customer classes located inside and outside a utility's jurisdictional boundaries.

Use of consistent procedures and reconciliation of assigned demands to those observed from individual utilities' system production or customer demand metering is important to ensure accuracy and prevent unintended interclass subsidizations. Especially insofar as system diversity and demand peaking factors are developed using a variety of assumptions related to individual class demand patterns, it is important to ensure consistency with individual utilities' monitored production and customer demands data.

Rate Design for Outside-Retail Customer Classes

As with service within the jurisdictional boundary of the utility, once outside retail water demands are appropriately estimated and costs are allocated to applicable outside-retail customer classes, water rates to recover allocated costs must be designed. Fundamental principles of rate design are applicable for outside-retail customer class rate designs as well. Accordingly, it may be quite appropriate for public water utilities providing service outside their jurisdictional limits to have multiple rate designs, each specifically intended to correspond to the unique cost and consumption characteristics of individual inside- and outside-retail customer rate classes. For example, a public water utility serving customers both inside and outside its jurisdictional limits in a major metropolitan area might bill some retail customer classes using a uniform rate design, other retail customer classes using various types of seasonal rate designs, and still other retail customer classes using various forms of inclining block rate designs. As discussed in chapter IV.1, the choice of rate structure is dependent on the philosophy and objectives of the utility and community, and subject to legal considerations. Notwithstanding the providing utility's discretion to impose different rate structures, many utilities choose to apply the same structure to both inside and outside customers with appropriate recognition for cost-based differentials determined in the cost-of-service analysis.

This page intentionally blank.

Chapter **VI.3**

Outside
Wholesale Rates

As discussed in chapter VI.1, public water utilities often provide service to customers located outside the local government's legal boundaries or service area on both a retail and/or wholesale basis. Using cost-based principles and methodologies to set rates for such customers is the most proven and accepted way to achieve equitable rates generally. This chapter discusses rate-setting considerations for wholesale service provided outside a utility's legal boundaries or service area.

Wholesale service can include several types of service arrangements but generally refers to those customers who buy water for resale. This service provision is generally provided pursuant to the terms of a negotiated service agreement between a providing utility, the "owner," who owns and operates assets necessary to deliver water to one or more points of delivery to a purchasing utility, and the wholesale customer, who buys water at those points of delivery and then resells it elsewhere. Wholesale customers tend to have a limited number of points of delivery with the owning utility's supply and/or transmission system and do not significantly use the owner utility's local distribution network, meter, or customer-service functions related to providing retail service. These types of costs are usually directly incurred by the purchasing utility as it conveys water through its own water delivery system to its own retail and/or other customers.

The guidance provided in this chapter may assist in addressing and limiting any regulatory and/or legal review, and may enhance owner and purchasing utility relationships in the establishment of the agreements and rates for wholesale water service.

DEFINITION OF WHOLESALE SERVICE

With the rise of regional partnerships in the water industry, variations of what constitutes wholesale service have become more prevalent. A simple definition is that wholesale service occurs when a purchasing utility is buying water services from a separate owner utility for the purpose of reselling such water to the purchasing utility's retail or other customers. Embedded in this definition is the notion of ownership. When a utility "owns" assets, it also owns the responsibility for operating and maintaining those assets, and it directly incurs all of the related costs and risks for service. The owner utility is then responsible for providing wholesale service to the purchasing utility.

Although the single-owner transaction is the most common wholesale service arrangement, there is a growing trend in the water industry for regional partnerships where, on a contractual or other legal basis, multiple parties jointly own water supply, treatment, and transmission facilities, and/or jointly own the costs of constructing, operating, and/or maintaining those facilities. There can be many forms of joint ownership of a regional facility (primary owner with other participants having contractual rights, separate entity created by all participants, etc.), but it is important to note that fractional rather than single ownership is emerging as an important trend. Understanding how the principles in this manual apply to such arrangements is therefore increasingly important, especially if both the owner and purchasing utility are parties to such a regional agreement.

In a typical wholesale arrangement, both the owner utility and the purchasing utility own certain assets, but the purchasing utility may own insufficient assets to provide all of the services it needs to serve its retail customers. This limitation in utility asset ownership by a purchasing utility can be for many reasons, including the recognition of economies of scale achieved from the operation of regional facilities, the lack of adequate sites for or access to water supply and treatment, among others. These limitations, either full or partial, are the gaps that wholesale service can fill and is the basis for identifying the owner utility's costs of providing wholesale service. Any costs incurred by the owner utility that are not otherwise compensated by the purchasing utility in some other way are legitimate costs to be recovered from a wholesale rate.

TYPES OF WHOLESALE SERVICE

There are several types of wholesale service including, but not limited to, the following:

- *Raw water service*—the owner utility has the contractual rights to the water supply and delivers raw water for subsequent treatment and distribution by the purchasing utility. An example of this service relationship would be if an owner utility owned a water supply reservoir and sold a portion of the water to a purchasing utility for subsequent treatment and delivery.

- *Potable (finished) water service*—the owner utility produces and treats the water for continuous or daily delivery to the purchasing utility that in turn distributes such water to its retail customers. This service could be on a full-requirements basis, whereby the owner utility provides all of the water to meet the capacity and usage demands of the purchasing utility, or on a partial-requirements basis, whereby the owner utility supplements the purchasing utility's own treated water supplies.

- *Water transmission (wheeling) service*—the owner utility provides for the conveyance of raw and/or finished water for the purchasing utility. An example could be where the purchasing utility owns water resources and treatment but does not have the necessary transmission capacity to convey the water to all or some of its retail service area; the owner utility in this case provides only for the transport of the water through its transmission system. (Note: this is sometimes referred to as "wheeling service," and in some areas, wheeling service has specific legal attributes.)

- *Emergency water service*—the owner utility contracts with the purchasing utility to provide water supply during emergency or major maintenance periods to provide enhanced reliability and avoid or minimize interruption of retail customer water service deliveries of the purchasing utility. Generally, the sale of emergency service water is of a limited duration and for a specific purpose (e.g., to provide supplemental water to repair a major line break), and helps ensure the short-term continuity of service.

In the establishment of rates for wholesale service, it is necessary to understand the contractual nature of the service arrangement, the funding relationships between the parties to the wholesale transaction for capital improvements (e.g., did the purchasing utility separately fund or contribute capital for the facilities?), and the types of utility plant facilities required to provide service. Additionally, consideration should be given as to whether the rate for wholesale service should be set on a contractual basis specific only to the particular wholesale customer or on a "utility-wide" or "system" basis in which the rate would be applicable to all wholesale customers receiving similar levels of service.

BENEFITS OF PROVIDING OUTSIDE WHOLESALE SERVICE

Public water utilities provide service to wholesale customers located outside of the local government's jurisdictional boundaries or service area for a variety of reasons. These reasons may include, but are not limited to,

- achieving economies of scale in providing water supply and treatment;
- managing the complex water treatment processes for the benefit of the purchasing utility (who may not have developed the required facilities and operational capacity to deliver these services);
- meeting existing or future regulations or consent order by the purchasing utility associated with the withdrawal or use of raw water and/or the treatment of finished water;
- regionalizing water resources and related treatment and delivery facilities; and
- improving the accessibility and cost of credit to secure financing for the construction or replacement of utility assets.

In most cases, the provision of wholesale water generally results in mutually beneficial efficiencies in the overall cost of service delivery. In addition to the cost savings usually achieved through economies of scale, there generally are regional benefits received by all users of the system: (1) improved regional planning for, and the financing of, capacity expansion and facility replacement, and the ability to comply with increased treatment regulations due to changing conditions; (2) improved regional management and planning; (3) reduction in number of water treatment facilities providing service, which eliminates redundant capacity and its related costs; and (4) the ability to implement regional programs promoting environmental goals and conservation.

WHOLESALE SERVICE RELATIONSHIP AND FINANCIAL CONSIDERATIONS

As mentioned in chapter VI.1, a government-owned utility is considered to be the property of the citizens within such local government who, as owners of the utility, bear the risks and responsibilities of utility ownership. Inside-city customers cannot withdraw from the utility, and the utility has a responsibility to develop the system to serve all retail customers within its jurisdictional boundaries as well as others that they are contractually obligated to serve. Although the public water agency's risks in providing service to wholesale customers may be mitigated based on the provisions of the service agreement between the parties, wholesale customers may have the ability and option to look to other entities to provide water service for them, or may have the option to develop their own water supply and systems, which could result in stranded investments and costs to the owner utility.

As discussed in chapter VI.1, a local government providing wholesale service for the benefit of customers located outside its jurisdictional boundaries or service area may incur substantial risks in making this investment. The reader is referred to chapter VI.1, "Risks Associated With Outside Customer Service," for a discussion of these risks and how they may affect the decision-making process relative to providing wholesale service.

Recognizing the above-mentioned risks, the overall financial and service conditions must be considered by the owner utility relative to providing wholesale service. Although each wholesale service transaction is unique, the following is a summary of the financial and service conditions that will affect the long-term risk of providing wholesale service and should be considered in establishing a wholesale service contract relationship:

- **Capitalization of the assets to be used in providing wholesale services.** Raising capital for the initial facility construction and eventual renewal and replacement of facilities is a substantial cost. Expectations for how these capital costs will be borne—by the owner exclusively or in some part by the purchasing utility—should be considered and agreed to as part of the wholesale service agreement. The wholesale service rate must consider how the funding of capital costs was or is to be accomplished (e.g., a separate contribution by the purchasing utility, funded over time through the payment of system development or impact fees, capital funded through issuance of debt by the owner utility and included as a component of wholesale rates to the purchasing utility). In general, the greater the owner's responsibility for capitalizing the assets, the greater the owner's risks (and potential for financial rewards) to provide service.

- **Contracted term of service.** The anticipated contract term (length) of service relative to the service life and the expected cost recovery of the assets used to provide wholesale service must be considered. If the contractual term of service is too short, it may not allow for the opportunity to fully recover the capital costs that the owner utility has invested to provide wholesale service and could result in future stranded capacity costs that could increase per customer operating, maintenance, and replacement costs of the owner utility.

- **Rate provisions and structure.** To maintain financial sufficiency, the owner utility must have the ability to adjust rates to fully recover the cost of service. Full cost recovery often provides for a fair return on investment to compensate the owner utility for its cost of capital and the risks incurred as a result of the owner's investment in providing wholesale service.

- **Reliability of service utilization by the wholesale customer.** If the wholesale customer's demand is highly variable, the risk to recovery of fixed operating, maintenance, and replacement costs is more uncertain. These risks could be mitigated by selection of an appropriate rate structure, which could employ fixed and variable cost recovery strategies to provide a stable, ongoing revenue stream. For example, minimum bills or minimum volume commitments within a wholesale agreement are one means of mitigating this risk.

- **Recovery of incremental costs.** Consideration of the facility requirements and the cost of operations must be evaluated if serving a wholesale customer results in an incremental increase in fixed costs that are allocated solely to, or as a result of, serving the wholesale customer. Such incremental costs should be borne by the purchasing utility rather than the owner.

DETERMINING WHOLESALE REVENUE REQUIREMENTS

As was noted in chapter VI.1, there are three generally accepted methods for establishing the revenue requirements to be recovered from wholesale service delivery: the cash-needs approach, the utility-basis approach, and a hybrid of these two generally accepted methods. A summary of the cash-needs approach and the utility-basis approach was presented earlier in Table VI.1-1, which provides a simple comparison of these two methodologies. In the situation where a utility serves wholesale customers, the cash-needs approach and the utility-basis approach may be used in the establishment of the rates, along with a third approach that is a hybrid of these two methodologies.

Development Fees and Capital Cost Recovery

In the development of the revenue requirements for wholesale service, a primary consideration related to the risk of providing service deals with the initial and ongoing capitalization of the infrastructure required to deliver wholesale services. The owner's capital investment may have already occurred or additional capital investment may yet be required. In any event, the owners will be dedicating resources for the provision of wholesale service and are entitled to recover those costs. Wholesale customers may be called on to pay for some or all of the capital costs as a condition of receipt of service. With respect to capital investment, the following general cost recovery strategies are available:

- Collect contributions in aid of construction (CIAC) from the wholesale customer up front (at the initiation of service agreement and when additional capital is required) for all or part of the capital cost of the facilities allocated to the purchasing utility. This payment would fund the capital cost applicable to the capacity requested by the purchasing utility and reduce the investment financed by the owner utility.

- Collect a system development charge (SDC), as described in chapter II.1, for the initial connections or capacity reserved by the purchasing utility and additional SDCs as new connections occur within the purchasing utility's service area.

- Collect the capital cost as a component of the rates for service. Using the methods described elsewhere in this manual, the normal rate for wholesale service will include the proportionate share of capital and operating costs applicable to the services provided to the purchasing utility. Including all such costs net of any other payments received (e.g., CIAC) in the rate charged for wholesale service is appropriate.

In some cases, to set fair and reasonable rates, it is necessary to identify the investment in utility plant facilities to provide service because most wholesale customers only use a portion of the owner utility's system facilities. The allocation of plant in service is conducted on the same basis as that described in chapter III.1 with special emphasis on the functional allocation of the plant accounts. Consideration as to the accounting for the funds collected from the wholesale customer for future capital reinvestment should also be made. Once the plant in service applicable to the wholesale service is known, the cash (or SDCs) and/or property contributions made by the wholesale customer are deducted to arrive at the net capital costs. If the utility-basis approach is used, the capital contributions directly offset the wholesale customer's rate base. In the cash-needs approach, capital contributions should reduce the related debt service and cash-funded capital investment requirements of the owner utility.

Cost Allocation for Wholesale Users

The cost allocation methodologies, as discussed in section III, are generally applicable in determining cost allocations to wholesale customers. While the general cost-of-service methodologies still apply, some additional cost allocation issues may arise when a utility's customers are segregated to include a wholesale customer or wholesale class.

The primary cost allocation issues associated with wholesale customers are (a) estimating and allocating water demand, and (b) determining applicable wholesale costs.

Estimating and allocating water demand. When wholesale classes of service are segregated within the cost-of-service analysis, the importance of accurately and fairly recognizing any differences in water demands between retail and wholesale customers and other customers is important. There are usually two common components to the demands for service: the amount of reserved capacity (as a share of total capacity) and the actual capacity used by the wholesale customer. Generally, the wholesale service agreement provides information for determining the water capacity being requested by and allocable to the wholesale customer and can form the basis for the allocation of capital costs, including the rate of return on investment. If costs are allocated based on current demand relationships, developing demand estimates requires a comprehensive understanding of both the owner utility and wholesale customer's demand characteristics. This can impose additional requirements on government-owned utilities providing wholesale service if, for no other reason, that it requires them to complete detailed analyses of the consumption characteristics of both their retail customers and the wholesale customer. Notably, wholesale customer demand patterns may be significantly different from those of retail classes for many reasons including, but not limited to, differences in customer mix among residential, commercial, and industrial customer classes; differences resulting from the aggregation of mixed demands as is the case for wholesale customers; and differences in expected water loss in the distribution system due to the relative quality of the wholesale customer's distribution system.

Determining applicable wholesale costs. An important element in determining wholesale costs is having an understanding and recognition of the facilities needed to serve these customers. The facilities needed to serve wholesale customers may vary based on the level of service, the geographic location of the wholesale customers, or some other distinguishing basis. In some cases, specific investments in facilities dedicated to serving only the wholesale customers need to be identified. Recognizing the facilities required to serve these customers while equitably and fairly distributing their costs within the cost-of-service analysis is often challenging. For example, segregating and removing costs associated with services, meters, and hydrants from wholesale service revenue requirements is fairly straightforward and relatively uncomplicated. However, a specific methodology may be needed to distinguish these costs if there are multiple points of delivery in the water distribution system or if there are specific requirements of the wholesale customer. The following is a discussion of some of these issues that need to be considered in developing rates for wholesale service.

Water supply and treatment. In many situations, the costs of water supply and treatment are jointly recovered from both retail and wholesale customers. For certain situations, some wholesale service agreements may identify a single source of supply (e.g., a particular reservoir or well field) or specific water treatment facility. This should be identified in the service agreement between the parties as a condition of service. If this is the situation, a careful evaluation or segregation of the fixed asset costs, available and used capacity, and costs of operation and maintenance (O&M) will be required. For example, if the wholesale customer is going to share in the cost of a particular water treatment plant based on peak-day-demand relationships and the owner utility has the ability to use other water facilities to meet its service area needs, the wholesale service agreement should address the reasonable use of the facility for cost allocation purposes.

Transmission versus distribution facilities. In many cases, wholesale customers are served at a transmission service level or by large-diameter water mains. An important component of establishing cost-based rates is defining what distinguishes the transmission system from the distribution system. These facilities would be separately identified from the raw water conveyance system to the water treatment and finished water pumping facilities. Although there is no single or unique definition of a transmission system, it is generally a system cost that is assumed to benefit all customers of a utility. In many cases, a utility may define their transmission system mains as any water main of a specified size or larger (e.g., mains with a diameter of being equal to or greater than XX in.), or perhaps water mains that have no service lines directly connected. While these approaches are widely practiced, they may not completely or accurately recognize the operational nature of the system. Therefore, operations personnel and references to distribution system maps may provide a more refined definition of the water mains that serve as the system backbone for water conveyance (i.e., the transmission system) and those water mains that are more properly classified as distribution system assets.

Another approach to determining distribution versus transmission mains, though less common in practice and more complex to perform, is to use system hydraulic analyses to determine which water mains, by size diameter and location, function as transmission mains. Given information on pipelines that serve transmission versus distribution functions, the associated costs of these assets may then be ascertained from the fixed asset records of the utility (if these records distinguish asset costs by pipe size). If the fixed assets are not readily available or known, "average pipe ($/linear foot) installed costs" relationships may be employed. Alternatively, the proportionate shares of diameter-weighted lengths of pipelines may be used to estimate (and allocate costs to customer classes) the capital and O&M costs associated with the transmission main system. However, care also needs to be taken in using this method because the diameter and the value of the mains may not have a meaningful relationship with the costs of service. For example, smaller mains on a system may be much older, nearly depreciated, and more costly to operate, whereas larger transmission mains may be newer and less costly to operate, or vice versa. The final method selected to assign water mains between the transmission and distribution functions may also form the basis for determining the water mains to be contributed to the owner utility by the wholesale customer and the wholesale customer responsibility for the construction and operation of the water distribution mains.

Distance and elevation. Distance and elevation of wholesale customers may be considered a factor in establishing wholesale rates when such physical characteristics are pronounced. In these cases, increased costs due to additional pumping over longer distances, higher elevations, or higher capacity factors may be judged to be significant enough to warrant separate treatment for cost recovery. Such rate differentials may also be applicable to the owner utility's retail customers (e.g., elevation surcharges). In addition, location of the customer relative to the source of supply or treatment plant is not necessarily an issue that would dictate a cost-of-service differential or the need for a different rate. However, some unique situations or circumstances may occur in which the location of customer relative to the source of supply or treatment plant (i.e., nearby) may suggest a limited amount of infrastructure to deliver water to the customers.

Peaking factors. Properly developed cost-based rates are designed to equitably allocate costs based on relative contributions to system demands (consumption) and peak-use events (e.g., maximum day and/or peak hour). In general, the wholesale class may simply be included in this cost allocation procedure and distributed its proportionate share of system costs. In this respect, there is no procedural distinction between retail and wholesale users for allocation of costs to service. However, peaking factors will have to be determined for all customer classes, including wholesale customers, to appropriately make allocations of costs of service.

Use of consistent procedures and reconciliation of assigned demands to those observed from system production or customer demand metering is important to ensure accuracy and prevent unintended interclass subsidizations. Especially insofar as system diversity and demand peaking factors are developed using a variety of assumptions related to individual class demand patterns, it is important to ensure consistency with individual utilities' monitored production and customer demand data.

Fire protection. In some cases, wholesale services may include the use of the owner utility's storage, transmission, and pumping capacity to provide not only for the maximum-day and maximum-hour of wholesale demand, but also fire flow capacity. For example, the wholesale customer may not have distribution reservoirs in its system at all, or insufficient storage, such that the wholesale customer relies on the owner's distribution storage to meet fire flow needs in the wholesale system. In such cases, a proportional allocation of fire flow capacity to the wholesale customer is appropriate.

Unmetered water. In allocating costs to wholesale customers, care must be taken to recognize the responsibility for unmetered or lost water. As discussed in AWWA Manual M36 (2016), much of a system's unmetered water is due to retail service (leaks in customer service lines, distribution leaks, water used for fire fighting, etc.). To account for this, costs can be allocated based on the volume of water supplied to retail and wholesale accounts, with the retail losses assigned to all retail customers and system-wide losses assigned to all customers in proportion to sales.

Customer accounting and service costs. Since the wholesale customer resells the purchased water on a retail basis to its own customers, there may be certain capital and operating costs incurred by the owner utility that may not be allocable to wholesale customers. Examples of such costs may include expenses related to customer call centers, meter reading and small-customer meter maintenance, customer billing and accounting, bad debts, public information, and water conservation programs that are incurred by the owner utility specifically for its retail customers. However, there may be certain costs that are directly related to providing wholesale service, such as the reading and replacement of meters at the wholesale water delivery or connection points, the annual calibration of such meters, and specialized billing costs (e.g., separate bills to the wholesale customer that cannot be generated from the utility billing system).

Other general service (administrative/overhead) costs. Other general service costs include, but are not limited to, utility management, finance and accounting, purchasing and human resources, information technology, insurance, and regulatory expenses related to the respective local government council, commission, or board that is empowered to regulate the utility and rates for service. These costs are necessary for the daily operation of the utility and should be allocated between the owner retail and wholesale customers based on the overall need or reason for the costs. Allocation factors based on the number of customers, allocated direct personnel, total operating expense relationships, and other cost allocation methods are used to apportion the costs to the wholesale customer class. In some instances, a predetermined percentage or dollar amount (e.g., a cap of not more than 10 percent of the total operating expenses) is used to determine the amount of other general service costs that should be apportioned. In many instances, the allocation of these costs can become problematic with respect to their applicability to wholesale service given that they tend to be indirect costs rather than easily identifiable direct costs associated with most of the operational costs. Special care may be needed to ensure that these costs do not become disproportionately large compared to other cost functions.

With respect to the determination of costs to serve the wholesale customer, the reasonableness standard should be exercised, because it is primarily based on an allocation process and not usually on the basis of exact identified costs. The allocation should be consistent with the terms of service as delineated in a water supply or service agreement and should promote fairness between the parties.

RATE DESIGN FOR WHOLESALE CUSTOMERS

As with retail service, once the wholesale water demands are appropriately identified and estimated and costs allocated between the retail and wholesale service classes, water rates to recover the allocated costs can be designed. Fundamental principles of rate design as described elsewhere in this Manual of Practice are applicable for wholesale service rate designs as well. Accordingly, it may be quite appropriate for government-owned utilities providing wholesale service to have multiple rate designs. Wholesale customers with unique cost and consumption characteristics could also be billed using different rate structures. As discussed in chapter IV.1, the choice of rate structure is dependent on the philosophy and objectives of the utility and community, and subject to legal considerations. In addition, the choice of rate structure in the case of wholesale service will depend greatly on the terms of the service agreement. Examples of rate structure components may include, but are not limited to, the following:

- Volumetric rate structure to recover those costs allocated on the basis of metered water consumption as measured at the point of delivery with the purchasing utility
- Capacity charge to recover costs associated with utility plant facilities (e.g., debt service, asset reinvestment, rate of return allowance on allocated rate base/plant investment) allocated to the wholesale customer or service based on capacity relationships
- Capacity charges and/or minimum demand based on a "take-or-pay" provision, or based on a designated peak demand or consumption requirement
- Application of an inclining block volumetric rate to promote conservation preferably based on the allocated costs associated with each block but, possibly, also as an excess demand charge to recover the cost of water use greater than the allocated demand to the wholesale customer
- A combination of the above components designed such that the sum of all charges can be reasonably expected to recover the total wholesale revenue requirement

IMPLEMENTATION AND ADMINISTRATION CONSIDERATIONS

The implementation and administration of wholesale rates can create a variety of accounting, data management, and financial reporting issues not generally encountered when a utility provides service solely within its jurisdiction. Further, as discussed, the application of cost-based rate-making practices can be more complex in wholesale rate-making situations. The need to isolate and/or allocate costs in support of the revenue requirement calculation and demand estimation requirements may be significantly different than those encountered when developing water rates for retail customers.

Wholesale Service Agreements

The wholesale service agreement is the primary contractual document that dictates the terms and conditions for service, specifies the basis for rate determinations, and identifies the capacity allocations or levels of service, the responsibilities of the parties, and other terms and conditions. A service agreement between the owner and purchasing utilities is often vital to ensuring lasting understanding of the terms, conditions, and requirements of service and should be executed prior to the provision of service. In developing an agreement, the utility should engage available resources and expertise to assist with terms and conditions used for pricing of the wholesale services. These wholesale service agreements often also include the following components:

- Term (length) of the agreement with (i) ability to extend service or (ii) specific notification provisions to terminate service

- Delineation of the allocated or reserved capacity and the basis for measuring such capacity (e.g., a peak-day demand expressed on a million-gallons-per-day basis and a total quantity demand expressed on an annual-average million-gallons-per-day basis)

- Payment for the initial reservation of capacity, including the cost of such capacity, amount to be paid, and when payment is due (at time of service agreement execution, installment payment over a predetermined time frame, etc.)

- Provisions for reserving additional capacity above the initial reservation, including the methodology for determination of the cost of such capacity, amount to be paid, and when payment is due (at time-of-service agreement execution, installment payment over a predetermined time frame, etc.)

- Special service provisions such as the pressure of water at the point of delivery, storage requirements, basis to interrupt service, provisions for emergency service (which would be in addition to the firm service), and other service provisions

- Delineation of the initial structure and level of rates for service and a rate formula or approach to determine future rate adjustments (The rate formula may also reference a price index adjustment formula to increase rates for inflation, certain pass-through costs, and an annual "true-up" provision to allow the amount billed during a year to be adjusted for actual costs.)

- Constraints on the ability of the purchasing utility to enter into an independent agreement to sell water to a third-party utility that relies on the purchase of wholesale water without the consent of the owner utility (i.e., no sales for resale)

- Delineation of how current and future capital investment (capacity purchase) and reinvestment (future renewals, replacements, and betterments) are recovered from the wholesale customer (CIAC, included as component of the rates for wholesale service)

- Regarding the costs to be recovered and if limited or no rate formula is reflected in the service agreement, any cost parameters that need to be identified, such as including the determination of the rate of return and basis for the calculation and the delineation of the amount of or basis for determining the recovery of administrative costs

- Listing of the specific facilities that are "used and useful" in providing service to the wholesale customer

- Description of delivery point location, responsibility for construction of the metering station and ownership provisions, and annual meter calibration requirements

- Responsibilities of the owner utility, including compliance with all existing and future regulations, maintaining prudent management and qualified personnel and obligations to adequately operate and maintain the facilities (including the implementation of renewals, replacements, and improvements to the assets shared by or allocated to the wholesale customer)

- Responsibilities of the purchasing utility, including a rate covenant that the wholesale customer rates will always be sufficient to pay the owner utility for the cost of wholesale service and will enforce the collection of such rates
- Responsibilities of the purchasing utility to maintain its distribution system to limit non-revenue water and any other special considerations relevant to the performance of the purchasing utility

Accounting Requirements

Government-owned utilities providing service to wholesale customers face expanded accounting and record-keeping issues when compared to providing only retail customer service. Wholesale service rates may reflect allocations of specifically assignable costs that, in turn, may require the accounting system to provide information regarding the location, function, and allocation of specific fixed assets and operating costs related to the wholesale services. In addition, if the wholesale customer provides capital contributions or SDCs, the accounting system needs to track those contributions accurately so they can be appropriately considered in the calculation of the wholesale rates.

Financial and Operational Reporting

Because wholesale users are not a constituency of the local government or its utility rate-setting body, interested stakeholders may require financial and operational data to gauge the appropriateness of the wholesale rates to which they are subject. Detailed and transparent financial and operational disclosure reports can reduce the possibility of future controversy or litigation. Such reports can also build trust and promote accountability in the wholesale rate-making process and make it easier to implement future rate adjustments or rate-design changes. The cost of providing such reports, if any, may be allocated in full or in part to the wholesale customer(s).

Regulatory Reporting Requirements

Public utility commissions or similar regulatory agencies impose a variety of ongoing reporting requirements on the utilities that they regulate. They also require substantial evidentiary support for proposed rate increases in the form of detailed revenue requirement calculations and cost-of-service studies. In the limited number of cases where a public utility commission does have regulatory authority over a government-owned utility, the reporting requirements they must comply with are generally similar to those of their investor-owned counterparts. In addition to the financial and operational reports previously described, state regulators may require government-owned utilities to submit the following:

- Annual reports presented in accordance with a mandated uniform system of accounts. Such annual reports often provide a variety of operational data in addition to traditional financial statements such as the statement of net position (balance sheet showing changes in assets, liabilities, and equity) and statement of revenues, expenses, and changes in net position (income statement).
- Annual and/or quarterly reports detailing specific costs, such as purchased water costs, especially if a utility is required to impose an explicit rate surcharge on customer bills for such costs
- Annual updates of the utility's integrated resource plan (if required)
- Integrated resource plans—which, if required, are usually filed with public utility commissions every three to five years—that require comprehensive long-range

demand forecasts, along with a detailed discussion of the portfolio of supply and demand-side management resources projected to meet the demand

Demand Management Issues

The demands placed on the government-owned utility providing wholesale service can often be significant. In many instances, the wholesale customer may be a substantial customer. Therefore, understanding the unique characteristics of a wholesale customer's current and future demand requirements is critical to having the necessary water supply, treatment, and conveyance systems constructed and available to meet such demands. Based on the demand relationship of the wholesale customer to the facilities identified or designated to serve the customer, five- to ten-year water demand projections (average and peak demands and equivalent residential connections) are beneficial. They allow the owner utility to adequately plan and define strategies for funding of future plant expansions or additions. Some of the data management issues potentially encountered by government-owned utilities providing wholesale service include the need to

- collect and analyze the water demands at the point of delivery on a daily basis to evaluate peak-day demands and coincident demands with the retail customer base;
- bill, store, and analyze water consumption and revenue information for multiple wholesale customer rate classes; and
- bill multiple wholesale customer rates according to a variety of rate designs. For example, a utility providing wholesale service to multiple users could bill different rate amounts or structures based on the conditions of service and the customers' contributions to financing infrastructure for their benefit (i.e., the receipt of cash and/or property CIAC from the wholesale customer).

Reviews and Updates

Prudent financial management practices dictate that all utilities, regardless of their size or complexity, should prepare demand forecasts, operating budgets, and revenue requirement calculations regularly. These respective analyses will assist the utility in assessing whether it should update the rate formula contained in the service agreement, perform a cost-of-service study, or consider financing for future capital needs, including capital cost sharing policies or allocations, to calculate updated wholesale rates.

In general, in situations of limited demand growth and stable operating expenses, debt service, and capital expenditures, a detailed cost-of-service analysis may not be warranted frequently. Updates of system revenue requirements and distributions of costs to customer classes in the same proportions as in prior years (i.e., based on detailed prior cost studies) may suffice. However, utilities that experience significant year-to-year changes in customer demands, operating expenses, debt service, and capital expenditures will likely need to revisit their allocations of costs to customer classes to preserve cost-of-service relationships and comply with the wholesale service agreements. The benefits of performing regular rate reviews and implementing updated wholesale rate evaluations include

- adequate revenue recovery to ensure the government-owned utility's cash flow and financial stability,
- accurate class-specific revenue requirement recovery for wholesale customers,
- water rates that fully recover the capital costs to provide wholesale service and reflect changes in regulations and demand patterns (e.g., water conservation)

relating to both the providing utility's wholesale customers and other customers, and

- enhanced transparency and trust in the wholesale service rate-making process among interested stakeholders.

STAKEHOLDER INVOLVEMENT AND PUBLIC COMMUNICATIONS

The process of developing and implementing wholesale rates is subject to a variety of political and public policy pressures not encountered when service is restricted to customers within a common jurisdictional boundary. Wholesale rates that are considered by the public to be having an impact on the retail rates (i.e., due to the need to expand utility plant facilities for the benefit of the wholesale customer) may become controversial and draw the scrutiny of a variety of interested stakeholders. In this context, the potential to build positive relationships with wholesale customers (and avoid costly and contentious litigation) is generally enhanced when government-owned utilities have reasonable, documented, and well-communicated rationales for their rate-making practices.

While these imperatives are true generally, stakeholder engagement and public communications related to wholesale service present many unique opportunities and challenges. In particular, there is often the need to distinguish the extent to which ratepayers' bills are driven by wholesale service costs, if at all, and what benefit ratepayers receive from providing wholesale service.

Finally, all parties involved in delivery of wholesale services should be fully cognizant of the legal framework within which rate-setting practices are adjudicated. This framework is defined by provisions in wholesale service agreements and/or any applicable state or federal legal standards. In addition, some utilities are regulated by public service commissions, many of whom have specific guidelines for calculating rates.

Wholesale customers do not enjoy the same level of legal and political representation as retail customers of the owner utility. Having no representation on the owner utility's elected body, wholesale customers are entirely dependent on the owner utility's performance within the terms of the service agreement and, failing that, court enforcement of the same. Poorly designed service agreements and lack of performance both contribute to the possibility of legal challenge related to the wholesale services. To avoid such contentious issues, it is often to the benefit of all parties to engage in continuous and transparent sharing of information where contract issues are routinely reviewed and addressed. For example, many utilities have had success in establishing an advisory committee to oversee rate-setting practices and the capital planning activities of the owner utility. Including wholesale customer representation on such committees may help ensure that contract issues are given a formal venue that can surface important issues before they become contentious.

SUMMARY

The provision of wholesale service holds the potential for significant benefits for both the owner and purchasing utility. Wholesale customers may avoid having to develop expensive water system infrastructure required to meet their service needs; owner utilities may reap the benefits of economies of scale, reducing the average cost of service for its retail customers within its jurisdictional boundaries or service area while utilizing otherwise idle capacity. In calculating wholesale water rates, there are different, generally accepted methods for determining the revenue requirements, each with relative advantages and disadvantages. Cost allocation requires specific attention with respect to wholesale customers because wholesale service generally requires the use of only a portion of the owner utility's facilities. Apart from recovering the direct costs of providing service, in setting rates for wholesale service, owner utilities should be mindful of the risks involved and the amount of capital contributed by the wholesale customer. To minimize risk and promote fairness, a service agreement between the parties is essential, because it identifies the basis for rate determination, methods for capital funding and recovery, and the provisions of service delivery. Providing wholesale service carries several additional stakeholder engagement and implementation requirements to ensure that all parties to the wholesale service contracts clearly understand and preserve the benefits anticipated by their original mutual agreement.

REFERENCE

AWWA (American Water Works Association). 2016. Manual M36. *Water Audits and Loss Control Programs*, 4th ed. Denver, Colo.: AWWA.

Section VII

Capacity and Development Charges

VII.1   Connection and Customer Facility Charges

VII.2   System Development Charges

VII.3   Availability Charges

This page intentionally blank.

Chapter **VII.1**

Connection and Customer Facility Charges

The cost of constructing lines and facilities to dedicate, expand, or extend service capability and to connect new properties to a water system can be recouped through capital cost recovery mechanisms. Capital cost recovery can be handled in various ways.

As water rates increase, separate capital charges are often considered as a way to relieve, reduce, or forestall general rate increases. Typically, capital charges are used where costs and revenues are significant, specific beneficiaries or customers can be clearly identified, and associated costs can be reasonably and accurately determined. Examples of special capital charges include charges related to costs for facilities installed between the water main and property line or for facilities located on the customer service site. These special capital charges should not be confused with common capital charges such as system development charges that recoup investments made in the "backbone" system facilities.

It is common policy for government-owned utilities to directly recover from the customer the costs of installing a tap or connection to a water main, the service line to the property, and the water meter. Many utilities have developed a standard connection and customer facility charge schedule based on meter or connection size. Other utilities develop customized charges based on site-specific costs. Still other utilities use a combination of standard and customized charges. In most cases, the charge is assessed when the customer or agent applies for new or expanded water service. In general, such charges increase with the size of the meter or connection and, in the case of customized charges, with the complexity and conditions of the service site.

This chapter addresses policy, cost, and pricing assumptions and concerns related to establishing customer facility and connection fees in the following areas:

- Allocation of costs
- Capital cost component
- Calculation of charges

In viewing a water system's capital charging practices, the source of supply, treatment plant, system storage, mains, and other facilities can be classified as customer facilities, connection facilities, and system facilities, as shown in Figure VII.1-1. *Customer facilities* include the meter, and other appurtenance facilities that must be constructed to meter the customer's water usage. Typically, the cost of installation and maintenance of the service line from the meter to the customer site (house or building) from the curb stop across the customer's property is the responsibility of the customer. *Connection facilities* are defined as the line, tap, and other facilities that must be constructed from the property line or curb stop/meter to the main in the street or right-of-way.

A key step in determining customer facility charges is the appropriate allocation of costs. In most cost-of-service analyses, the basis for allocating costs is cost causation, by recognizing the key parameter or parameters that most influence the level of cost incurred. Determining the appropriate method of cost recovery, whether through the general rate structure or an up-front charge, is critical. Also, costs associated with appurtenances that are onsite or customer specific (rather than off-site or common to all customers) need to be considered in the allocation process.

When identifying the capital cost to be recovered through customer facility and connection charges, the utility needs to define what portion of the cost of installing the facilities between the utility main and the customer's property is allocable to the utility and

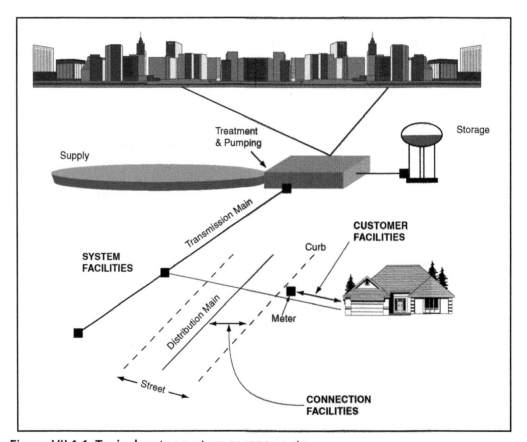

Figure VII.1-1 Typical water system components

what portion is allocable to the customer. Also, the utility needs to determine the variation in capital costs of installation caused by the differences in material costs and methods of construction.

Example calculations of a basic model for both a connection charge and a customer facility charge are provided later in this chapter. The specific method of calculating these charges, however, will vary from one utility to another because of the unique circumstances of each utility. When charges are established for an investor-owned utility, the taxable nature of such revenues needs to be recognized. Another consideration for the utility is to choose the terminology to define the connection and customer facility charges. It is common for utilities to impose multiple types of capital charges that recoup the investment made in system facilities, connection facilities, and customer facilities.

The utility should use appropriate terminology to identify each capital charge to clearly convey to the customer the purpose of each charge. Historically, it has not been uncommon for utilities to combine capital charges for system facilities, connection facilities, and customer facilities into one or two charges. However, this approach limits the ability of the utility to appropriately allocate each portion of the capital costs based on customer-specific characteristics and therefore is generally discouraged.

ALLOCATING COSTS

The purpose of a cost allocation process in rate setting is to assign costs to the customers who benefit from or cause those costs to be incurred. In allocating costs associated with installing customer connections, the utility must first address these questions:

- Are there legal constraints on the ability of the utility to charge a connection charge or on the amount of the charge?
- Should the costs of connecting new customers be included in the system revenue requirements for allocation to all customers through general water rates?
- Should these costs be allocated to a specific customer class and recovered through rates for that class?
- Should the cost be recognized as an incremental capital cost and recovered directly through a specific customer connection charge?

Utilities may choose to allocate and recover all, or a portion, of such costs through the general water rates rather than through a specific connection or customer facility charge.

To determine whether a specific capital charge should be established for a new connection, the utility should consider the following issues:

- **Frequency.** Is the number of occurrences significant enough to justify a specific connection charge?
- **Data availability.** Is there reasonable and sufficient information available to support a charge for the installation?
- **Justification.** Are costs sufficient to justify creating such a charge?
- **Affordability.** Is the magnitude of the calculated charge cost-prohibitive to economically disadvantaged customers?
- **Consistency and predictability.** Are the material costs and labor requirements relatively consistent and uniform?
- **Equity.** Would isolation of customer-connection costs significantly increase equity among customers?

After evaluating these key issues, the utility may determine that a separate capital charge to recover the cost of new connections is not needed. Alternatively, the utility may determine that a policy for collecting all or some of the costs associated with new connections is justified through either a standard or customized system of charges. Or the utility may determine that a separate standard charge is justified only for residential, small business, and other small service connections. The policy for customers with larger connections, on the other hand, may require customized charges or, alternatively, recovery of the actual cost of installing customer facilities.

Standardized Versus Customized Charges

Usually, connection and customer facility charges for small-volume customers are standardized because the installation of smaller connections tends to be more frequent; therefore, the cost is generally affordable and relatively consistent from one installation to another. These charges can be standardized with limited financial risk to the utility and without undue equity burdens on individual customers. However, the utility may determine that certain large connections do not satisfy the criteria for standard charges. In such cases, it would be more appropriate to charge the customer for the actual cost of the service connection and meter installation, thereby customizing the charges based on site-specific conditions. Because of the high cost often associated with larger installations, it may also be appropriate to require payment of an advance deposit based on the estimated cost of installation. A similar deposit may be required of a developer who is concurrently applying for service to several smaller properties.

CAPITAL COST COMPONENT

After a utility has determined the need for separate capital charges to recover new connection costs, it needs to delineate the capital costs to be included in such charges at the point where responsibility for installation shifts from the utility to the customer. Factors that may affect the actual cost of a service connection include the size of the service connection, requirements for backflow or cross-connection protection, and meter location (on a public right-of-way or private property). In addition, building restrictions, such as local building code requirements or pressure problems related to a building's height, may affect cost.

Measuring water consumption is essential to the financial planning of water utilities and is usually required for new service connections. Currently, most water utilities have meters for the majority of their customers; however, there may be a few exceptions to this general rule. Metered services provide

- an equitable basis to charge customers for services,
- a history of water consumption,
- the means to evaluate growth and changes in water use patterns,
- the means to measure conservation,
- an indication of water loss or leaks,
- a method of establishing long-term consumption trends, and
- a method of establishing seasonal consumption trends.

The decision to install a metered service connection may have ramifications when establishing connection and customer facility charges. The cost of metering needs to be balanced against the benefits and the increased equity in billing customers. In some cases, regulatory orders, local ordinances, or resolutions require the installation of meters for all customers.

Additional factors related to installing service line appurtenances may have a significant bearing on the proposed installation pricing structure. One factor is determining where the utility's responsibility for the cost of the installation ends and where the customer's responsibility begins. Often, the responsibility shifts at the customer's property line. The issue of cost responsibility is less clear if the utility must incur significant costs to extend the existing system to the customer's property line. In this case, the customer is likely to bear a portion or all of the costs to extend the system to the property line. After the responsibilities of the utility and the customer are determined, it is relatively simple to calculate the associated charge.

Typically, a residential service connection involves the installation of connection facilities (including a corporation stop, service line, curb stop, and miscellaneous fittings) and customer facilities (including the meter box, meter, and miscellaneous fittings). It is common practice for utilities to install this equipment in the road right-of-way up to the customer's property line. This delineates a clear point of cost responsibility and establishes a level of consistency relative to the average cost of a service connection. Utility systems in areas that experience freezing temperatures may require meters to be installed inside the customer's building.

In contrast to the basic installation of a residential service connection, large, complex service connections serving high-rise buildings, shopping centers, industrial sites, and high-density apartment complexes involve far greater capital investment. In these situations, capital costs typically vary significantly from one location to another.

It is important to determine the portions of the connection and customer facilities that will be capitalized, rather than expensed, by the utility. This has specific ramifications for utilities that calculate general water rates according to the utility method of developing revenue requirements, where the calculation of rate base is required.

CALCULATING CONNECTION AND CUSTOMER FACILITY CHARGES

The first step in determining connection and customer facility charges is to collect data on both direct and indirect costs (Tables VII.1-1–VII.1-3).

Direct Costs

Individual work orders provide a primary source of direct-cost data. By examining historical work orders, utilities can determine the consistency in the cost and type of materials used, the amount of time and cost for labor, and the cost associated with equipment. Analysis of work orders as well as inventory reports may also yield information about how these costs fluctuate with the size of the connection. Average costs for each component of the installation can be calculated by examining the direct-cost data. Because future costs often vary from historical costs, it is appropriate to use an allowance for inflation when forecasting costs for parts and materials. This escalation may be appropriate when fees are being set for several subsequent budget years.

Labor costs. Direct labor rates also need to be examined to determine the average labor cost of installation. Often, this is done by considering the staff positions required and is based on personnel cost records and related pay rates for these positions. Typically, estimated hourly labor costs are forecast based on expected salary increases. Total labor costs are based on estimated hourly salaries in conjunction with expected hours of labor (see chapter V.9 for a more extensive discussion about direct costs).

Table VII.1-1 Calculation of connection and customer facility charges

Labor Costs			
Staff Member	Current Direct Labor Costs, $/h	Adjusted Direct Labor Costs,* $/h	Fully Loaded Rate,[†] $/h
Crew Foreman	33.00	33.99	67.98
Crew Member	24.00	24.72	49.44
Engineering Technician	30.00	30.90	61.80

Materials Costs			
		Current Cost by Meter Size	
Materials	¾ in., $	1 in., $	1½ in., $
Connection Facilities:			
Asphalt Repair (25 ft²)	408.75	408.75	408.75
Service Line (30 ft)	19.86	44.40	48.00
Corporation Stop (1)	25.83	48.00	62.85
Miscellaneous Fittings	18.00	36.00	54.00
Total Current Costs	472.44	537.15	573.60
Adjusted Costs*	486.61	553.26	590.81
Customer Facilities:			
Meter Box (1)	123.45	318.60	375.00
Meter (1)	93.00	284.70	630.00
Saddle (1)	31.50	38.25	56.70
Total Current Costs	247.95	641.55	1,061.70
Adjusted Costs*	255.39	660.80	1,093.55

Equipment Costs		
Equipment	Current Cost, $	Adjusted Cost,* $
Compressor, $/h	27.00	27.81
Backhoe, $/h	66.00	67.98
Service Truck, $/mi	1.05	1.08

*Reflects 3 percent salary or inflation adjustment.

†Reflects indirect cost multiplier of 2.0 to include all applicable administrative and general overhead costs.

Equipment costs. Equipment costs can be developed based on accounting data, including depreciation and maintenance records. The average cost of renting similar equipment is sometimes used for these estimates.

Indirect Costs

Indirect costs should also be factored into the development of appropriate connection fees. These costs are not directly attributed to one specific cost center and generally include, but are not limited to, such overhead costs as administrative salaries, administrative supplies, and employee fringe benefit programs. Direct labor costs, as well as materials, supplies, and equipment expenses, should include an allowance for indirect costs. Typically, an indirect cost multiplier, obtained by relating the indirect costs as a percentage of direct costs, is used to establish a "fully loaded" cost.

Table VII.1-2 Calculation of connection charges

Item	Quantity	Connection Charge by Meter Size		
		¾ in., $	1 in., $	1½ in., $
Labor Costs				
Crew Foreman (hours)	1.5	101.97	101.97	101.97
Crew Member (hours)	3.0	148.32	148.32	148.32
Engineering Technician (hours)	0.5	30.90	30.90	30.90
Subtotal		281.19	281.19	281.19
Materials Costs				
Subtotal		486.61	553.26	590.81
Equipment Costs				
Compressor (hours)	1.5	41.72	41.72	41.72
Backhoe (hours)	1.5	101.97	101.97	101.97
Service Truck (miles)	10.0	10.82	10.82	10.82
Subtotal		154.50	154.50	154.50
Total Connection Charges		922.30	988.95	1,026.50

EXAMPLES

Tables VII.1-1 through VII.1-3 illustrate the calculation of connection charges and customer facility charges. The tables show the determination of average current cost, inflated for expectations of direct cost changes, and the use of an indirect cost multiplier to account for all indirect costs as a function of direct labor.

For this example, a one-year time horizon was used to project the charges. In some cases, a multiyear time horizon may be applicable, and the salary adjustment and inflation assumptions should be adjusted to reflect the multiple-year time horizon. However, state commissions may not allow a projected multiyear method to be used for investor-owned or regulated government-owned utilities. The method allowed by a particular state commission should be followed in determining appropriate costs for use in that particular jurisdiction. Also, if an inside meter setting is used, costs associated with that type of installation would apply. This would eliminate the outside meter box but would include a meter yoke and possibly installation of a remote reading device.

Table VII.1-1 provides a summary of the information obtained when gathering data to determine indirect costs. The table is divided into three sections. The top portion lists applicable utility staff positions, current average hourly salaries, and projected average hourly salaries. Projected hourly salaries are based on the current hourly salaries multiplied by an expected average wage increase. In addition, an indirect overhead multiplier is applied to compensate for fringe benefits and other costs related to administrative, general, and indirect overhead.

The middle section of Table VII.1-1 lists typical materials and their per-unit cost. In the example, costs are escalated by applying an estimated allowance for inflation. The current equipment costs shown in the third section of the table are based on average unit costs for the types of equipment required. Future equipment costs are estimated based on the same inflation allowance used for materials costs. Based on historical records obtained during the data-gathering phase, the average time required for each crew member to install a new connection was multiplied by the hourly labor rates from Table VII.1-1 to determine total labor costs (see the labor costs sections of Tables VII.1-2 and VII.1-3). It is assumed that the number of hours required for each crew member is the same for all three

Table VII.1-3 Calculation of customer facility charges

Item	Quantity	Customer Facility Charge by Meter Size		
		¾ in., $	1 in., $	1½ in., $
Labor Costs				
Crew Foreman (hours)	1.0	67.98	67.98	67.98
Crew Member (hours)	2.0	98.88	98.88	98.88
Engineering Technician (hours)	0.5	30.90	30.90	30.90
Subtotal		197.76	197.76	197.76
Materials Costs				
Subtotal		255.39	660.80	1,093.55
Equipment Costs				
Service Truck (miles)	10.0	10.82	10.82	10.82
Total Customer Facility Charges		463.96	869.37	1,302.13

meter connection sizes. This may vary for each utility, and actual field experience should be relied on in establishing charges for a particular utility.

The total average materials costs as developed in Table VII.1-1 are further developed in Tables VII.1-2 and VII.1-3. Similarly, Tables VII.1-2 and VII.1-3 state the expected equipment cost obtained by applying the required number of hours or miles to the equipment rates developed in Table VII.1-1. Finally, all costs are totaled and the connection and customer facility charges are shown in Tables VII.1-2 and VII.1-3, respectively.

Chapter **VII.2**

System Development Charges

A *system development charge* (SDC) is a one-time charge paid by a new water system customer for system capacity. It is also assessed to existing customers requiring increased system capacity. The receipts from this charge are used to finance the development of growth-related or capacity-related water facilities and are an important funding/financing source for these facilities.

Although a one-time charge, SDCs are not always paid up front. Some states require utilities to offer an option to pay the SDC in installments if the fee is over a certain amount. Utilities often offer such an option with the potential for financing terms that allow for installment payments spread over several months or years.

The development of the appropriate level of SDCs provides utilities and policymakers with a cost-based analysis of the value of existing and planned capacity that is available or will be developed to serve and accommodate new capacity demands. By understanding the costs of providing capacity, policymakers can make an informed decision concerning the equity of allocating system capacity costs between existing and new customers.

Utilities make investments in capacity-related facilities that will provide service to new development in advance of when the new development occurs. Typically, the capacity-related facilities are constructed in fairly large increments, and the new customers that this capacity is intended to serve will typically connect to the system over many years. As a result of the size of the capacity expansion and the timing of when customers connect to the system, the timing of receipts generated from the SDCs is rarely synchronized with the construction of the capacity-related facility. Therefore, SDCs provide an equitable method for recovering the costs of system capacity additions from those who will use the increased capacity; although in most cases, some portion of the capacity-related costs must still be recovered from user rates and charges assessed to all customers due to the aforementioned timing issues.

In general, SDCs are based on the costs for major backbone infrastructure components that are necessary to provide service to all customers, including source-of-supply facilities, raw water transmission, treatment facilities, pumping facilities, storage tanks, and major treated-water transmission mains (e.g., "general benefit" facilities; see

Figure VII.1-1). Much less common, and only when local circumstances or applicable state or local government statutes specifically allow for it, the costs of water distribution mains and other facilities might also be recovered from SDCs.

The development of SDCs and the use of SDC receipts are often governed by state or provincial legislation as well as case law. Most jurisdictions have specific legislation, and the language and requirements vary from jurisdiction to jurisdiction and are subject to change. Therefore, an important starting point in determining SDCs is to understand any applicable and current legislation or laws related to SDCs to help ensure that the utility's SDCs are calculated and administered in a defensible manner.

System development charges, or SDCs, is the commonly used terminology to describe these charges, but it is not unusual for utilities to use another name for them. Other commonly used names include, but are not limited to,

- impact fees or development impact fees,
- system capacity charges or capacity fees,
- capital facility fees,
- development fees,
- general facility charges,
- expansion charges,
- plant investment fees,
- system buy-in charges,
- capital charges,
- capital recovery fees, and
- dedicated capacity charges.

It is important for utilities to ensure that the persons preparing the SDC calculations are considered qualified in the utility industry and in the applicable state. Some states require that a registered professional engineer prepare the SDC calculations (e.g., Arizona at the time of this manual's publication).

Finally, this chapter is meant as a guide for utilities when considering an SDC program. Each agency has specific circumstances when it comes to system planning, facility requirements, and cost structures. Final consideration should be given to local characteristics and policies, state legislation (if applicable), and legal counsel opinion.

FINANCIAL GOALS AND OBJECTIVES

A critical step in developing SDCs is to identify the objectives to be achieved by the SDC program, which might include some or all of the following:

- Require new development to pay its own way—that is, "growth pays for growth."
- Fund major system expansions.
- Minimize debt or reduce the need for future debt.
- Equitably recover capacity-related capital costs from current and future customers to achieve equity between the different generations of ratepayers (intergenerational equity).
- Maintain an appropriate level of retained earnings and cash reserves to meet other capital needs of the system.

- Equitably reimburse the existing ratepayers for their investment in oversizing of infrastructure to accommodate future customers.

The development of SDCs must also consider

- any local and state/provincial legal or statutory requirements,
- financial objectives of the utility,
- generally accepted water utility industry financing and pricing practices, and
- methodologies for determining SDCs based on industry standard practices.

The use of SDC receipts is generally limited. First, SDC receipts can be used to directly pay for a growth-related capital improvement project. In using the SDC receipts in this manner, the utility will likely have avoided, or at least minimized, the use of long-term debt or pay-as-you-go rate funding for the project that shelters the existing ratepayers from the cost of expansion of the system and, hence, may reduce the need for monthly user rate increases. The other typical use of SDC receipts is to apply them against growth-related debt service. When a utility issues long-term debt to pay for a growth-related capital project, the associated debt service is generally paid using SDC receipts. In doing so, the utility may be able to better align the cash flows related to the debt service with the timing of the new connections and receipts derived from SDCs. However, it is important to be aware of any legal restriction or bond covenants related to the use of SDC receipts being applied to debt-service payments. The utility should also be cautious, and not overly reliant, on the use of SDC receipts to pay for debt service because SDC receipts are growth-dependent and not necessarily a stable source of funding from year to year.

Utilities may experience some opposition to the implementation of SDCs. For example, in some cases, local builders and developers oppose the charges because SDCs add to their up-front development costs. Working closely with the building and development community to provide a better understanding of the derivation of the SDCs, along with the dedicated purpose and use of the SDC receipts, is often an important step in the implementation of these charges. Some states have statutory requirements for involving advisory committees consisting of members of the development community. An SDC is a financial commitment on the part of both the development community and the utility. In the absence of SDCs, a utility may be unwilling to raise their existing customers' rates to build the facilities needed to accommodate the capacity requirements of future development.

METHODOLOGY AND LEGAL CONSIDERATIONS

The development of an SDC should include a review of the legal authority and relevant legislation related to the establishment of SDCs. Legal authority to impose an SDC may be granted through enabling legislation, statutes regarding general law or home rule authorities, local charter, utility operation permits, utility service certifications, regulatory guidance, or judicial rulings. For municipal utilities, there may be specific legislative guidelines or requirements that govern the SDC determination, and its implementation and assessment practices. For investor-owned utilities, and in some cases municipal utilities, the public utility commissions have rules of practice concerning capital cost recovery and rate-making.

When considering the development and implementation of SDCs, a utility should

- consider statutes or public utility commission rules of practice (many legislatures have searchable statutes on their Internet sites);

- review the relevant case law for commission and judicial decisions relating to SDC practices and procedures for developing and implementing SDCs;
- seek competent legal advice, particularly when litigation risks are uncertain; and
- evaluate the underlying criteria important to a specific water system or jurisdictional environment.

The Rational Nexus Test

A common legal consideration related to SDCs is establishing a reasonable relationship, or rational nexus, between the amount of the SDC and the cost associated with serving the new development. In general terms, the rational nexus test requires that there be a connection (nexus) established between new development and the new or expanded facilities required to accommodate new development, and appropriate apportionment of the cost to the new development in relation to benefits reasonably expected to be received by the new development. These requirements have been reinforced by the US Supreme Court through landmark decisions on private property rights, especially in the cases of *Nollan v. California Coastal Commission* in 1987 (483 US 825) and *Dolan v. City of Tigard* in 1994 (512 US 687). The precedence established by the rulings in these two cases has helped to establish the standard for rational nexus incorporated in many state statutes and case law.

To establish the rational nexus, several key criteria are often used, including, at a minimum, the following:

- System planning criteria
- Financing criteria
- State and provincial or local laws

According to Arthur C. Nelson (1995), the rational nexus test examines the following:

1. A connection should be established between new development and the new or expanded facilities required to accommodate such development. This establishes the rational basis of public policy.
2. Identification of the cost of these new or expanded facilities needed to accommodate new development. This establishes the burden to the public of providing new facilities to new development and the rational basis on which to hold new development accountable for such costs. This may be determined using the so-called *Banberry* factors [*Banberry Development Company v. South Jordan City* (631 P.2d 899, Utah 1981)].
3. Appropriate apportionment of that cost to new development in relation to the benefits it reasonably receives. This establishes the nexus between the fees being paid to finance new facilities that accommodate new development and the benefit new development receives from such new facilities.

The first element of the rational nexus test examines the establishment of a rational basis for the policy being implemented through the fees. This implies that planning and capital improvement studies are used to establish the need for new facilities to accommodate anticipated growth. Adopted master or comprehensive plans or facility plans, or similar types of studies, should satisfy this first element because these plans assess existing facilities and capacity, project future capacity requirements, and determine the future capital infrastructure and new facilities needed to accommodate anticipated growth.

The referenced nexus test can be satisfied based on an assessment of both current and future capacity available to meet growth-related demands. For example, a utility that has, in the extreme, constructed all of the water system capacity required through the planned "build-out" of the service area can still make the nexus between the charge and the facilities needed to accommodate the anticipated growth. In this example, the basis for the charge would be the existing capacity available to serve new demands.

The second element of the rational nexus test examines factors such as the so-called *Banberry* factors, which include seven factors the Banberry court used "to determine the proportionate share of costs to be borne by new development" (Nelson 1995):

1. The cost of existing facilities.
2. The means by which existing facilities have been financed and who paid those costs.
3. The extent to which new development has already contributed to the cost of providing existing excess capacity.
4. The extent to which existing development will, in the future, contribute to the cost of providing existing facilities used community-wide or non-occupants of new development.
5. The extent to which new development should receive credit for providing at its cost facilities the community has provided in the past without charge to other development in the service area.
6. Extraordinary costs incurred in serving new development.
7. The time-price differential inherent in fair comparisons of the amount of money paid at different times.

Although these factors provide reasonable guidance in the development of SDCs, they should not be required in all jurisdictions.

The final element of the rational nexus test is the reasonable apportionment of the cost to new development in relation to benefits the new development will reasonably receive. This is accomplished by using a generally accepted methodology to establish the SDC. The financing criteria for establishing SDCs relates to the method used to finance infrastructure and ensures that customers are not paying twice for infrastructure—once through SDCs and again through rates.

Most statutes require a *reasonable relationship* between the fee charged and the cost associated with providing capacity to the customer. The charges do not need to be mathematically exact or reflect the cost to serve a specific customer (i.e., the SDC must be indicative to serve a class or group of customers) but must bear a reasonable relationship to the cost burden imposed. Implementation of the planning criteria and the actual and planned costs of construction will typically establish compliance with the reasonable relationship requirement. Some states require that SDCs must be based on the most recent and localized data, and this practice is recommended for all SDC calculations.

Given that fee factors and capacity-related cost structures differ among jurisdictions, benchmarking or comparing a utility's SDCs with "peer" or neighboring/regional agencies must be performed with caution. Reasons why SDCs can differ among utilities include the following:

- Source of supply
- Proximity to source of supply
- Type/complexity of treatment
- Effluent disposal method
- Availability of grant funding

- Administrative policies
- Time elapsed since last SDC fee review
- Density within service area/size of system
- Utility life cycle (growth-oriented versus mature)
- Level of service standards
- Local policy decisions

Depending on relevant legal and accounting requirements, it is important for utilities that charge SDCs to track the receipts carefully and separately so they can ensure that the receipts are applied to offset growth or expansion-related capital costs and are not used for operations and maintenance (O&M) or any other purpose not allowed by the pertinent regulations.

INFORMATION AND DOCUMENTATION FOR CALCULATIONS

Information needed to calculate SDCs may include asset records, a line inventory, the multiyear capital program often developed through the master planning process, and planning documentation. Each of these items is discussed in the following sections.

Asset Records

A utility should maintain detailed asset records to improve the accuracy of impact fee calculations. SDC calculations often consider the costs of a utility's system costs—the backbone or primary supply, treatment and transmission facilities in-service that have capacity available to serve new growth. If a utility has substantial unused capacity and no planned capacity expansions in the intermediate term, the SDC calculations may be based exclusively on the costs of the existing facilities.

To facilitate the accurate identification of these costs, the utility's asset records should ideally include the following items for each asset

- Asset number
- Asset location
- Acquisition date
- Purchase price
- Accumulated depreciation
- Whether the asset was purchased, funded through grants, or contributed

The costs of grant-funded and contributed assets are ineligible to be recovered through SDCs because such costs were not incurred by the utility and SDCs should not provide a "windfall" to existing users. The total costs for all the assets should closely match what is reported in the utility's annual financial report for the appropriate time period.

Line Inventory

A utility should maintain an up-to-date inventory of the amount of linear feet of water transmission and distribution mains by line size (diameter), and reclaimed water mains by line size. This information can assist in classifying water transmission versus distribution mains. (Given less than perfect information, the inventory data can be used to develop a reasonable allocation assumption.) Some utilities have incorporated the classification standards into their code of ordinances (e.g., transmission lines are generally any main greater than 12 in. in diameter).

Capital Program

If SDCs are to be calculated based on a multiyear projected capital improvement program, utility management should first ensure that the capital program from which the SDC calculations are derived is necessary, reasonable, attainable, and fundable. The utility should clearly indicate those projects that are growth related and will create additional capacity versus those projects that are renewals, replacements, and upgrades that will primarily benefit existing customers.

The projects should also be classified into functional categories such that the costs eligible to be recovered through SDCs can be identified.

Planning Documentation

Some states require land-use assumptions and improvement plans within the SDC methodology and documentation. Master plans, comprehensive plans, and facility use plans as adopted by the utility's governing body often provide important assumptions from which the SDC calculations are based, such as level-of-service standards, multiyear capital plan with cost estimates, and capacity of facilities and planned improvements and expansions.

NEW CUSTOMER DEMANDS (LEVEL OF SERVICE)

SDCs are most commonly charged on a per-equivalent residential unit (ERU) basis. An ERU—sometimes known as an equivalent residential connection (ERC), residential equivalent unit (REU), equivalent dwelling unit (EDU), equivalent living unit (ELU), or capacity unit—is representative of the water capacity (average or peak) required to serve a typical individually metered single-family residential customer. This class of users usually represents the largest group of customers served by a utility and typically has the lowest level of usage requirements for a specifically metered account.

An important assumption in calculating an SDC is the level-of-service standard assigned to an ERU. For water service, the level-of-service standard that is commonly used in the utility industry is the amount of capacity (service) allocable to an ERU expressed as the amount of usage (e.g., gallons, cubic feet) on an average-day or peak basis. This allocation of capacity represents the amount of capacity allowable to an ERU for system engineering and planning purposes, whether or not such capacity is actually used by the customer.

It is very important for a utility to be able to provide justification for any level-of-service standards used in the SDC calculations. A review of historical customer and per capita flows and peak-to-average-daily-flow water production relationships and trends can indicate whether an existing level-of-service standard is still appropriate or whether it should be updated. The water usage per customer may have decreased with some degree of permanence such that a lower level-of-service standard should be considered. Factors that could cause such a downward trend may include

- continued water conservation pricing efforts by local governments;
- improvements in water use requirements for household appliances, such as clothes washers and dishwashers, low-flow toilets, and water fixtures;
- increases in customer densities to reduce the costs of construction that result in less pervious surface to irrigate; and

- general customer awareness of the need to reduce water use (e.g., installation of xeriscape landscaping).

Sources that recognize or establish general level-of-service standards for water facilities include

- utility governing documents;
- the local government's code of ordinances for public utilities;
- the growth management plan;
- the utility's master plans and engineering design criteria used to establish the need for additional capacity;
- state regulatory agencies for private utilities;
- state departments of health; and
- state departments of environmental protection.

It may also be appropriate to survey the level-of-service standards used by neighboring utilities, especially those with similar service area characteristics.

The total ERUs—often expressed in gallons—assigned to a new customer comprise the "new customer demands" referenced in this chapter.

APPROACHES TO CALCULATING SDCs

Potential Costs in SDC Calculations

The costs that might be recovered through the imposition of SDCs depend on the calculation approach and the utility's specific circumstances. Some state laws specify that any capital costs included in SDC calculations must have a minimum useful life (5 years in some states, 10 years in others). A discussion of the major cost categories follows.

Installed system assets. The proportionate share of the cost of system assets available to serve growth may be eligible to be recovered through SDCs if the utility actually incurred the cost. The costs of contributed assets or assets funded through grants or other relatively cost-free means are ineligible to be included in SDC calculations.

Estimated capital program. The projects in the capital program should also be classified into functional categories in a similar fashion as described previously for the existing assets. Once the projects are classified, standards for including the capital project costs in the SDC calculations could be as follows:

- The project is related to the utility's water supply, water treatment, or primary transmission/storage.
- The project is identified as being growth related or provides a system-wide benefit, the cost of which should be shared by growth connecting to the system and existing customers.
- The project will result in a fixed asset(s) being added to the system and will not be recognized as operating expense. (New or revised accounting standards sometimes mandate the reclassification of certain capital expenditures represented in the capital program as operating expenses.)
- The project is not anticipated to be funded through grants or other contributed capital.

All of the aforementioned standards would need to be met for a project cost to be included in the SDC calculations.

The utility should be prepared to defend the inclusion of every project in the SDC calculations (e.g., explain the purpose and the benefit to new growth). If a project is ambiguous in scope (e.g., a placeholder) or does not provide a clear benefit to new growth, it should not be included in the calculations. "When in doubt, leave it out" is a good principle to follow.

One issue to consider is the treatment of renewal and replacement (R&R) projects in a multiyear capital improvement program for the purpose of calculating SDCs, especially if the R&R projects involve assets with capacity remaining to serve growth. The most conservative approach is to not include any R&R projects in the calculations. However, R&R projects are typically replacing existing fixed assets with more expensive assets (e.g., due to historical inflation and technology improvements). If the new assets represented in the capital improvement program are included in the impact fee calculations while the assets being replaced are removed from the calculations, then the utility has essentially created a pro forma fixed asset register that "right-sizes," or updates into today's dollars, the costs of the facilities in service that have capacity to serve growth. This approach promotes inter-period equity. (Once the capital improvement is executed, the then-current fixed asset register would presumably match the pro forma fixed asset register developed years earlier.)

Notably, existing customers may not be responsible for the needs for all of the utility's R&R projects. Sometimes assets must be replaced because of premature aging (e.g., as a result of contaminant intrusion) or as a result of limited or no use (e.g., the assets were built for growth that never materialized as expected).

Another issue relates to the costs of relocating water and wastewater lines due to the widening of roads that is necessitated by new growth. The incremental increase in the costs of the lines, or any upsizing component, may be eligible to be recovered through SDCs.

Interest costs. Interest costs associated with financing system assets may be eligible to be recovered through an SDC, or such costs might be recovered through a separate fee charged to growth.

Administrative costs. In addition to the costs of existing facilities and capital improvements, utilities are typically allowed to recoup the administrative costs of managing SDC fee programs within their calculated SDCs.

Reclaimed/reuse water system costs. The reclaimed water system of a utility is a form of (treated) wastewater disposal, and the capital costs associated with a reclaimed water system can justifiably be included in wastewater SDC fee calculations. However, reclaimed water, which is typically used for irrigation purposes, also reduces system potable water demand. Therefore, it also provides a clear benefit to the water system. Without the availability of reclaimed water, the utility may need to invest in costly water treatment plant expansions or new water supply sources. As such, it may be appropriate to include a portion of the reclaimed water system capital costs in the water SDC calculations.

Basic Approaches

There are many different methods that may be used to calculate cost-based system development charges. The three basic or common methods for calculating the SDCs are as follows:

1. The *buy-in method* is based on the value of the existing system's capacity. This method is typically used when the existing system has sufficient capacity to serve new development now and into the future.

2. The *incremental cost method* is based on the value or cost to expand the existing system's capacity. This method is typically used when the existing system has limited or no capacity to serve new development and new or incremental facilities are needed to serve new development now and into the future.

3. The *combined approach* is based on a blended value of both the existing and expanded system's capacity. This method is typically used where some capacity is available in parts of the existing system (e.g., source of supply), but new or incremental capacity will need to be built in other parts (e.g., treatment plant) to serve new development at some point in the future.

Fundamental Formula

According to any of the basic approaches discussed previously, the fundamental formula for calculating an SDC is

$$\frac{\text{System Value}}{\text{System Capacity}} \times \text{New Customer Capacity Demands} = \text{SDC}$$

This formula starts by determining the unit value of the water system's capacity and multiplies that unit value by the amount of capacity the new customer will demand. (See the level-of-service discussion in the previous section.) The result is an SDC that apportions the value of the system capacity to a new customer based on how much of the capacity the new customer will use.

Because system capacity is generally not available in the same proportions throughout the various functional components of the water system (e.g., source of supply, treatment, pumping), the formula may be used for each functional area to calculate the SDC component cost by functional component (e.g., source of supply, pumping, treatment). This allows the utility to recognize variations in system capacity, system value, and customer capacity needs by functional area. Summing the SDC functional component costs results in the water system SDC.

Also, by applying the formula to each functional area of the water system, the analysis can recognize that the design and operating criteria for each functional area may differ. For example, an impounded reservoir supply may have annual average-day usage as the basis of capacity while treatment, pumping, and transmission mains are more likely to have a maximum-day demand capacity in terms of million gallons per day.

The key steps in the analysis are the same, regardless of the overall methodology selected:

1. Determine system planning criteria.
2. Determine the associated cost or value and available capacity of capacity-related facilities.
3. Determine new customer demands for each functional area of the system.
4. Calculate system component costs.
5. Determine any credits.

EXAMPLES OF SDC METHODOLOGIES

The mathematical examples presented in this chapter are intended to assist the reader to understand the calculations involved in determining SDCs and are not intended to be used as step-by-step templates for calculating SDCs. These examples are designed to illustrate the basic concepts associated with calculating SDCs according to each methodology. There may be variations on these approaches that would still be considered legally defensible.

For purposes of simplification of the examples, it is presumed that an adopted master plan has been used to determine the system planning criteria. This plan defines and establishes the existing capacity and projected future customer growth to the build-out of the service area or a defined planning period (e.g., 20 years). The adopted master plan also specifies the expansion or growth-related facilities that will be required to accommodate the projected future growth. Given those key assumptions, the examples presented in the following sections focus primarily on the calculation of the system component costs and, more specifically, on the valuation of capacity according to each of the methodologies.

In the example calculation of the SDC, in very basic terms, the total value of each functional backbone component is divided by the appropriate gallons of system capacity provided to establish a unit cost ($/gal) for the SDC calculation. A commonly used approach for determining new customer capacity demands is to use the demands for the base-size connection (usually ⅝-in. or ¾-in. meters). Once the unit cost ($/gal) is determined, the average capacity demands of the base customer (average day and maximum day as applicable) is multiplied by the unit cost ($/gal) to derive a total SDC cost. Therefore, if the calculated unit cost of one backbone component is $1.50/gal and a base-size connection has an average-day requirement of 250 gallons, the charge for that component of the SDC, before any credits (see the "System Liabilities and Equity" subsection later in this chapter), would be $375.00 ($1.50 × 250 gal). This type of approach is well suited to backbone components such as treatment plants, reservoirs, and so on, where the total capacity of the treatment plant or reservoir is well established.

In the examples presented in the following sections, pump stations are used for the purpose of illustrating the various methodologies. To calculate a full and complete SDC, each component of the backbone system (source of supply, treatment, pumping, transmission, etc.) would be separately analyzed. Each backbone component is added together to determine the *gross* SDC before any debt-service credits. At that point, any debt credits to the SDC should be deducted from the gross SDC to establish the net allowable system development charge.

Buy-in Method

The buy-in method is typically used where there is sufficient capacity in the existing system such that it is capable of meeting both near-term and long-term capacity needs. Under the buy-in methodology, new development "buys" a proportionate share of capacity at cost (value) of the existing facilities. It is important to note that while this methodology is labeled a *buy-in method*, payment of an SDC does not transfer or impart ownership of assets to the customer. Payment of an SDC, under this method, is generally considered to provide access to capacity in the amount purchased at a status equal to that of existing customers of the system.

The buy-in method is based on the principle of achieving capital equity between existing and new customers. This approach attempts to assess new customers an SDC to approximate the average equity or debt-free investment position of existing customers.

Valuation and system equity. There are different methods used to establish a value to the existing assets under the buy-in methodology. If the existing assets are valued at their original cost or depreciated original cost, this is often referred to as the *original cost method*. An alternative valuation approach is to value the existing assets at a replacement cost or a depreciated replacement cost. This is commonly referred to as the *replacement cost method*. According to the replacement cost method, the existing system components are valued at the current-day cost of replicating the existing assets. This is typically accomplished through the use of a construction cost index or other comparable valuation method to bring the historical costs up to current-day value. In summary form, the four valuation approaches for system assets under the buy-in method are as follows:

1. **Original cost (OC)** is the cost of construction in the year of construction.
2. **Original cost less accumulated depreciation (OCLD)** is also known as the net book value of the system assets.
3. **Replacement cost new (RCN)** is the original cost escalated to current-day dollars, providing an estimate of the current-day cost of replicating the existing facilities.
4. **Replacement cost new less depreciation (RCNLD)** is the original cost escalated to current-day dollars, less accumulated replacement cost depreciation. This provides an estimate of the current-day cost of replicating the existing facilities that is then adjusted by an estimate of the replacement cost depreciation, resulting in a replacement cost valuation that reflects the remaining depreciable life of the facility.

A combination of the approaches may also be used. Using the OC and OCLD valuations, the SDC reflects the original investment in the existing capacity. The new customer "buys in" to the capacity at the OC or the net book value cost (OCLD) for the facilities and as a result pays an amount similar to what the existing customers paid for the capacity (OC) or the remaining value of the original investment (OCLD).

Using the RCN and the RCNLD valuations, the SDC reasonably reflects the cost of providing new expansion capacity to customers as if the capacity was added at the time the new customers connected to the water system. It may also be thought of as a valuation method to fairly compensate the existing customers for the carrying costs of the excess capacity built into the system in advance of when the new customers connect to the system. This is because, up to the point of the new customer connecting to the system, the existing customers have been financially responsible for the carrying costs of that excess capacity that is available for development.

System liabilities and equity. Balance-sheet liabilities and equity that are recognized in the valuation method should equitably address the issue of the outstanding principal portion of long-term debt. When debt is issued to finance a growth- or expansion-related project, the principal portion of the debt service will be repaid over time, possibly through a customer's rates after connection to the system and payment of an SDC. Given that, a debt credit may be applicable to avoid the potential double-charging of these debt costs through both the SDC and user rates. In a situation where the SDC is separated into functional components (source of supply, treatment, pumping, transmission, etc.), the analysis may provide these debt credits at the functional level or on a combined system level at the end of the analysis.

SDC calculation adjustments. Valuation adjustments may be necessary if grants or other contributions were used to develop the capacity-related facilities or if a facility is replaced and the resulting replacement provides additional capacity to accommodate future customers. This may be addressed within the valuation process by determining the percentage of the asset eligible for the SDC (i.e., percent SDC eligible). For example, if grants were provided specifically for the water treatment facilities, these grant contributions should be credited to the value (cost) of those specific facilities, and the grant-related portion of the water treatment plant's value should not be included in the SDC.

SDC determination—buy-in method. For purposes of the example SDC calculation under the buy-in method shown in Table VII.2-1, the RCNLD valuation method has been used. The backbone component of pumping plant has been selected for purposes

Table VII.2-1 Illustrative example of the development of the SDC for a pumping plant using the buy-in method and RCNLD valuation approach for a ⅝-in. connection

Asset Description	Useful Life, Years	Years in Service	Original Cost	Cost Index	Replacement Cost Value	% Depreciated	% SDC Eligible*	Pump Station SDC Component
Pump Station 1	25	29	$541,075	1.97	$1,065,918	100	100	$0
Pump Station 2	25	19	1,352,780	1.61	2,177,976	76	100	522,714
Land	Land	N/A†	1,048,750	1.53	1,604,588	0	100	1,604,588
Pump Station 4B	40	10	777,615	1.37	1,065,333	25	100	798,999
Zone 3 Pump Station	40	2	1,397,100	1.04	1,452,984	5	50	690,167
Pump Station Improvements	35	1	580,675	1	580,675	3	100	563,255
Total								**$4,179,723**

Less: Outstanding Debt Principal on Pump Station Facilities	$(500,000)
Equals: Net Pump Station Value	$3,679,723
Divided by: Pump Station Capacity (mgd)	24
Equals: Unit Valuation of Pump Station ($/mgd)	$153,321.80
Divided by: 1,000,000 gallons ($/gpd)	$0.1533
Multiplied by: New ⅝-in. Customer Demand (gpd)‡	625.0
Equals: Pump Station Component Value of SDC	$95.83

*% SDC eligible reflects the amount of the facility to be included in the SDC calculation. The portions not included reflect contributions such as grants, contributions in aid of construction, etc.

†N/A = not available.

‡Assumes a new ⅝-in. customer uses 91,250 gallons of water per year, with a maximum-day peaking factor of 2.50, yielding a maximum-day demand of 625 gpd.

of illustrating the buy-in methodology. The RCNLD approach shown in Table VII.2-1 can be easily adapted to reflect the other valuation methods: original cost, original cost less depreciation, and replacement cost.

As can be seen, this methodology uses the original cost of the assets and their useful lives to develop the RCNLD value. The methodology also considers any contributed assets (e.g., grants) that should be excluded from the SDC. In this example, the total depreciated replacement cost is calculated as $4,179,723. This valuation is reduced by outstanding debt principal associated and issued for the facilities, and the net value is then divided by the pump station capacity to determine its unit value. The unit value of the capacity ($0.1533/gpd) is then multiplied by the amount of capacity needed by the new customer (625 gpd). The example uses a ⅝-in. connection as the basis for the calculation. This results in the pumping plant component of the SDC of $95.83 for a customer with a ⅝-in. connection.

The process used in this example must be repeated for each functional portion of the water system that is to be included in the SDC calculation. It is important to note that the pumping plant example previously shown uses maximum-day capacity. Other plant components may use different design criteria (e.g., average-day use), and the calculated SDC should reflect the capacity (design criteria) required for that particular plant component. Once each component cost of the backbone system has been calculated, they may be summarized into a total net allowable SDC. Provided in Table VII.2-2 is an illustrative example of how this information may be summarized for a ⅝-in. connection. In this example, the total ⅝-in. SDC, after debt credits or other adjustments, is $2,454.18.

Table VII.2-2 Illustrative example of the summary of the net allowable SDC using the buy-in method and RCNLD valuation approach for a ⅝-in. connection

System Component	Gross SDC	Less: SDC Debt Credits	Net Allowable ⅝-in. SDC
Source of Supply	$1,048.25	($220.00)	$828.25
Treatment	1,845.90	(543.50)	1,302.40
Pumping*	108.85	(13.02)	95.83
Transmission	228.45	(55.65)	172.80
General Plant	54.90	0.0	54.90
Total	$3,286.35	($832.17)	$2,454.18

*Calculations are based on data contained in Table VII.2-1:

- Pumping Gross SDC is based on this calculation: [($4,179,723/24 mgd)/1,000,000] × 625 gpd.

- Pumping SDC Debt Credit is based on this calculation: [($500,000/24 mgd)/1,000,000] × 625 gpd.

Incremental Cost Method

The incremental cost method, also referred to as the marginal cost method, differs in perspective from the buy-in method. While the buy-in method uses existing assets for the valuation of the SDC, the incremental cost method assigns to new development the incremental cost of future system expansion needed to serve the new development. Generally, this method is considered most appropriate when the existing system does not have sufficient available capacity, and a significant portion of the capacity required to serve new customers must be provided by the construction of new facilities. When using this method, it is important to have a capital improvement plan (CIP) that identifies the costs associated with new capacity, the timing of the expenditure, and the proposed source(s) of funds for those capital improvements.

The incremental cost method is designed to equitably distribute these capital costs to new customers in proportion to the new customer's usage of the facilities and the investment required to develop the facilities. Similar to the buy-in method, the valuation of the incremental assets are developed, adjusted for any grants or other contributions, and then divided by the capacity (in gallons or gallons per day) to derive a cost per gallon on new facilities. The result is an SDC for new customers that reflects the capital costs associated with providing the capacity needed by customer growth. However, it is important to realize that under this method, as is the case for the buy-in method, there will typically be a cash-flow timing difference because the facilities have to be built (and financed) before new customers can connect to them.

There are a number of factors or considerations in establishing SDCs using the incremental cost method. To calculate SDCs according to the incremental cost method, the practitioner must determine, among various factors, the period of growth, growth rates, type of growth, capacity associated with the various improvements needed to serve the projected growth, and cost of these improvements. Provided in the following sections is a discussion of some of the key considerations along with an example.

Service area. The area to be served must be determined before the SDC can be computed. Commonly, the total service area of the utility system is used, but some utilities divide their system into separate service areas. Particular care should be used when dividing a utility system into subsets to ensure that the subsets are based on identifiable and significant cost-of-service differences from the system as a whole.

The delineation of the utility service area is important for growth planning and for assessing capital improvements needed for new development. Typical service areas are municipal corporate limits and public-utility-commission certificated or franchised service areas. The inclusion of extraterritorial jurisdictions may be appropriate where service is currently provided or the provision of service is imminent.

Municipalities that serve communities outside their borders typically use one of the following approaches for calculating outside-city SDCs:

1. They do not charge outside-city customers an SDC.
2. They charge the same SDC charged to inside-city customers.
3. They charge a different SDC than inside-city customers based on specific customer demand estimates and identification of new facility and cost analysis for serving inside- versus outside-city customers.

Outside-municipality surcharges are not recommended to be applied to an SDC. Such a surcharge could possibly make the total collected amount exceed the development's or entity's pro-rata share of the infrastructure costs (i.e., the fee exceeds the benefit cost); hence, it could potentially be challenged as a violation of case law pertaining to SDCs. There should be a nexus between the costs and the SDC charged.

Planning period. The SDC planning period is needed to project the growth and service requirements of the system. Though utilities have used various lengths of time for planning purposes, the planning period for determining SDCs is generally the same as the utility's standard planning period. This planning period is typically defined within their planning documents, but it usually ranges from 10 to 20 years for distribution and treatment facilities planning but may exceed 50 years for water supply planning. Another criterion for determining a planning period is the financial cycle for long-term financing, which can typically be 10 to 30 years. Sometimes legislation governs the length of the planning period.

Growth rate and magnitude of expansion. A projection of the future system growth is an integral part of the incremental cost method. The rate and type (customer class) of growth has a direct effect on the type of system expansion needed to serve new development over the planning period. Ideally, a utility's facility planning documents will provide the basis for much of this information.

Capital improvement plan for system expansion. Ideally, the capital improvements needed to meet system expansion and growth will be provided within the utility's adopted master, comprehensive, or facility planning documents. These adopted documents provide a clear connection between projected growth, system planning criteria, and the needed improvements to serve future development. Some utilities will also have CIPs that segregate projects between replacement projects and capacity expansion (i.e., growth-related) projects.

In reviewing the CIP, some decisions may be needed regarding the proportion of an improvement that provides expanded capacity versus replacing existing capacity. While some capital improvements may clearly be 100 percent expansion related, the difficulty with replacement projects is that they may replace existing capacity and provide expanded capacity (e.g., a transmission line that is replaced but oversized for future growth and expansion). For replacement projects that provide expanded capacity, only the proportion of the project that provides new capacity is included within the SDC. The same situation may occur for improvement projects primarily driven by regulatory requirements (e.g., upgraded improvements at a water treatment plant). Again, if the improvement provides capacity for new customers, that portion of the improvement that provides new or additional capacity for growth and expansion may be included within the SDC.

SDC determination—incremental methodology. For purposes of the example SDC calculation under the incremental cost method shown in Table VII.2-3, it is presumed that an adopted comprehensive water system plan was used as the source document for

Table VII.2-3 Illustrative example of the development of the SDC for a pumping plant using the incremental cost method for a ⅝-in. connection

Future System Improvement	Cost of Improvement*	% Expansion[†]	% SDC Eligible[‡]	Pump Station SDC Component
Pump Station 1 Expansion	$565,000	50	100	$282,500
Land	128,000	100	100	128,000
Pump Station 5	425,000	25	100	106,250
Zone 8 Pump Expansion	538,000	100	50	269,000
General Improvements	125,000	0	100	0
Total Pumping Improvements				**$785,750**
Divided by: Additional Capacity (mgd)[§]				4
Equals: Unit Valuation of Additional Pumping Capacity ($/mgd)				$196,438
Divided by: 1,000,000 gallons ($/gpd)				$0.1964
Multiplied by: New ⅝-in. Customer Demand (gpd)**				625.00
Equals: Pump Station Component Value of SDC				**$122.77**

*Improvements are stated in current-day dollars.

†Reflects the proportion of the project that provides expansion capacity.

‡SDC eligible reflects amount to be included in the calculation of the SDC and may exclude contributions such as grants, developer contributions, ad valorem tax payments, etc. It should also reflect the removal of any future costs that are related to the quality of service for old customers (better treatment) as well as the costs of any facilities that serve existing customers (replacement of a pipe with a larger one).

§Derived from planning documents.

**Assumes a new ⅝-in. customer uses 91,250 gallons of water per year, with a maximum-day peaking factor of 2.50, yielding a maximum-day demand of 625 gpd.

the assumed customer growth, planning capital projects, and the proportion of the projects that are related to providing system capacity expansion. Furthermore, although the improvements will be made in future years, the analysis uses current-day dollars for all plant costs.

As shown in Table VII.2-3, the SDC component for a pumping plant under the incremental cost method would be $122.77. The pump plant component of the SDC would be summed with the other backbone SDC components to determine the total ⅝-in. SDC.

In viewing Table VII.2-3, the approach is similar yet different from the buy-in approach (Table VII.2-1). According to this approach, the improvements have been identified within the comprehensive water system planning document. All the plant values have been placed in current-day dollars (i.e., any escalated values in the planning document are present valued to convert them into current-day dollars for purposes of the SDC calculation). Next, a determination of the percentage of each project that provides capacity expansion, along with the percentage of the project that is SDC eligible, is made. Similar to the buy-in methodology, projects funded in part from grants, developer contributions, and so forth, may not be eligible for inclusion within the SDC calculation. The total eligible projects are summed then divided by the total capacity that will be added to the system. This allows a unit value of the additional capacity to be determined ($0.1964/gpd) and, when multiplied by the capacity needs of the future customer (625 gpd), the pump station component of the SDC is determined ($122.77).

Table VII.2-4 Illustrative example of the development of the SDC for a pumping plant using the combined cost method for a ⅝-in. connection

Capacity Item	Value	Capacity, mgd	Unit Value, $/mgd
Existing Capacity	$4,179,723	24.0	N/A*
Future Capacity	$785,750	4.0	N/A
Total	$4,965,473	28.0	$177,338.33
Divided by: 1,000,000 gallons ($/gpd)			$0.1773
Multiplied by: New ⅝-in. Customer Demand (gpd)			625.00
Equals: Pump Station Component Value of SDC			$110.84

*N/A = not applicable

Combined Cost Approach

The combined cost approach, as shown in Table VII.2-4, is, as the name implies, a technique for averaging the buy-in and incremental cost methods. The average is not a simple summed average, but rather, it is a weighted average. In the example illustrated in Table VII.2-4, it is assumed that the utility has capacity within the existing system that can serve growth but will also need to add capacity in the future to serve growth. In such cases, it is logical to base the SDC on the weighted average cost of the existing capacity and future capacity additions. By doing so, new customers pay an SDC that reflects the value of existing and planned capacity.

As was the case for the buy-in and incremental cost methods, the example in Table VII.2-4 provides the pumping plant cost component for the SDC. In this case, using the combined cost method, the SDC for a ⅝-in. connection is $110.84. This is based on a unit cost of $0.1773/gpd and a customer demand of 625 gpd. A similar analysis should be done for the other functional areas of the system, and the sum of the component SDCs will result in the total allowable SDC for a new customer.

SDC Schedule Methods

The examples used in this chapter have determined an SDC for a new ⅝-in. connection. However, new customers will likely have different connection sizes and place different capacity demands on the system. Therefore, a utility must have a method of administering the SDCs that fairly and equitably reflect the capacity costs of the varying new customer capacity needs. There are four common methods for determining the SDCs for varying capacity requirements:

1. Meter size
2. Fixture units
3. Customer attributes
4. Estimated usage

Meter size. A common method for administering SDCs is based on meter size. One of the advantages of this method is that it is relatively easy to administer and explain to new customers. According to the meter size approach, SDCs for new customers increase as the size (capacity) of the meter increases. To accomplish this, an equivalent meter ratio is developed that expresses the capacity of larger meters in relation to the capacity of the utility's "base" meter size (e.g., a ⅝-in. meter).

Table VII.2-5 Meter equivalencies based on meter capacity and establishing SDCs by meter size using the buy-in method and RCNLD valuation approach

Meter Size	Maximum-Rated Safe Operating Flow, gpm*	Meter Equivalent Ratio[†]	SDC
⅝-in. Displacement	20	1.0	$2,454[‡]
¾-in. Displacement	30	1.5	3,681
1-in. Displacement	50	2.5	6,135
1½-in. Displacement	100	5.0	12,271
2-in. Displacement	160	8.0	19,633
3-in. Singlejet	320	16.0	39,267
3-in. Compound, Class I	320	16.0	39,267
3-in. Turbine, Class I	350	17.5	42,948
4-in. Singlejet	500	25.0	61,354
4-in. Compound, Class I	500	25.0	61,354
4-in. Turbine Class I	630	31.5	77,307
6-in. Singlejet	1,000	50.0	122,709
6-in. Compound, Class I	1,000	50.0	122,709
6-in. Turbine Class I	1,300	65.0	159,521
8-in. Compound, Class I	1,600	80.0	196,334
8-in. Turbine Class II	2,800	140.0	343,585
10-in. Turbine Class II	4,200	210.0	515,377
12-in. Turbine Class II	5,300	265.0	650,357

*Source: AWWA Standards: Displacement, C700-15; Singlejet, C712-10; Turbine Classes I and II, C701-12; Compound Class I, C702-10.

†Using standard maximum meter-flow capacity ratios (e.g., 2 in. = 160 gpm, 20 gpm (⅝ in.) = 8.0:1.0 capacity ratio).

‡⅝-in. SDC based on example presented in Table VII.2-2.

The equivalent meter ratio is used as the basis for the increased SDC for larger meters. For example, the safe operating capacity of a ⅝-in. meter is 20 gpm. In contrast, a 2-in. meter has a safe operating capacity of 160 gpm. Thus, on a capacity basis, a 2-in. meter is the equivalent of eight ⅝-in. meters, and the SDC for the 2-in. meter should be set at 8 times the ⅝-in.-meter SDC.

Table VII.2-5 provides an example for the development of SDC schedules based on a ⅝-in. meter as the base meter size. In this example, the base SDC is $2,454 or the amount calculated in the buy-in example displayed in Table VII.2-2.

As shown in Table VII.2-5, for each type of meter, there is a corresponding maximum-rated safe operating flow. This provides the basis for the meter equivalency ratios. These ratios are then multiplied by the base cost SDC ($2,454) to provide a schedule of SDCs for new customers connecting to the system. For example, a customer with a 2-in. meter would be charged $19,633, since the capacity of a 2-in. meter is eight times that of a ⅝-in. meter. Stated another way, a customer with a 2-in. meter has the capacity of the equivalent of eight ⅝-in. meters. The manufacturer specifications of the actual meters used by a utility may also be used to develop meter equivalency ratios.

One of the disadvantages of the meter size approach is that for larger meters, the meter capacity may not be a reasonable indicator for the actual capacity demand of the customer. It should be remembered that the $2,454 SDC for a ⅝-in. connection reflects the usage patterns of that size meter (i.e., a residential customer with a ⅝-in. meter).

A new customer with a larger connection size—for example, an industrial customer with a 6-in. meter—may use far more capacity than shown in Table VII.2-5 for a 6-in. meter. Therefore, an individual determination of the number of equivalent units or capacity requirements may be appropriate.

Fixture units. The fixture unit approach is based on a count of the fixture units (water-using devices like toilets, dishwashers, etc.) of the dwelling or building. This method is commonly used for unmetered customers. The basic concept of this approach is that each water-using fixture of the building is equal to a specified volume stated in gallons per day and that can be equated to an equivalent residential unit (ERU). The values for each fixture unit of the building are then summed, and the total ERUs for purposes of establishing the SDC can be determined.

Customer attributes. The attributes method for determining ERUs is based on the type of establishment and standardized usage characteristics for certain business attributes rather than meter size or fixtures (plumbing) of the new structure. For example, the capacity of a restaurant may be based on the number of permitted seats, or the capacity of an office based on square feet of the office building. The advantage of the attributes method is that it may be a better indicator of actual use compared to a fixture or meter equivalent approach that does not consider how the facility will be used. However, one downside is that compared to fixture counts or meter size, the attributes method can be more administratively burdensome, especially when involving the redevelopment of property. For example, under the attributes method, additional SDCs may be required for the redevelopment of a particular property even if there is no change in meter size or overall number of plumbing fixtures compared to the original development on the property. Under the attributes method, there may be difficulty in surveying the capacity requirements associated with different types of nonresidential establishments (some may not be easily categorized). Therefore, customers of the same type could have different plumbing configurations, resulting in differences in potential demand.

Estimated usage. This approach is often used by utilities to establish the SDC for new customers needing a meter size that is larger than a certain threshold (e.g., larger than 2 in.). In these cases, for new connections up to the threshold size, the utility will use the meter size, or other standard approach. Then, for meters larger than the threshold, the utility will estimate the capacity needs of the new customer and base the SDC on those estimates. Ideally, the utility will have other similar customers with historical data on which to make the estimate.

Credits for "green" initiatives. Utilities should consider the applicability of SDC credits for customers that may have lower demand on the water system due to low-flow toilets or the structure of their facilities. Customers that have achieved Leadership in Energy and Environmental Design certification often have water-conserving fixtures throughout the applicable building(s). In these situations, it may be appropriate for the utility to provide an SDC credit that is proportionate to the reduced system demand compared with the demand of a standard unit if the reduced demand can be verified.

Review or true-up of SDC. Some utilities, within their adopted SDC ordinance or resolution, provide for the ability to review capacity use of customers with larger connections after a specified period of time after which a baseline of historical usage has been established. With this review comes the opportunity to true-up the SDC payment based on the baseline consumption data. In some cases where estimated usage is used to determine the customer's SDC, the utility may consider a true-up to the SDC after some reasonable time period of historical usage that has allowed for a clearer understanding of the customer's patterns of use. The use of such a true-up should be evaluated based on any applicable legal/legislative requirements governing the assessment of SDCs.

Timing of SDC assessment and collection. Another factor that should be considered when selecting the SDC schedule approach is the timing of the SDC assessment and collection. Depending on when the SDC is assessed and collected, it may be possible that the data required for one or more of the four approaches will not be available. However, if the SDC is collected at the time of building permit issuance or service initiation (e.g., at the time the meter is set), the data for any of the four approaches would be available; therefore any one of them could be selected. The estimated usage approach involves additional collection steps in cases where the customer's usage during the monitoring period demonstrates the need to collect an incremental SDC. When the monitoring period extends over years, it is possible that the utility may find itself dealing with customer turnover at the service location. Again, the determination of when the SDC may be assessed and/or collected may be governed by local or state requirements.

OTHER SDC TECHNICAL AND ADMINISTRATIVE ISSUES

While the previous discussion and examples have provided an overview of the development of SDCs, there are many other technical and administrative issues associated with SDCs.

SDC Revenue (Debt) Credits

SDC calculations should consider the applicability of credits for capital costs that are embedded in system revenue requirements (e.g., outstanding debt) and will be recovered through user rates. Typically, this credit is for the debt related to capital expansion projects. As such, the debt credit adjusts the SDC to avoid collecting capital costs through the SDC and then again through water rates.

As noted previously, determination of SDCs differs significantly from user rate development because of the prevalence of enabling legislation, which in many states is prescriptive. This is specifically true with respect to revenue credit calculations, and the credit calculation may include items such as growth-related debt service embedded within user fees, taxes, assessments, and intergovernmental transfers. Accordingly, it is important to review applicable legislation and recognize that what is appropriate in one state or province may be invalid in another.

In general, there are several options for the calculation of revenue credits, each of which should be reviewed for conformance with applicable legislation and each with relative advantages and disadvantages. The applicability of revenue credits may depend on the costs included in the SDC calculations (e.g., capital costs plus interest/financing costs or only capital costs) and how the utility uses its SDC collections. For example, if SDCs are used to directly pay for project costs, reducing the amount of debt financing required, a debt credit may not be applicable.

Outstanding debt principal. One approach for making revenue adjustments and to prevent double recovery of debt-related costs (or other credits) in calculating SDCs is to deduct the outstanding debt principal balance from the cost basis used in the calculation of the unit costs of capacity. By doing so, SDCs do not recover costs that will potentially be collected from the new customer in future water rates (i.e., debt service within the revenue requirements and user rates). According to this approach, the amount of the credit will decrease as the principle of the debt is repaid through rate revenue. Thus, in order for the SDC to continue reflecting the cost of capacity, the credit needs regular adjustments. The primary advantage of using the outstanding debt principal approach is its simplicity and transparency.

Present value of revenue payments. The present value approach is another method for calculating revenue credits. This approach is used when the credit will be applied to the total SDC calculation as opposed to the components. It is based on a deduction of the present value of new customer debt-service payments that will be included in future water rate charges paid by new customers.

The present value approach can be complex because of the need to determine whether the present value analysis is done for total debt-service payments (principal and interest) or just principal payments, and related to this decision is the selection of the proper discount rate. Another consideration is whether there are specific jurisdictional (e.g., state) legal requirements for the calculation of these credits.

Utilities often incur debt to defray the costs of capacity-expanding improvements (both existing and future improvements). To pay the annual costs of debt service, agencies often rely on customer rates but may use other revenue sources including system development charges. If SDCs are utilized to fund debt service, then interest and financing costs can be included to derive the charges. The utility would simply add such costs to the capital or system improvement costs in its SDC calculation process. If customer rates are used to fund debt-service payments, in whole or in part, debt-service credits to SDC calculations should be considered to avoid the potential of charging a connection twice for the same cost of capacity-expanding system improvements.

In some SDC calculations, both principal and interest payments are considered as legitimate expenses. Principal is included because it is capitalized into existing facilities, and interest costs are considered given that they are costs that are recovered by existing and future ratepayers through their regular user rates. The question then becomes one of methodology used to include these financing costs. One approach advocates the simple summing of future interest costs, reducing them to a unit value (e.g., per-gallon basis) and deducting from the gross SDC calculated amount. Another approach takes the net present value of future interest costs discounted at an appropriate rate to determine the unit cost of credit. This is a more widely used approach in the calculation of SDC debt-service credits. The rate utilized would be a discount rate. The discount rate converts the future stream of financing costs into their value in current terms. The question of what discount rate to use is one where utility finance professionals often disagree. One approach is to use the cost of debt issued to finance the system improvements. Another approach is to set the discount rate at the real interest rate of the debt issued for such improvements (nominal rate less an inflation rate). The argument made to support the use of the real rate is that it appropriately reflects the opportunity cost of the utility's investment dollars that could have gone to other uses (albeit other uses for a single-purpose utility are limited, whereas there are other considerations in a municipality that owns and operates a utility).

Outstanding bond payments as well as future bond payments linked to planned capital projects would be considered in the present value analysis. If future bond payments are considered, estimations will have to be made on the terms of the potential financing. In addition, the utility should be confident that the bond sale will occur at the specified time as considered in the SDC analysis. Delays in the issue date, construction amount, or other terms of the issue will have an effect on the output of the present value analysis.

Use of SDC Receipts

SDCs can be a major source of funding for financing growth-related projects that limit the amount of new debt needed, or in the alternative, for making debt-service payments on past growth-related debt. A utility desiring to use SDC receipts for debt-service payments should use caution because customer growth may not be stable or consistent over time. Therefore, the SDC receipts in any single year may be significantly deficient when compared to the debt-service payments. In cases where SDC receipts are used for debt-service payments, the utility should be proactive and adopt written financial policies that outline the preference for using the SDC receipts for debt-service payments and identify the alternative funding sources that may be available should growth and the SDC receipts not materialize as expected. It is prudent to not rely solely on SDC receipts for debt-service payments but rather to protect against the growth risks by identifying other sources, such as transfers from reserve funds, water rates, or contributions from the general fund (e.g., property taxes) that can be used when SDC receipts are insufficient in meeting debt-service requirements.

Reimbursement Policies

Reimbursement contracts are sometimes used by water utilities for infrastructure contributions. These contracts typically provide for reimbursement of some contributed facility costs from SDCs collected from future customers who will use the contributed facility. Limitations on the amount of, and the time period for, reimbursement should be included in the contracts. For example, reimbursements may be limited to a period of 10 years after the contribution and limited to the same system component (i.e., source, treatment, distribution, or transmission) of the SDCs collected in the service area of the contributed facilities. Reimbursement contracts should clearly explain the formulas for determining credits and/or refunds, and for administrative reasons, excessively complex formulas should be avoided. Simplifying solutions, such as much smaller but up-front reimbursement for a portion of the contributed asset, can be far preferable to contracts requiring management over many years.

Timing of SDC Assessment and Collection

The timing of collection involves two conflicting issues that must be reconciled. First, the utility needs to collect SDCs early enough for the SDC program to make a meaningful improvement in the availability of funds for system improvements. Second, the utility can accurately assess the SDC only later in the development process, when the actual meter size or number of fixture units is known. In some cases, SDCs are charged at the time the plat is approved, but more common is the assessment and collection of SDCs at the time the building permit is issued or at the time service is provided (e.g., when the meter is set or when a certificate of occupancy is issued during the development process). The utility must determine what it considers to be the "trigger" for assessing and collecting its SDCs. In making this type of decision, utilities and their governing bodies should be aware that deferring collection of the SDC to later in the development process shifts some of the speculation risk from the developer to the utility. Deferral of SDC collection extends the cash-flow timing issue mentioned previously in this chapter and puts existing utility customers in the position of investing up-front for potential new customers that may take longer than expected to materialize. This decision is essentially the same choice as determining to whom SDCs are charged and when the charge should occur. Utilities apply SDCs in several ways, triggered by several conditions, including

- creation of a new plant,
- issuance of a building permit,
- application for new service,
- application for additional service, and
- provision of new service.

Alternative SDC Calculation Procedures

It is important for utilities to have an adopted, official procedure for applicants to submit an alternative SDC calculation—this may be required by state law. If an applicant believes that the nature, timing, or location of a proposed development would make it likely to generate impacts costing less than the amounts calculated under the utility's current methodology for determining the number of ERUs, the applicant has the right to submit an alternative SDC calculation—prepared and certified by a qualified professional in the utility industry under generally accepted methods—often to the utility director or city/county manager (or his/her designee). The purpose of the alternative SDC fee calculation is not to simply switch one accepted ERU determination methodology for another, but to present compelling evidence that the ERU calculations under the current methodology significantly overstate the applicant's capacity demand. If the calculation is not accepted, the applicant may appeal to the governing board, commission, or council.

The applicant is often expected to pay in full the SDC calculated under the utility's current methodology in advance of the alternative SDC review. The utility may have the option of charging a nonrefundable alternative SDC review fee. The alternative SDC review policy should specify the time frame of the various stages of review (e.g., utility director will complete review within days).

If the alternative SDC calculation is accepted, the utility should still reserve the right to true-up the calculation based on the actual use of the development once connected to the system, as it is important that each customer pay its fair share of the demand for the utility's capacity. If actual consumption during a specified period (e.g., 24 months) after initiation of service reflects a greater demand on the water facilities than what was represented in the alternative fee calculation, the utility should retain the right to increase the total amount of SDCs collected from the applicant.

There are several examples of alternative SDC calculation procedures available in city and county ordinances. Utilities that have not yet established a formal procedure can reference those of peers and derive one that fits their organization.

SDCs and Private Fire Protection

SDCs are often established in relation to the size of the meter being installed. An issue being considered by the utility industry is how to fairly assess SDCs when a customer requires an oversized meter due to standby (fire protection) capacity, which may never be required or used over the life of the building structure.

ADMINISTRATIVE AND ACCOUNTING POLICIES AND PROCEDURES

The utility should adopt general administrative and accounting procedures to ensure that the SDC collections are managed and used for the facilities needed to provide service to new development in the utility's service area. Some statutes require all such funds to be used for the specific facilities that the SDCs were designed to finance. (A utility should always maintain documentation showing how the existing SDCs were derived.) SDC funds should be identified and segregated from the utility's unrestricted assets. To avoid spending a large portion of revenues on administration, the utility may find it helpful to first document the current development process and try to integrate the SDCs into the existing organization. In no case should SDC funds be used to fund annual O&M expenses.

Administrative Issues

Utility managers should develop procedures to administer the SDC program, including establishing a process for hearing appeals and exceptions to the SDC policies and procedures. In the case of regulated utilities, the regulatory authority may oversee this process. The multitude of development and contribution scenarios requires some procedure for dealing with unusual circumstances.

Customer notification requirements. Some states (e.g., Florida as of the date of this manual's publication) have a requirement that notice must be provided within a certain time frame (e.g., 90 days) before the effective date of an ordinance or resolution imposing a new or increased SDC. However, the waiting period may not apply if the SDC is being decreased, suspended, or eliminated. As a courtesy to the development community, the utility can make full use of various media (e.g., newspapers, public announcements, letters, Internet) to communicate changes in fees as well as to explain any justification for the changes.

Refunds. The utility should consider refunds of SDCs under the following circumstances (note that refunds may be required in some states under different circumstances):

- When service is not provided in a reasonable period of time after the charges are paid.
- When collected charges are not spent on system expansion (or projects that the SDC calculations are based on) within a reasonable time period.

These provisions, or similar thereto, are sometimes included in enabling legislation.

Interest income. The utility should dedicate interest income from SDCs to the SDC accounts. This helps to offset inflationary cost increases for system expansion projects. In most jurisdictions, such dedication of interest income is a legal requirement.

Income taxes. For investor-owned utilities, SDCs are generally included as ordinary taxable income for federal tax purposes.

Regulatory issues. When setting water rates using the utility basis for determining revenue requirements, most regulatory commissions exclude contributions of facilities and the related depreciation on contributed assets from the rate base in the rate-making process. Generally, SDCs are considered as an offset to plant investment in determining the rate base. Typically, any income tax liability generated from the collection of SDCs would be included in the rate base to determine rates for an investor-owned utility, unless such liability is already included in the SDC.

Maintenance of expansion-related debt factor or percentage. SDCs can typically be used to make principal and interest payments on growth- or expansion-related debt. Therefore, it is important for utilities to know the percentage of annual debt-service requirements that are expansion related and, hence, eligible to be paid with SDCs.

Ideally, the utility should have detailed accounting of how each dollar from debt proceeds was spent. Table VII.2-6 contains a sample debt-service expansion percentage calculation. As the debt mix of the utility changes, the debt expansion percentage calculation should be updated as appropriate.

Accounting Issues

Collection records. Because SDCs are imposed to recover some or all of the cost of new development, proper accounting of receipts is important to document authorized use of those funds. Assessment and collection records should be maintained by individual lot if SDCs are collected at the time of platting. This practice requires accounting for each new lot in all subdivisions. Assessment at the time service is requested requires accounting for SDC by service connection. With this approach, collection of SDCs is similar to regular customer service accounting.

Receipts. The utility should account for SDC receipts with the same procedure used for contributed facilities. Specifically, SDCs should not be included as a part of general operating revenues. SDCs should be used for capital-related purposes, including either retiring debt or constructing capital facilities related to system growth.

Table VII.2-6 Sample debt-service expansion percentage calculations

Project Analysis for Each Debt Issue:

Bond Issue 2

Project	Amount Borrowed	Expansion	Water System Projects Expansion Related	Non-Expansion Related
Expansion of the Reverse Osmosis Water Treatment Plant	$18,000,000	100.0%	$18,000,000	—
Water Main Rehabilitation	6,000,000	0.0%	—	6,000,000
New Water Transmission Main	8,000,000	100.0%	8,000,000	—
New Wells	3,000,000	100.0%	3,000,000	—
Pump Station Rehabilitation	1,000,000	0.0%	—	1,000,000
Total	$36,000,000		$29,000,000	$7,000,000
Percentage of Total			81%	19%

Calculating Overall Debt-Service Expansion Factor:

Outstanding Debt Issue	Total Debt-Service Payments 2012	Water System Allocated Water System Debt Service	Expansion	Expansion-Related Debt Service
Bond Issue 1	$9,927,500	$5,410,488	95%	$5,139,963
Bond Issue 2	2,458,944	2,458,944	81%	1,980,816
Bond Issue 3	14,249,788	10,259,847	72%	7,387,090
State Revolving Fund Loan 1	1,246,301	—	N/A	N/A
State Revolving Fund Loan 2	1,524,424	—	N/A	N/A
Total Payments	$29,406,957	$18,129,279		$14,507,869
Overall Expansion-Related Debt-Service Factor				80%

N/A = not applicable

Expenditures. SDCs should be expended in a manner consistent with the financial goals and basis for which the charges were established. Expenditure accounting for SDCs should be maintained to support the revenues derived from the charges.

Restricted fund. A restricted fund should be established for capital improvements funded by SDCs to facilitate the accounting of the income and expenditures for the capital improvements.

BEST MANAGEMENT PRACTICES

It is advisable for utilities to prepare for the cyclicality and timing of SDC collections by maintaining a strong financial position and high credit rating as well as adequate cash reserves for capital spending. There are often significant differences in timing among a utility's capacity construction schedule, the dates on which the capacity becomes available, and the receipts of SDCs from the new growth to be served by such capacity. Since SDC collections can be one of the utility's most unpredictable revenue streams and can vary significantly with changes in the economy, the utility should not be overly dependent on SDCs to fund its expansion program. Sometimes utilities issue debt to fund growth-related projects and then expect the SDC collection stream to pay the annual debt service. Although this strategy may result in lower user rates during periods of high growth, SDC collections are likely to diminish during economic downturns, requiring the debt service to be paid with user rate revenues. In this situation, significant additional user rate increases may be required to meet rate covenants.

To manage the timing of cash flows associated with an expansion program, a utility should maintain a strong system financial position to enable the utility to secure optimal credit ratings that typically lead to lower interest rates on debt financings. In addition, the utility should maintain adequate cash reserves for capital spending to serve as working capital for the expansion program. Credit rating agencies (i.e., Moody's Investors Service, Standard and Poor's Financial Services, and Fitch Ratings) frequently publish their criteria for evaluating the creditworthiness of utilities. High credit ratings are typically linked to strong debt-service coverage ratios and favorable cash positions. Because of the greater unpredictability of SDC collections versus user rate revenues, the rating agencies place more value on the all-in net revenues debt-service coverage ratio (net revenues divided by the sum of senior and subordinate lien annual debt service) calculated without SDCs (i.e., due to lower financial risk). Therefore, the utility's user rates should ideally be set at a level to achieve operating margins that result in strong all-in net revenues debt-service coverage and allow the utility to fund its capital needs—including those related to growth—through a mixture of debt and pay-as-you-go financing. If the utility's net revenues without SDCs can pay all system debt service plus provide strong coverage, and if the utility has adequate working capital for capital spending, the utility should be in a good position to handle fluctuations in SDC collections.

UPDATES OF THE SDC ANALYSIS

As development occurs and the economic mix of the community that the utility serves changes, growth and development assumptions may also change. Similarly, the facilities needed to serve customers will transform over time, and the costs associated with these facilities will be different from the past. As this occurs, the utility may update its master plan, comprehensive plan, or facility plan, which typically provides the basis for many key assumptions used within the development of the SDCs. Because of these changes, utilities need to, on a periodic basis, reassess their SDC assumptions and compare the historical development, capital spending, and capacity utilization levels achieved with that originally planned or projected. Legislation may also govern how often SDC assumptions and calculations should be reviewed.

SDCs are not typically as sensitive to annual changes in customer demand as are water rates, but it is still appropriate to update SDC calculations to ensure that they remain at appropriate levels. It is recommended that utilities review their SDC calculations

- at least every five years;
- when major capital improvements (expansion or upgrade) are proposed for the water system;
- when policymakers are reviewing the reasons for the underlying methodologies;
- when a significant change occurs in capacity usage, demand forecasts, or in capital planning; and
- when required per governing legislation.

Depending on local laws and for short-term administrative convenience, SDCs may be adjusted on an annual basis using a construction cost index or other reasonable indices to reflect the time value of money. This is particularly appropriate when the initial calculation of the SDC has valued the costs in current-day dollars.

REFERENCES

AWWA (American Water Works Association). 2009. C700-15 *Standard for Cold-Water Meters—Displacement Type, Metal Alloy Main Case.* Denver, Colo.: AWWA.

AWWA (American Water Works Association). 2010a. C702-10 *Standard for Cold-Water Meters—Compound Type.* Denver, Colo.: AWWA.

AWWA (American Water Works Association). 2010b. C712-10 *Standard for Cold-Water Meters—Singlejet Type.* Denver, Colo.: AWWA.

AWWA (American Water Works Association). 2012. C701-12 *Standard for Cold-Water Meters—Turbine Type, for Customer Service.* Denver, Colo.: AWWA.

Nelson, A.C. 1995. *System Development Charges for Water, Wastewater and Stormwater Utilities.* Boca Raton, Fla.: CRC Press. pp. 16–19.

This page intentionally blank.

Chapter **VII.3**

Availability Charges

Charges that recover a portion of the cost of a water utility's available capacity for future and existing customers in the form of an *availability charge* are used in certain settings. For rural water systems or systems with mature service areas, the availability charge may be used effectively as a financial tool to allocate such costs to properties within the dedicated service area that are not presently connected to the water system. New water systems with a finite customer base and limited growth potential can apply the availability charge to recover sufficient revenues to enhance the financial feasibility of the system.

The charge can be incorporated under ordinance for regular water rates as a distinct charge or as a separate fee schedule, but it only applies until the benefited property is connected for service. These charges are often assessed on a front footage or similar basis to those properties with access to the water main in the street, even though the property is not physically connected to the system. The availability charge covers the operation and maintenance (O&M) expenses and capital costs incurred to extend service to a specific area to serve potential future customers. The benefiting properties that are not currently water system customers constitute a portion of this potential customer base.

Even when the utility has an effective program for customer contribution of capital outlays for local mains and other local facilities, the utility can incur other fixed costs associated with backup facilities. In establishing availability charges, these costs may be apportioned among the existing customer base through their regular general service rate structure, and to the benefiting property owners who are not customers of the water utility through availability charges. However, because a portion of the costs of backup facilities not allocable to existing customers may also be included in the calculation of other charges (i.e., system development charges and standby charges), utilities should be careful to avoid double recovery in determining fees through the availability charges.

Another rationale for the assessment of availability charges applies where the majority of costs for public fire protection service are recovered through the regular water rates. Adjacent properties not connected to the water system would benefit from the availability of fire protection that is provided by the water system. An availability charge can be determined, in part, to equate the proportionate share of public fire protection costs to the benefit received.

Table VII.3-1 Example calculation of availability charge

Line No.	Item	Cost
1	Total invested capital	$600,000
2	Total annual debt service (assume 6% interest, 30 years)	$43,200
3	Annual operation and maintenance	$48,000
4	Payment in lieu of taxes	$30,000
5	Total annual dedicated facilities cost (sum of lines 2–4)	$121,200
6	Linear feet of main frontage	20,000
7	Number of benefiting properties	200
8	Average linear footage per property (divide line 6 by line 7)	100
9	Unit charge per frontage foot per month*	$0.505
10	Average monthly cost (availability charge) per property (multiply line 9 by line 8)	$50.50

*$121,200 ÷ 20,000 ft = $6.06/ft; $6.06 per foot ÷ 12 months = $0.505/ft/month.

Other suitable applications of the availability charge may be identified, but the principal need for the charge is to recoup the significant investment required to extend facilities with the capability to serve properties not presently connected to the water system.

In establishing the form and amount of the availability charge, the utility must determine the specific facilities for which costs are to be recovered and establish an equitable unit basis for assessing the charge. For government-owned water systems, appropriate costs include related capital expenditures, either in the form of the capital expenditure of the project plus indirect costs or debt service as applicable, plus apportionment of related annual O&M expenses (e.g., certain maintenance and inspection costs, customer billing, payment in lieu of taxes, and administrative expenditures). For investor-owned utilities, a fixed rate would include depreciation expense, taxes, and return (as applied to the value of the plant in question), as well as O&M expenses.

After the utility determines total costs applicable to the availability charge, it must define the appropriate unit basis for applying the charge. Though several methods have been adopted by utilities in North America, a generally acceptable unit basis is linear feet of main frontage accessible to benefiting properties. A charge per frontage foot is established by dividing the total annual cost of the dedicated facilities by the total frontage length of mains. The example in Table VII.3-1 illustrates the calculation of an availability charge.

One of the difficulties a utility may encounter with availability charges is enforcing payment. Because the entity to which the charge is assessed is not connected to the water system, discontinuing service is not an option in response to nonpayment of the availability charge. Accordingly, the utility must use other means to enforce payment, such as placing a lien on the property. Typically, investor-owned utilities do not have the same enforcement powers as do municipal utilities. Accordingly, investor-owned utilities may find availability fees to have limited usefulness.

Section VIII

Implementation Issues

VIII.1   Public Involvement in Rate-Making

VIII.2   Data Requirements

This page intentionally blank.

Chapter **VIII.1**

Public Involvement
in Rate-Making

Involving the public in the rate-making process can provide many benefits; it can also generate additional complications and challenges for a utility. Because many utilities continue to use public involvement strategies, for these utilities, the benefits outweigh the costs. The public involvement process provides a forum for an interactive exchange of ideas and information between utility decision makers and public stakeholders. It requires that involved stakeholders have the ability to meaningfully participate in the decision-making process, and as such, should be distinguished from public relations or public education efforts. Public relations and education largely involve one-way communications from the water utility to affected or interested members of the community, where public involvement requires two-way communications and interaction.

The interactive nature of public involvement in water rate-making demands the use of communications techniques that facilitate information exchange. These techniques range from use of citizens advisory committees (CACs) to Internet site survey instruments. Open interaction also demands the establishment of a structured decision process to provide appropriate exposure to the democratic process.

GENERAL CONSIDERATIONS AND POLICY ISSUES

Public involvement is not required to design water rates that meet utility requirements. In fact, under certain circumstances, public involvement may not be a viable option. However, public involvement in decision-making processes that affect community stakeholders (over a broad range of issues) is a proven approach to enhancing public acceptance of utility policies. The general considerations involved in determining the involvement of the public in water rate development, and the form of this involvement, relate to the

- magnitude of potential impacts on community stakeholders;
- extent to which options may reflect community values; and

- extent to which the utility can (and is willing to), on certain selected issues, allow community stakeholders greater feedback and input in the decision-making process.

Beyond these general considerations, the development of water rates raises several important policy issues. For example,

- How should revenue responsibilities be distributed across customer classes?
- Should variances from cost-of-service-based rates be eliminated, and if so, over what time period?
- Should subsidies be provided to support economic development?
- Should water rates be structured to encourage water conservation, and if so, what conservation rate designs are appropriate for which customer classes?
- Should water rates be structured to address affordability concerns, and if so, how?

Resolution of these policy issues often involves finding the balance between conflicting community values. For example, rates are often considered fair and equitable if they are based on cost of service. However, shifts in revenue responsibilities to effect cost-based rates may compromise economic development or affordability objectives.

Public involvement during the development of the water rates recognizes that affected parties are more likely to accept rate decisions if they have had the opportunity to participate in the rate development process. This principle is not unique to rate development but rather has been the basis for the use of public involvement and structured public decision processes for a broad range of issues. Furthermore, involving the public in rate development recognizes that affected parties may identify unique cost-allocation and rate-design approaches that reflect community circumstances and values better than rate designs developed in isolation.

HISTORICAL PERSPECTIVES

Water rate development, like most utility decision-making, historically has been a relatively closed process. Typically, utility staff or consultants conduct all major steps of the rate development process—projection of usage characteristics, estimation of revenue requirements, allocation of costs to customer classes, and rate design—with limited or no input or review by affected customer representatives. For regulated utilities, this process culminates in submittals of rate filing packages in support of rate increase requests to the applicable regulatory body. Public involvement is essentially confined to participation by interveners in subsequent rate hearings. For municipal utilities, the annual municipal budget adoption process or public hearing on rates is analogous to a rate filing package; public involvement occurs at or very near to the end of the process.

A meaningful public involvement effort must begin long before and continue well after the rate study process in any given year. The timeline required to organize, educate the participants, make a recommendation, and conduct a public outreach to the ratepayers will be substantial.

For water rate changes that preserved relatively low-cost water service, as was largely the case though the 1970s, this limited level of public involvement was not particularly problematic. However, several factors have heightened interest in water rate design and public involvement in rate development.

Perhaps the most significant factor has been a trend of substantial increases in water rates in this century. As the water bill has become a more significant percentage of income, utility customers have increasingly demanded assurance that they pay only their "fair

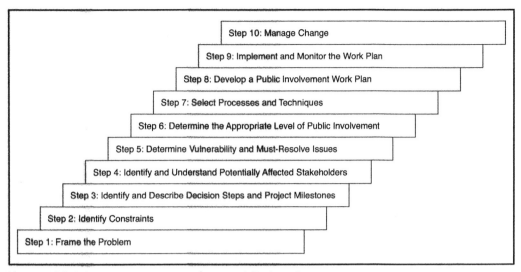

Figure VIII.1-1 10-step approach to public involvement

share" of utility costs. Additionally, increased public interest in environmental steward-ship in general, and water conservation in particular, has generated interest in conserva-tion rate designs. Also, significant changes in the costs and rate designs of other utility services, most notably electric and telephone service, have raised the question of whether similar changes may be available for water service.

PUBLIC INVOLVEMENT PLANNING

Heightened public interest in water rate development has increasingly led to implementa-tion of public involvement strategies to gain acceptance of water rate changes. Utilities can follow the general 10-step process outlined in the AWWA and AwwaRF report titled *Public Involvement Strategies: A Manager's Handbook* to structure a public water rate decision pro-cess (AWWA and AwwaRF 1995). This general 10-step process is shown in Figure VIII.1-1.

The 10-step process highlights the importance of effective planning of public involve-ment programs. Eight of the ten steps precede implementation and focus on establish-ing a strategy that is responsive to the specific circumstances and interests of potentially impacted stakeholders. By employing these steps to develop public involvement strategies for water rate-making, specific issues or questions are raised.

Step 1. Frame the Problem

Water rate development, by definition, involves determining the appropriate distribution of revenue responsibilities among customer classes. Rate design relates to the selection of a particular structure of charges that will recover allocated revenue responsibilities. Decisions on these issues may, in part, reflect community values related to financial responsibilities of different ratepayer groups. Accordingly, public involvement on water rate issues will address questions of how costs are allocated between customer classes; whether one customer class subsidizes another; and whether incentives are provided to use, or conserve, water resources. In this step, it is generally useful to prepare a brief prob-lem statement, review factual information about customer demands and utility revenue requirements, and identify critical assumptions needed to develop rate alternatives.

Step 2. Identify Constraints

Water rates are required to serve specific functions—most notably, generating adequate revenues to support utility performance and ensure the financial integrity of utility operations. Furthermore, in most jurisdictions, utility rates are legally required to be "just, reasonable, and nondiscriminatory." Beyond these constraints, water rates generally will not obtain public or political acceptance if community values and sensitivities are not respected. This step of identifying constraints on water rate changes, therefore, will determine the boundaries within which water rate alternatives may fall. For example, if implementation of cost-of-service-based rates will require substantial increases in residential rates, movement to cost-of-service-based rates may dictate the need for a multiyear rate transition plan. Candidate rate structures generally will not be acceptable if they impose dramatic bill increases on selected users. If environmental stewardship and promotion of water conservation is a strong community value, declining block rate designs may be problematic. Similarly, inclining block rates may be equally troublesome in communities seeking to encourage water-using development. Lastly, there may be logistical constraints on the level of public involvement available for water rate-making. For example, rate adoption may be required within an internally or externally specified time frame or budgetary constraints may limit available communication vehicles.

These rate-making constraints reflect the need to develop rate options that can gain the acceptance of utility decision makers, municipal and regulatory authorities, and ratepayers in general.

Step 3. Identify and Describe Decision Steps and Project Milestones

Designing a public involvement program requires integration of the public decision process with the formal, legal process required to enact rate changes. Accordingly, the steps by which rate changes are approved and enacted should be clearly understood by all participants in the public decision process. Moreover, public involvement program planning should identify the vehicles and timing by which program participants will have an opportunity to influence rate decision-making.

Careful delineation of how public involvement efforts will affect formal rate adoption steps is particularly important in the event that selected ratepayer representatives are asked to dedicate a substantial amount of time and effort to execute a public involvement program. For example, CACs are commonly formed to serve as advisory bodies to either utility management or governing boards. The members of the CAC should understand that the governing body may not agree with their recommendations. These CACs are often not vested with decision-making authority, serving only in an advisory capacity. This aspect of the CAC's role should be clearly articulated at the outset of any public decision process to avoid unfounded expectations of decision-making authority.

Step 4. Identify and Understand Potentially Affected Stakeholders

Alternative assignments of class revenue responsibilities and rate designs will affect customer bills differently. Evaluating the merits of one alternative over another requires an understanding of the affected parties. Moreover, an understanding of stakeholder perspectives is required to develop effective communication strategies about rate alternatives.

Importantly, stakeholder groups are not typically defined by the customer class groupings used to establish rates. Therefore, it is important to avoid the danger of evaluating stakeholder interests on the basis of customer class rate impacts. In many instances, stakeholder group interests cut across customer classes while in other cases they are quite specific. For example, environmental groups may be concerned about rate designs for industrial, commercial, and residential customers while gardening club members are primarily composed of a subset of residential users. Although each of these groups may have residential class members, their views about water conservation rate designs are likely to be much different, as are the communications media by which the various stakeholders obtain information. At a minimum, it is important to identify and engage stakeholders whose support is required to secure rate adoption or whose opposition could compromise public acceptance of proposed rates.

Step 5. Determine Vulnerability and Must-Resolve Issues

Public involvement in water rate-making is fundamentally a tool for utility managers to gain acceptance of water rate changes by customers. Preserving existing rates is generally not a problem. Accordingly, when planning a public involvement program, it is important to structure a public decision process that will be conducive to the resolution of fundamental rate challenges. In some cases, this may be the adoption of some form of system-wide rate increase. In other situations, the distribution of revenue responsibilities across customer classes may be at issue. In still other instances, rate designs to support water conservation, economic development, or other community goals may be of fundamental interest.

In any case, public involvement programs for water rate-making should be focused on specific rate issues and be structured to ensure timely development of acceptable rate options. To do so, while honoring stakeholder interests and concerns, an honest assessment of vulnerabilities is helpful. Vulnerabilities may be in the form of the potential for legal challenge of a given class's rates or simply (and commonly) the potential for given stakeholder groups to employ political influence to circumvent structured public decision processes. Vulnerabilities may range from a utility's credibility with potentially impacted stakeholders, to decision-maker inexperience with rate issues, to changes in economic conditions that alter perspectives on the viability of potential water rate changes.

Step 6. Determine the Appropriate Level of Public Involvement

Answers to Step 5 will indicate the extent to which public involvement may help resolve critical water rate issues and gain acceptance of water rate changes. In many instances, the must-resolve issues are limited and relatively simple. For example, acceptance of a limited system-wide rate increase without modifications to the distribution of class revenue responsibilities or rate structures is unlikely to require extensive public involvement. An appropriate level may be achieved through a limited number of public meetings (or other forms of information exchange) in advance of the annual budget adoption process. This level would typically be supplemented by one-way forms of communications to advise interested stakeholders of proposed rate changes. In other cases, a concerted effort using multiple outreach forms may be required. These cases will often involve consideration of changes in the distribution of revenue responsibilities across and within customer classes or acceptance of substantial increases in overall rate levels.

Step 7. Select Processes and Techniques

Once the appropriate level of public involvement has been determined, utility managers can select from a broad range of processes and techniques to solicit ratepayer input and inform interested stakeholders. For all but the most limited of rate issues, an effective public involvement program will employ multiple outreach mechanisms to access the broad diversity of stakeholder groups. Processes and techniques should be selected based on their effectiveness in communicating information to, and soliciting input from, particular ratepayer groups. Techniques should also be appropriate for the level of information detail to be communicated and the relative complexity of rate-making decisions.

For example, cost-of-service studies focus on relatively complex issues of inter-class revenue distribution and rate structures. Public involvement programs for these studies often involve CACs composed of a broad spectrum of stakeholder representatives. CACs are particularly useful because of the zero-sum game nature of cost-of-service questions—every dollar of revenue responsibility not distributed to one customer class must be borne by other customer classes. For such studies, a forum for public discussion among representatives of all customer classes may avoid challenges by one customer class of preferential treatment of other classes. Because CACs are generally comprised of a diverse mix of community representatives with competing interests, it is important to establish guidelines for committee interaction and its role in the public decision process. An example of such guidelines is provided in appendix D.

For complicated rate issues, public involvement approaches may also include distribution of informational brochures or newsletters (possibly with accompanying survey instruments), speakers' bureaus, print or broadcast media articles, as well as a variety of public meeting forums. Most utilities have Internet (web) home pages that can provide to ratepayers immediate access to a wealth of information (e.g., PDF copies of studies and reports, proposed rates, and customer-specific bill impacts). The utility's website can also be a useful tool to survey these same customers and gain feedback on the specific rate issues being reviewed.

Step 8. Develop a Public Involvement Work Plan

The previously described steps involved in planning a public involvement program address many activities that typically will cross the responsibilities of several functional organizations within a utility. Customer service personnel need to know about the planned rate development process and be able to direct inquiries appropriately. Financial management staff will be required to develop (and possibly present) information on utility costs. Frequently, plant and field operations managers and engineering staff will need to provide information and respond to questions. Public communications or top utility management personnel will need to represent the utility in public discourse and ensure logistical support of public involvement activities.

If the utility fails to coordinate these activities effectively and to properly support a public decision process, it will undermine rather than enhance the utility's credibility and public trust. Consequently, it is extremely important that public involvement programs be well planned and appropriately budgeted. A public involvement plan should provide a clear delineation of responsibilities, the scheduling of program activities, communications protocols, and the linkages between public input and the rate development process. It is often useful to develop a public involvement program mission statement to promote internal commitment to the program as well as external understanding. This statement is typically separate from that used to guide development of rate options, and it deals specifically with objectives of the public involvement program. For example, while the rate development process may be oriented to developing cost-based, equitable water rates, the public involvement program may be developed to ensure that water rates reflect community values through balanced and informed input of interested stakeholders.

Step 9. Implement and Monitor the Work Plan

Insofar as facilitation of public involvement activities is not the primary background of most utility personnel, implementing the public involvement work plan is likely to be uncomfortable. This is particularly true for water rate-making in which a measure of controversy is generally unavoidable and concerns tend to be acute. Although effective program planning can go a long way toward easing the discomfort, several guidelines are key to successful program implementation. These include the following:

- Utility representatives must be able to communicate effectively and respectfully with stakeholder groups.
- Communication on the status of public involvement and rate development tasks must be regular and comprehensive to ensure against miscommunications.
- Responses to information requests should be carefully reviewed and checked against other information provided to interested parties. Discrepancies should be clearly reconciled.

Step 10. Manage Change

Public involvement programs for water rate development will typically support some form of rate study (e.g., cost-of-service analysis, rate structure evaluation) that will generate new information on the utility's existing water rates and future rate options. As a consequence, the framework for public decisions on water rate issues will evolve. Additionally, external factors may alter the decision-making environment. These factors may range from unanticipated additions to utility revenue requirements to changes in the political landscape. The inevitability of change means that the public decision process must be responsive to new information and viewpoints. As changes occur, all participants in the decision process should be fully advised of modifications to the public involvement program and the reasons for these modifications. Utility representatives should also be extremely careful not to commit to granting authority that may be altered under new circumstances.

COMMUNICATION TOOLS

Applying the 10-step (or similarly comprehensive) process to developing public involvement strategies gives utility managers the opportunity to employ public outreach and communication tools to the greatest effect. Ultimately, water rate decision-making may be improved by greater understanding of rate development challenges and informed community participation. As noted in Step 7, select processes and techniques, there is a broad range of communication tools that may be used to implement a successful public involvement program, each with its relative advantages and disadvantages. Several of the most commonly used tools for water rate public involvement programs are listed in the following sections.

Bill Inserts/Stuffers

Brief letters or small-sized inserts that are distributed with each customer's bill offer a way to communicate with the entire customer population, but unfortunately, these inserts are frequently viewed as "junk mail." Responses to insert survey instruments or service offerings typically obtain 10 to 20 percent response rates. Generally, bill inserts are recommended to announce significant rate study events, such as the commencement of CAC meetings, reports of findings, and rate change implementation dates.

Newsletters

Topic-specific newsletters may be published and distributed to key community groups or mailed to all customers as a way of providing more in-depth information than is typically afforded through a bill insert. Newsletters can be particularly useful if a high level of interest or concern about the rate study has been expressed and interested parties have requested detailed information. The cost of publishing a newsletter, including staff time and printing and mailing costs, tends to be justified only in cases where significant issues are to be addressed and a sizable readership may be reasonably anticipated.

Speakers' Bureau/Community Group Presentations

A less expensive, and often more informative, vehicle for disseminating information to interested customers is to make presentations to requesting community groups. In-person contact allows utility representatives to communicate directly with customers and may express the utility's commitment to inform and involve the public more strongly than printed materials. Nevertheless, to be useful, in-person contact requires effective public speaking and facilitation skills by rate study representatives and community group use of the available service.

Information line

A 24-hour telephone line with a recorded message can inform the public about rate study events, such as CAC meeting times and dates, locations of published study materials, and public hearing times and dates. In addition, the phone numbers of utility staff members are listed so customers can contact them with specific questions.

Print and Broadcast Media Relations

Announcements of the times and dates of public hearings and work sessions on rates should almost certainly be made in the local print media and, if possible, broadcast media. Local public access channels may be used to broadcast CAC meetings or special informational programs on the rate study. Accurate coverage by the local press may be encouraged through media briefing sessions and advance notices of potentially "newsworthy" decision making.

Internet Site

Internet sites may be used to allow access to a wealth of information about water rate issues. In addition to quick access to information about public involvement program events (e.g., CAC meeting or public hearing dates), actual materials from the rate study may be made available on the site. These may include issue papers generated as part of the rate study, presentations made to utility decision makers, and general reference data. Information may be solicited from those accessing the site through survey instruments or general requests for comment. The public tends to use Internet sites as well as various forms of social media for a wide variety of information, and this form of communication is likely to become an increasingly important tool for water utilities.

This listing may serve as a "menu" of public communications options. Some, but likely not all, of these methods can be used effectively. The selection of methods should be oriented toward ensuring opportunities for all ratepayers to learn about and become involved in the project without incurring unnecessary expenditures.

EVALUATING COMMUNICATIONS

Successful implementation of public involvement programs is promoted through continuous evaluation of the effectiveness of communication methods and responsiveness to change. However, while the ultimate evaluation standard for a public decision process is acceptance and adoption of proposed rates, this measure may be compromised by influences outside the scope of public discourse. Accordingly, the criteria used to evaluate public involvement programs should relate to those aspects of the program over which participants have a reasonable measure of control. For example, while consensus recommendations may not be reached, commendable public involvement programs are generally structured to provide the interested parties with the opportunity to learn about rate issues and participate in the discussion of proposed rates. Similarly, although attendance at public meetings on rates may be limited, utilities that attempt to provide information and solicit public input through a variety of communications vehicles are considerably less likely to be criticized for arbitrary rate development practices. Lastly, because public involvement simultaneously invites criticism and collaboration by members of the public, an important criterion for evaluation of public involvement activities relates to the professionalism and respect utility representatives demonstrate in the public decision process. Success in this effort will convey benefit far beyond the scope of rate development issues.

SUMMARY

Several factors, most notably substantial increases in system revenue requirements and conservation issues, have heightened public interest in water rate-making. Concerns include questions about the distribution of revenue responsibilities across customer classes, incentives provided through rate structures, and the affordability of basic levels of service. Public involvement in water rate-making is a potentially powerful tool to enhance community understanding of rate issues and gain acceptance of proposed rate changes. Public decision processes generally require careful planning and a high level of utility commitment. Comprehensive planning may be facilitated by reference to established processes for developing public involvement strategies. This planning will help identify the communication tools to be used to inform and engage community stakeholders. Fundamentally, public involvement requires that community stakeholders have the ability to participate in the water rate decision process; public involvement programs should be evaluated on the quality of this participation.

REFERENCE

AWWA (American Water Works Association) and AwwaRF (Awwa Research Foundation). 1995. *Public Involvement Strategies: A Manager's Handbook.* Denver, Colo.: AWWA and AwwaRF.

This page intentionally blank.

Chapter **VIII.2**

Data Requirements

The key factors in developing supportable utility rates are the availability of sound, accurate records and data. Maintaining good records is not only helpful to the rate practitioner in establishing rates, but it is also critical to the ability of the utility to adequately ensure and assess the impact of alternative rate forms on such issues as revenue sufficiency and stability, individual customer or customer class equitability, and conservation goals and objectives. Among the areas in which accurate and detailed records are important in preparing the cost-of-service analysis, developing rates, and evaluating the impact of rates on customers are (1) customer records (number of customers, billed usage, revenues, demographics, seasonal variations in use, and demand factors); (2) plant investment (functional breakdown and design capacities); (3) operation and maintenance expenses (functional and object class breakdowns, seasonal variations); (4) periodic (monthly or annual) cash flow for the utility; and (5) customer survey information. This chapter addresses these elements as well as why and how the maintenance of adequate records in these areas is important and helpful in establishing various alternative rate forms.

CUSTOMER RECORDS

From a rate-making standpoint, the most important areas in which the utility should maintain accurate and extensive records are that of customer-related data and statistics. By far the most significant source of revenue for most water utilities is that produced from water sales or "rate" revenue. The application of a particular rate structure to the number of bills and/or metered water usage produces the billings and revenue that sustain the utility's financial well-being. Without accurate customer billing records, the development of a rate structure can be hampered, resulting in rates that do not generate sufficient revenue to meet the utility's revenue requirements and revenue bond covenants.

Number of Customers

Most utilities do maintain certain standard customer-related statistics. These typically include the number of customers by size of meter and by customer class (if customers are classified for rate-making or other purposes). These records are generally kept on either a monthly or year-end count. Because billing frequencies may vary by type or classification of customer (e.g., residential accounts may be billed bimonthly while other accounts are billed monthly), it is also common and important for utilities to maintain records regarding the number of bills issued by meter size and/or customer class. Detailed information on the number of customers and bills by meter size and class of customer is used in the development of customer-related charges such as minimum bills or service charges. These types of charges are common to virtually every type of alternative rate form and are therefore necessary data requirements for all utilities. If customer classifications are used by the utility, it is important to develop sound, consistent definitions for the classifications. This is very important if different rate forms are developed and applied to different classifications of customers.

Metered Consumption

Another common customer statistic that is often maintained is metered consumption by meter size or by class of customer, or both. Ideally, this information should be maintained in as much detail as the utility's billing system or customer database will permit. At the least, the data should be maintained on an annual basis, but preferably on a billing cycle basis (monthly, bimonthly, etc.) by class and/or meter size. In the development of seasonal rates, it is necessary to know the metered consumption for each month, because there is a different rate for defined monthly periods or seasons under this rate form. The maintenance of consumption data for individual customers is also important, particularly for certain types of rate structures, such as water-budget rates or excess-use rates, whereby each customer is charged at a higher unit rate when their water usage exceeds an established threshold (e.g., more than 125 percent of winter period use).

To design and evaluate different rate structures against a utility's goals and objectives, which as previously mentioned may include such elements as financial stability, enhanced equitability, and conservation, it is important to maintain detailed customer records, such as number of bills and metered consumption, for as many years as possible. This is particularly necessary in areas of the country where the weather can vary significantly from year to year and where water sales are sensitive to weather patterns. This would include regions in which discretionary uses such as lawn irrigation constitute a large proportion of annual water sales. The maintenance of these types of records for a period of years (e.g., 3–5 years) should enable the utility to have a database that encompasses a wide range of weather conditions and related water usage and demands on the system. The availability of this type of data enables the rate practitioner to "test" various alternative rate structures against a variety of weather conditions. This permits the determination of the sensitivity and variation in monthly and/or annual revenue of alternative rate forms to weather conditions. This further allows the establishment of necessary reserves or working capital balances that need to be maintained to protect the revenue stability of the utility.

Another important reason to keep detailed records of metered consumption by class of customer and/or meter size on a billing period basis is to enable the development of a bill frequency distribution analysis or bill tabulation. These analyses are particularly important in the development of declining or inverted block rate structures, or in the establishment of lifeline rates, where a different unit rate is assigned to metered consumption that falls in predetermined consumption or rate blocks. In these rate forms, it is necessary to know the percentage distribution of the annual usage of the utility by class, if appropriate or germane to the particular utility, into each of the rate blocks.

Billed Revenue Data

A third customer statistic that is important in the development of rates, and commonly maintained by most utilities, is customer billing information in dollars. Most often this information is available by customer class or meter size. It is important to keep this information to have a gauge or benchmark against which to measure the revenue anticipated from proposed new rates. Application of existing rates to the customer statistics previously discussed (bills and consumption) to develop a "pro forma" level of billings, and comparison of those billings with actual known billings, provides the rate practitioner with a measure of the "accuracy" of the billing statistics or units of service with which he or she is working. Therefore, when the proposed rates are applied to these billing units, the anticipated billings and revenue will be achieved.

Billing information by individual customer should be retained in the utility's billing database. This is particularly true whenever a change in the rate form is planned. Often with a change in rate structure, there are more customer inquiries. It is helpful to the customer service representatives to have billing history available to aid in answering the customers' questions. It is also helpful to the rate practitioner and the utility's customer information or public relations staff to have such information available to establish profiles of "typical" customer impacts of changes in rates. These profiles are good tools to have available when addressing and explaining the new rate structure in public forums or when the customer is able to access account information on-line.

Peak-Period Demand Data

Customer class demand data are extremely beneficial to the rate practitioner in cost-of-service allocations and in designing rates. Very few water utilities have this type of information. To develop maximum-day and maximum-hour demand data on a customer or customer class basis can require significant financial resources. Demand meters must be purchased and installed, and the data must be reviewed, interpolated, and expanded to fit the entire class of customers. For measuring residential customers, careful planning, statistically valid samples, and coordination with other municipal agencies, such as the fire department when certain areas must be valved off, are required. If done properly, the results of these studies can be quite useful not only to the rate practitioner, but also to the water utility's engineering and planning staff, because the demand data are also useful in sizing mains, storage reservoirs, and so forth. With the movement toward fixed network automated meter reading (AMR) systems, a utility has far greater ability to better understand customer consumption patterns and, in particular, peak-period demands.

In those situations where detailed peak-demand data are not available, most often the information on customer class demands is based on system-wide coincident maximum daily and hourly demands, which are generally available or can be obtained from treatment plant pumping records and storage tank drawdown data. (See appendix A for a more detailed discussion.) This information, combined with monthly metered consumption data by customer class, is used to estimate customer class demand data. While some utilities are installing AMR systems that can gather demand data, specific customer class demand data is not usually available to most utilities at present. Therefore, it is important to maintain good records of system-wide maximum daily and hourly demands to enable the simulation of class demands.

Other Data Requirements

Demographic distribution of the utility's customer base is not typically maintained by water utilities; however, it is becoming an increasingly important piece of information as water rates across the country continue to climb because of increasing regulatory requirements. Many utilities are implementing discount rates or lifeline rates to accommodate the growing number of fixed-income and low-income families and customers in their service areas. Whether the discount rates are targeted to a specific group of customers or are available to the entire customer base, as in the case of some lifeline rates, it is necessary to know how many customers are impacted, and, if targeted to a specific group, who they are. Oftentimes, utilities find it useful and cost-effective to coordinate with other agencies in the community that already have a system and database in place to address the needs of low-income customers. Checking with these agencies and using their available resources is important when a utility is considering implementing these types of rates.

One final area of customer record keeping that is, in effect, a fallout of the information previously discussed is the ability to measure the price elasticity of customer demand for water. Price elasticity is the relationship of the change in the demand for a commodity (water, in this case) relative to the change in the price of the commodity (see chapter V.7). The need to have information regarding price elasticity is important whenever a utility is faced with implementing a rate increase. This need is particularly enhanced when a conservation rate structure is being implemented because the intent of this type of rate structure is to encourage or achieve a reduction in water usage, either during peak-demand periods or in total over the year. To properly design the water rates and to maintain financial stability for the utility, it is necessary to make some allowance for the amount of water-use reduction that is anticipated to occur as a result of the rate increase. Measurement of price elasticity for water is a difficult and a somewhat judgmental undertaking because there are many variables involved, including climatological considerations, educational and information programs regarding conservation, and efficient use of water, economic cycles, and so forth. However, without sufficient detail and accuracy of customer billing records, the task of assessing price elasticity becomes extremely difficult and the results are not as meaningful.

The frequency of customer billing is particularly important during the implementation of any adjustment in the utility's water rates. Due to stipulations or constraints that may exist in the utility's regulations, ordinances, or policies, the billing frequency of each utility must be recognized in determining billings and collections under the new rates during the first year in which the rates become effective. Depending on the utility's specific rate ordinance or regulation, the first bill rendered to each customer subsequent to the effective date of a rate adjustment must often be prorated between the previous rates and the new rates. This proration is generally based on the number of days of service received by the customer before and after the effective date of the new rates. This proration may be applicable to both the volume-related portion of the customer's bill and the fixed, or customer-related, portion. The net impact of this proration process is that the new rates will not be fully effective the first year.

In establishing the necessary adjustments to rate levels to meet the utility's revenue requirements, in addition to the potential lag in realizing full billings under new rates due to the proration process, the timing of the collections of the billings must also be recognized. This latter consideration is particularly important for those utilities whose accounting records and/or revenue bond debt-service coverage requirements are legally established on the "cash" basis as opposed to the accrual basis of accounting. When implementing proposed rate adjustments, both the billing lag and the collection lag should be recognized in fully recovering revenues under revised rates. Absent these considerations, utility revenues may fall short of the intended level of billings and receipts.

PLANT INVESTMENT

Accurate and sufficiently detailed plant investment/asset information should be used in developing supportable rates. Plant investment is used in the rate-making process in the allocation of capital-related costs, such as debt service and annual cash-financed capital additions and replacements under the cash approach to revenue requirements and rate-making, and for allocation of return-on-investment-related costs under the utility-basis approach. It is recommended that the utility use the *Uniform System of Accounts for Class A Water Utilities* published by the National Association of Regulatory Utility Commissioners (NARUC 1996) or another fully developed chart of accounts. Such an accounting system provides for the accumulation and accounting for additions, replacements, and retirements of utility property on a functionalized basis, representative of the various distinct service functions that various categories of property provide. Functionalization of plant investment under the NARUC system includes source of supply, raw water pumping and transmission, water treatment, treated water pumping, transmission and distribution, system storage, hydrants, meters and services, and administrative and general property. Functional classification of plant investment is necessary to allocate capital-related costs to the appropriate functional category, whereby these functionally allocated costs can subsequently be distributed to the various classes of customers in proportion to their respective demands and usage of each of the plant facilities. In those instances where a utility does not have plant data maintained using the NARUC chart of accounts, the utility should attempt to functionalize its plant data and information as much as reasonably possible.

An associated element of plant investment that is useful in designing certain alternative rate forms is the design capacity of the various plant facilities. The majority of water system facilities is designed to meet peak system demands, whether they be maximum-day demands (river source of supply, well fields, raw water pumping and transmission, treatment, treated water pumping, and certain treated water transmission mains) or maximum-hour demands (transmission and distribution mains, system storage, booster pumps). In the design of certain types of rates, including seasonal, inverted, and off-peak rates, it may be useful to know what the nonpeak season demands or capacity requirements of the utility system are and what the associated plant investment is to provide for these non-peak season demands. If this type of information can be determined by the utility staff, perhaps in conjunction with the utility's design engineer, this information can prove to be valuable in the determination of the costs of the system associated with providing off-peak demands, and the unit cost of service and appropriate rates associated with those demands.

OPERATION AND MAINTENANCE EXPENSES

Detailed records of historical operation and maintenance (O&M) expenses should also be maintained on a functionalized basis. The *Uniform System of Accounts for Class A Water Utilities* published by NARUC (1996) also provides guidelines for establishing accounting records that capture annual O&M data on a functionalized basis. For O&M expenses, in addition to recording the total expenses by function, the functionalized expenses should be broken down by the object classifications for these expenses, which are used by the utility in its budgetary processes. These object classes typically include personal services (and related fringe benefit expenses), purchase of services (including power, which should be recorded separately from other expenses for cost allocation purposes), materials and supplies (including chemicals, which should also be recorded separately), and equipment expenses. As in the case of plant investment, the detailed accounting of O&M expenses, in accordance with the NARUC guidelines, provides for an adequate breakdown of expenses for cost-of-service allocation and appropriated distribution of functionally allocated expenses to customer classes in proportion to their respective demands on the water system.

In designing certain types of rates—again including seasonal, inverted, and off-peak rates—O&M expenses should be provided, in the detail previously described, on a monthly basis. This information would be extremely helpful in determining the cost of water service in an off-peak period or season.

PERIODIC CASH FLOW FOR THE UTILITY

A principal objective of any rate structure should be to maintain the financial stability of the utility. Revenues must be sufficient—certainly on an annual basis—to meet the revenue requirements and revenue bond covenants, as applicable, of the utility. Reserve funds and rate stabilization funds may be available to assist in meeting these financial obligations on either a planned or an emergency basis. However, stable and adequate rate revenue, over the long run, must be the cornerstone of the utility's financial integrity.

During the course of the year, many utilities have seasonal demands on their system caused by climatological or economic cycles, or other events. This variation in demand also creates a variation in the associated billings and revenues throughout the year. Most water utilities' monthly costs, on the other hand, remain relatively fixed during the year, with perhaps the only monthly fluctuation being for power and chemical expenses, which tend to vary directly with water production. For utilities that have significant monthly swings in demand during the year, the monthly cash flow should be analyzed to determine in which months a cash-flow shortfall can be expected. Working capital reserves or other sources of readily available funds for meeting the fixed costs of doing business during the negative cash-flow months must be provided. When implementing a rate form that has, as one of its objectives, to encourage conservation or more efficient use of water, it is doubly important to have good knowledge of the monthly cash-flow situation, because revenue that may be counted on from, for example, higher peak season rates may not materialize if the climatological conditions are such that the higher priced consumption does not occur.

CUSTOMER SURVEY INFORMATION

As a final element of the data requirements and information that may be of assistance to the utility in establishing a rate form that meets the objectives and goals of the utility, it is important to find out what your customers want or perceive to be important. Before embarking on the implementation of a new rate form, or even continuing to use the existing rate form, the utility should investigate its customers' needs, attitudes, and preferences. A well-designed customer attitude survey should yield information that the utility can use in developing rates and other programs to best meet its customers' requirements.

SUMMARY

Many utilities maintain records, data, and statistics of the nature and detail described in this chapter (Table VIII.2-1). It is very important from a rate-making standpoint to capture as much detail as possible in terms of customer information and cost and expense data. Not only does this facilitate the task of rate setting, but it also provides for a more defensible rate structure. When and where data are lacking or could be improved, the utility should note such details and make a concerted effort to collect the appropriate information to improve future rate studies.

REFERENCE

NARUC (National Association of Regulatory Utility Commissioners). 1996. *Uniform System of Accounts for Class A Water Utilities.* Washington, D.C.: NARUC.

Table VIII.2-1 Data requirements checklist

I. Customer Records
   A. Number of Customers/Bills
      1. By Meter Size
      2. By Customer Class
      3. By Billing Frequency (if different for different classes)
      4. Monthly Summary
      5. Annual Summary
      6. Maintain Consistent Definition of Customer Classes (if applicable)
      7. Maintain Historical Data for 3 to 5 Years
      8. Number of Public Fire Hydrants
      9. Number of Private Fire Services by Size
   B. Metered Consumption
      1. By Meter Size
         a. By Billing Frequency (if varies by class)
         b. Monthly Summary
         c. Annual Summary
      2. By Customer Class
         a. Monthly Summary
         b. Annual Summary
      3. By Individual Customer
         a. For Customer Relations and Customer Service Purposes
         b. Necessary for Certain Rate Forms (i.e., "Excess Use" Rates Tied to Individual Characteristics)
            (1) Bill Frequency Distribution (number of bills with zero usage, 1 unit, 2 units, etc.)
            (2) Maintain Historical Data for 3 to 5 Years
   C. Billed Revenue Data
      1. By Meter Size
         a. Monthly Summary
         b. Annual Summary
      2. By Customer Class
         a. Monthly Summary
         b. Annual Summary
      3. Maintain Historical Data for 3 to 5 Years
   D. Peak-Period Demand Data
      1. System Coincident Demands
         a. Total Production or Output to Distribution System
         b. Maximum-Day Demand
         c. Maximum-Hour Demand
         d. Monthly Data for Each of Above Items
         e. Maintain History for 5 to 10 Years
      2. Customer Class Demands
         a. Requires Demand Meter Study (can be an expensive undertaking)
         b. Nonresidential Demands
             (1) Select Representative Sample Accounts
            (2) Use Individual Demand Recording Meters or Establish Hourly Meter Reading Schedule by Utility Staff
II. Plant Investment Records
   A. Establish Uniform System of Accounts
      1. Classify Plant Investment by Function (raw water, treatment, etc.)
      2. Provide for Recording Annual Additions and Retirements
      3. Provide for Depreciation Accounting Records to Parallel Plant Investment
   B. Determine System Capacity for Each Functional Plant Element
   C. Separate Plant Investment Between Peak Season and Nonpeak Season Demand (as necessary)
III. Operation and Maintenance Expense
   A. Establish Uniform System of Accounts
      1. Classify Operation and Maintenance by Function (raw water, treatment, etc.)
      2. Classify Operation and Maintenance by Object Classification (salaries, purchase of services, materials and supplies, and equipment)
      3. Separately Identify Expenditures for Power and Chemicals
   B. Identify Specific Expenses Associated With Seasonal or Peak Usage
   C. Summarize Operation and Maintenance Expenses Monthly and Annually
   D. Maintain Historical Data for 3 to 5 Years

This page intentionally blank.

Appendixes

This page intentionally blank.

Appendix **A**

Development of Peaking Factors by Customer Class

The determination of appropriate peaking factors by customer class for use in cost-of-service allocations and/or rate design is a significant challenge in rate-making. One means for determining peaking factors by customer class is to undertake a formal demand study. Formal demand studies involve daily and hourly consumption records of samples of customers from each class of service and are analyzed over a period of weeks or months. With the increasing availability of automated meter-reading equipment, enhanced billing software, and data processing capabilities, these formal design studies, although still costly, are not as difficult or costly as they were in the past. However, they are not without costs, and there are less sophisticated though adequate calculations that may be employed to estimate customer class peaking factors using readily available data in the utility's records. This appendix offers relatively straightforward procedures that can be used in developing customer class peaking factors from system demand data and customer billing records that are available to many utilities.

The system-wide demand data that are necessary to undertake the analysis include (1) the highest ratio of system maximum-day (MD) demand to system average-day (AD) demand over a representative number of recent years; (2) the system maximum month (MM) for that highest ratio year; and (3) the system maximum-hour (MH) demand for that year. The customer billing records necessary to complete the analysis are the monthly billed consumption records by customer class, the annual billed consumption by class, and a general knowledge of the daily variation in usage throughout the day and the week for each customer class. For utilities with other than monthly billing frequency, the available billing records will need to be used, but the results of the analysis will be less accurate. For purposes of this appendix, it is assumed that the example utility bills all customers on a monthly basis.

The use of the noncoincident peaking factors for each class is the commonly used approach for the allocation of costs to the various customer classes. In some specific cases,

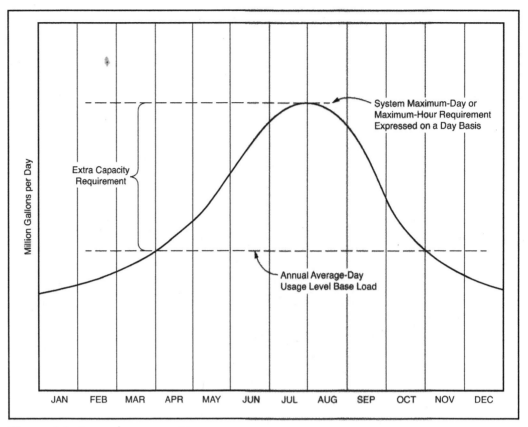

Figure A-1 Annual usage pattern

it may be appropriate to use the coincident demands for each class. The derivation of peaking factors for customer classes under each of these methods is discussed in this appendix.

Figure A-1 presents an example of the coincident or system-wide usage for each month. As shown in Figure A-1, the maximum extra capacity demand for the example system occurs at the end of July. The coincident system demands of each customer class would be their demands on that day.

Figure A-2 shows that the peak demands of each customer class may not occur on the same day (or hour, in the case of peak-hour demands) as the system peak demand. The peak of each class does not coincide with the same day (or hour) of the peak of other classes. In the example in Figure A-2, the commercial class's peak occurs prior to the system peak, the residential class's peak coincides with the system peak, and the industrial class's peak occurs after the system-wide peak.

With the use of noncoincident peaks as the basis for calculating class peaking factors, the sum of each class's peak demand is greater than the overall system demand. If coincident peaks are used, each class's actual demand at the time of the system peak is used. In this case, the peak assigned to a particular class may be less than the class's actual peak demand.

DETERMINATION OF NONCOINCIDENT PEAKING FACTORS

It is important that the reader understands the rationale of using the noncoincident demands in distributing the functionally allocated costs to each class. The rationale for supporting the use of noncoincident peaking factors is that the benefits of diversity in customer class consumption patterns should accrue to all classes in proportion to their use

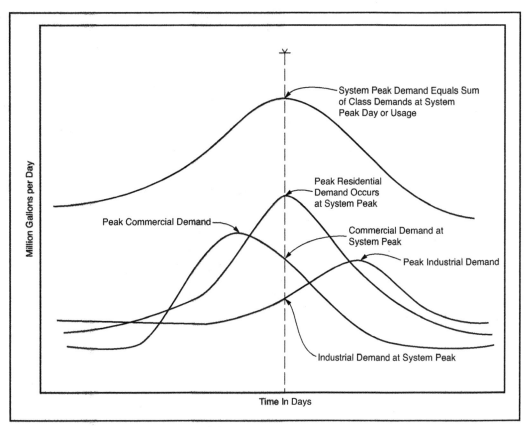

Figure A-2 Peaks that occur at different times

of the system, and not be allocated primarily to a particular class that happens to peak at a time different from other users of the system. The concept is illustrated through the following example: Assume that a utility was going to build a *separate system* (source of supply, treatment, pumping, transmission and distribution, etc.) for *each of the customer classes* served by the utility. These separate water systems would need to be sized to meet the base, maximum-day extra capacity, and maximum-hour extra capacity demands related to each class. The sum of those systems would compose the overall water system, and the costs associated with each of the individual systems would be allocable to each class (based on their respective noncoincident demands that were the basis for sizing the individual components of the system).

Assume that a concept is developed that efficiencies, economies of scale, and reduction in the overall size of the "system" could be achieved if the system is integrated and diversified. With this concept in mind, recognizing the diversities of demands of the various classes and using the coincident demands of all classes to size the plant, a smaller system could be built. Total fixed capital costs and most operation and maintenance expenses, except perhaps for power and chemical costs, would be reduced in sizing the overall system facilities on the basis of the coincident demands of all the classes of customers.

The question at hand is, considering that there is a smaller, more efficient, and less costly system, how should the cost savings of that system be allocated among the individual customer classes? One appropriate manner to allocate these costs, and have each customer class share equitably in the overall cost savings, is to allocate the total new, smaller system costs on the basis of the noncoincident demands of each customer class. In this manner, all classes share proportionately in the economies of scale and cost savings of this smaller, integrated, and diverse system.

The system demands for this example are the same as those used in the example in chapters III.1 and III.2. Accordingly, the system annual average-day production is 7.5 mgd, the system coincident maximum-day demand is 11.55 mgd, and the system coincident maximum-hour demand is 16.65 mgd. For purposes of this example, the system coincident maximum-month demand is assumed to be 8.60 mgd.

In terms of the necessary information regarding customer class billed consumption, the following data are applicable. From Table III.2-1, the annual average-day billed consumption for each of the retail service classes is as follows: residential (2.65 mgd); commercial (1.30 mgd); and industrial (3.00 mgd). From the example utility's billing records, the following average-day consumption for the maximum month for each class (it may be a different month for each class) is as follows: residential (3.60 mgd); commercial (1.70 mgd); and industrial (3.09 mgd).

Maximum-Day Peaking Factors

The first step in determining the noncoincident peaking factor by customer class is to calculate the ratio of the average-day consumption for the maximum month to the annual average-day consumption for each class. This calculation results in the following factors, which represent the minimum maximum-day peaking factor for each customer class:

- Residential: 3.60 mgd / 2.65 mgd = 1.36
- Commercial: 1.70 mgd / 1.30 mgd = 1.31
- Industrial: 3.09 mgd / 3.00 mgd = 1.03

The ratio of the overall system coincident maximum-day demand (11.55 mgd) to the average-day demand for the system maximum month (8.60 mgd) [11.55 mgd/8.60 mgd = 1.34] is an indication of the potential relationship between these two demands for each of the retail customer classes for the example utility. It must be recognized, however, that daily fluctuations do occur throughout the month of maximum consumption for each customer class. These variations would tend to understate the actual maximum daily demand for the class that occurs during the maximum month if only the 1.34 factor applicable to the system were applied to the maximum-month ratios previously developed for each class. Accordingly, there should be an allowance for such fluctuations factored into the calculation of the maximum-day peaking factor for each class.

For purposes of this example, it is assumed that for the commercial and industrial customers, the vast majority of the water demand throughout the week occurs only six out of seven days. Thus, an adjustment factor to recognize the daily variations in usage for these classes of 1.17 (7 total days/6 days of water use) might be used. For residential customers, there will also be daily variation in usage throughout the maximum month. For purposes of this example, an adjustment factor of 1.35 is chosen for the residential class. It should be emphasized that these adjustment factors are assumed for purposes of this example only. Consideration should be given to the particular usage characteristics and periods of demands for the various customer classes of each individual utility when analyzing and determining the applicable class peaking factors.

Multiplying the results of the analyses and factors previously described to arrive at an initial estimate of the maximum-day peaking factors yields the following factors by class:

	Residential	Commercial	Industrial
MM/AD Factor	1.36	1.31	1.03
System MD/MM Ratio	1.34	1.34	1.34
Weekly Usage Adjustment	1.35	1.17	1.17
Calculated MD Peaking Factor	2.46	2.05	1.61
Peaking Factor (from chapter III.2)	2.50	2.00	1.50

To test the reasonableness of the maximum-day peaking factors, the noncoincident demands resulting from the application of the example peaking factors to the annual average-day demands of each class should be summed and compared against the actual coincident system demands. This relationship of the noncoincident to coincident demands is referred to as the measure of the system diversity of demand. The system diversity ratio is often in the range of 1.1 to 1.4, though different system diversity measures may arise for communities with more atypical customer class usage patterns. For example, a system that consists almost entirely of residential customers would have a diversity factor very close to 1.0 because the noncoincident demand of the residential customer class would be approximately equal to the coincident demand of the system.

The test of the system diversity, using the example peaking factors, is demonstrated in the following analysis:

Residential MD Demand	2.65 mgd × 2.50	= 6.63 mgd
Commercial MD Demand	1.30 mgd × 2.00	= 2.60 mgd
Industrial MD Demand	3.00 mgd × 1.50	= 4.50 mgd
Wholesale MD Demand*		= 1.42 mgd
Noncoincident Demand		15.15 mgd
Noncoincident MD Peaking Factor	15.15 mgd/7.50 mgd	= 2.02
Coincident MD Peaking Factor	11.55 mgd/7.50 mgd	= 1.54
System MD Diversity	2.02/1.54	= 1.31

*Wholesale customer noncoincident maximum-day demand based on actual meter readings.

As indicated by the example analysis, the initial maximum-day peaking factors computed for the retail customer classes produce an overall maximum-day system diversity factor of 1.31, which falls within a common range of 1.1 to 1.4. This means that the maximum-day peaking factors selected for each of the classes, based on the data available and the assumptions regarding variation in consumption patterns, likely result in reasonable approximations of the overall class maximum-day demands for cost allocation purposes.

Maximum-Hour Peaking Factors

The determination of maximum-hour peaking factors by customer class is similar to, and builds on, the previous determination of the maximum-day peaking factors.

For industrial customers, the relationship of maximum-hour and maximum-day peaking factors may be a function of manufacturing processes, input/output logistics scheduling, or simply the hours of operation during the day in which the maximum hour for the class is likely to occur. For purposes of this example, it is assumed that the industries in the example utility operate two equal 9-hour shifts each day during the six-day work week. Thus, the maximum-hour demand is at least 1.33 times the maximum-day demand (24 hours per day/18-hour work period). Care must be taken to recognize the usage characteristics of each utility's customers; the assumptions in this appendix are for illustrative purposes only.

The relationship between the maximum-hour demand and maximum-day demand for the residential and commercial customer classes is a function of even more factors due to the diversity of customers within these classes. It is likely that the overall relationship of maximum-hour to maximum-day demands for these two classes is greater than that previously discussed for the industrial class, because the time of peak consumption for these two classes may be concentrated in a shorter time frame throughout the day. For purposes of this example, a maximum-hour to maximum-day ratio of 1.66 is selected for the residential and commercial classes. This assumed ratio, and the resulting maximum-day peaking factors for the three retail classes, can be tested using the diversity analysis that was previously described for the maximum-day capacity ratios.

The initial determination of the maximum-hour peaking factors for the residential, commercial, and industrial classes is shown in the following example:

	Residential	Commercial	Industrial
MD Peaking Factor	2.50	2.00	1.50
Estimated MH/MD Ratio	1.66	1.66	1.33
Calculated MH Peaking Factor	4.15	3.32	2.00
MH Peaking Factor (from chapter III.2)	4.00	3.25	2.00

The diversity test to indicate whether the maximum-hour peaking factors developed in the example are reasonable is similar to the analysis performed for the maximum-day peaking factors. This analysis results in the following findings:

Residential MH Demand	2.65 mgd × 4.00	= 10.60 mgd
Commercial MH Demand	1.30 mgd × 3.25	= 4.23 mgd
Industrial MH Demand	3.00 mgd × 2.00	= 6.00 mgd
Wholesale MH Demand*		= 2.36 mgd
Noncoincident Demand		23.19 mgd
Noncoincident MH Peaking Factor	23.19 mgd/7.50 mgd	= 3.09
Coincident MH Peaking Factor	16.65 mgd/7.50 mgd	= 2.22
System MH Diversity	3.09/2.22	= 1.39

*Wholesale customer maximum-hour demand based on actual meter readings.

As indicated by this analysis, the maximum-hour peaking factors computed for the retail customer classes produce an overall maximum-hour system diversity factor of 1.39, which is within a typical range of 1.10 to 1.40. This means that the maximum-hour peaking factors selected for each of the classes, based on the data available and the assumptions regarding variation in consumption throughout the day, likely result in reasonable approximations of the overall class maximum-hour demands for cost allocation purposes.

DETERMINATION OF COINCIDENT PEAKING FACTORS

The use of peaking factors by customer class based on the estimated demands for each class that are coincident with system maximum-day or maximum-hour demands is an alternative to the use of estimated noncoincident demands. Depending on the specific circumstances, the use of coincident peaking factors may be appropriate. A utility system serving a predominately bedroom residential community may be an example of where coincident system-based class capacity factors may be appropriate. Coincident peaking factors may also be appropriate in situations where the utility is trying to encourage the shift of the demands by one or more classes to off-peak periods. This section discusses the development of coincident peaking factors.

Estimation of coincident customer class peaking factors may be accomplished using the same general types of data as are used for estimation of noncoincident peaking factors. The estimation procedure involves imputation of class peaking factors based on the ratio of each respective class's monthly usage in the month of the system-wide coincident peak to the annual average monthly usage for each class and the system peak to system maximum-month demands.

Maximum-Day Peaking Factor

The formula for the maximum-day peaking factor is

$$\left(\frac{\text{Class Consumption During System MM}}{\text{Annual Average Month for Class}} \right) \times \left(\frac{\text{System Peak-Day Rate of Flow}}{\text{System MM Rate of Flow}} \right)$$

Maximum-Hour Peaking Factor

The formula for the maximum-hour peaking factor is

$$\left(\frac{\text{Class Consumption During System MM}}{\text{Average Month for Class}} \right) \times \left(\frac{\text{System Peak-Day Rate of Flow}}{\text{System MM Rate of Flow}} \right)$$

Accordingly, initial calculations of class peaking factors using data from the example utility are as follows:

Maximum-Day	
Residential:	(3.60 mgd/2.65 mgd) × (11.55 mgd/8.60 mgd) = 1.82
Commercial:	(1.50 mgd/1.30 mgd) × (11.55 mgd/8.60 mgd) = 1.55
Industrial:	(3.04 mgd/3.00 mgd) × (11.55 mgd/8.60 mgd) = 1.36
Maximum-Hour	
Residential:	(3.60 mgd/2.65 mgd) × (16.65 mgd/8.60 mgd) = 2.63
Commercial:	(1.50 mgd/1.30 mgd) × (16.65 mgd/8.60 mgd) = 2.23
Industrial:	(3.04 mgd/3.00 mgd) × (16.65 mgd/8.60 mgd) = 1.96

The estimate of the coincident demands (both daily and hourly) for each customer class can be adjusted in a manner similar to the way these demands are adjusted for noncoincident peaking factors. These adjustments may increase the accuracy of the calculations. This example does not include adjustment factors.

The coincident demands resulting from the application of the example peaking factors to the annual average-day demands of each class should be summed and compared against the actual system demands. The relationship of the estimated coincident demand to the actual system demand is a measure of the accuracy of the aggregate daily and hourly demand estimates. This relationship is expressed as an accuracy factor:

Maximum-Day		
Residential:	2.65 mgd × 1.82	= 4.83 mgd
Commercial:	1.30 mgd × 1.55	= 2.02 mgd
Industrial:	3.00 mgd × 1.36	= 4.08 mgd
Wholesale:*		= 1.42 mgd
Total:		12.35 mgd
Accuracy Factors	11.55/12.35 = 93.5%	
Maximum-Hour		
Residential:	2.65 mgd × 2.63	= 6.97 mgd
Commercial:	1.30 mgd × 2.23	= 2.90 mgd
Industrial:	3.00 mgd × 1.96	= 5.88 mgd
Wholesale:*		= 2.36 mgd
Total:		18.11 mgd
Accuracy Factors	16.65/18.11 = 91.9%	

*Wholesale customer maximum-day and maximum-hour demands based on actual meter readings in the system maximum month.

Accordingly, the class peaking factors may be adjusted by applying these accuracy factors to the calculated factors, whereby the sum of the individual class demands will equal the system demands. The resulting factors are estimated demands that closely approximate those actually experienced by the utility system, as illustrated for the maximum-day peaking factors in the following example:

Maximum-Day		
Residential:	4.83 mgd × 0.935	= 4.52 mgd
Commercial:	2.02 mgd × 0.935	= 1.89 mgd
Industrial:	4.08 mgd × 0.935	= 3.81 mgd
Wholesale:*	1.42 mgd × 0.935	= 1.33 mgd
Total:		11.55 mgd
Maximum-Hour		
Residential:	6.97 mgd × 0.919	= 6.41 mgd
Commercial:	2.90 mgd × 0.919	= 2.67 mgd
Industrial:	5.88 mgd × 0.919	= 5.40 mgd
Wholesale:*	2.36 mgd × 0.919	= 2.17 mgd
Total:		16.65 mgd

*Wholesale customer maximum-day and maximum-hour demands based on actual meter readings.

SUMMARY

The examples and explanations regarding the determination of customer class maximum-day and maximum-hour peaking factors discussed in this appendix are intended to add clarity to this aspect of the cost-of-service process. As may be inferred from the examples, to make these determinations, it is imperative that the utility maintain adequate system demand and customer class billing records to complete the calculations that are necessary for the development of these factors.

An important technical decision in completing cost allocations by customer class as described in this appendix is whether to use noncoincident or coincident peaking factors by customer class in the cost-of-service analysis. The resulting allocations using the two sets of factors could be materially different, depending on the water demand characteristics of a system and its customers. Therefore, the choice of which method to use is important with respect to rate-making principles, data and costs required to conduct the analysis, and assumptions that may need to be made. Selection of the appropriate methodology for determining customer class peaking factors should be considered on an individual utility basis.

This page intentionally blank.

Appendix **B**

Equivalent Meter Ratios

In the overall rate-setting process, there is often the need to establish a minimum threshold or base level of cost or demand for service against which the costs or demands of larger-volume customers can be measured. A convenient and readily available parameter for this purpose is the size of the customer's water meter. Typically the meter size, which is generally used as the *base* or *minimum*, is the smallest available. The ⅝-in. meter has traditionally been the most prevalent meter size found in many water utilities, and, until recently, has also been the size most often used for single-family residential customers. However, this is subject to local code requirements that may vary by location, with some utilities using ¾-in. meters as the minimum size for residential customers. Accordingly, care should be taken to select the meter size for the base that is most relevant to the particular utility. In the overall rate-setting process, residential user characteristics are often used as the measure of the base level of service or on which service equivalency units are measured.

There are different methodologies for measuring or computing equivalent ratios for larger meters as compared to a ⅝-in. meter or the standard base size meter as determined by the utility. The appropriate methodology depends on the use of the equivalent ratios. The two most commonly used ratios in the water rate-making industry are (1) equivalent meter-and-service cost ratios and (2) equivalent meter capacity ratios. Generally, equivalent meter-and-service cost ratios should be used when assigning elements specifically related to the initial installation cost of meters and service line connections, depreciation of meters and services, replacement of meters, and testing of meters among the various sizes of meters in the system. The allocation of many customer-related costs associated with meters in conjunction with a cost-of-service study is an example of a use of equivalent meter cost ratios.*

Meter capacity ratios, on the other hand, are most often used when estimating potential capacity or demand requirements for customers on the basis of the size of the water

---

* This may not include customer costs associated with meter reading, billing, and collection that are typically the same for all meter sizes and are more a function of bill frequency.

Table B-1 Example costs of meter installations

Cost Item	⅝-in.	¾-in.	1-in.	1½-in.
Service Connection	$922.32	$922.32	$988.97	$1,026.52
Meter Installation	$385.46	$463.97	$869.38	$1,302.13
Total Cost	$1,307.78	$1,386.29	$1,858.35	$2,328.65
Ratio to ⅝ in.	1.00	1.06	1.42	1.78
Ratio Used	1.0	1.1	1.4	1.8

meter. The determination of system development charges or impact fees for meters greater than the base size, where potential customer demand is assumed to be proportional to meter size, is an example of the use of meter capacity ratios. Meter capacity ratios may also be appropriate in the design of the service charge portion of the general rate schedule when such charges include some recovery of fixed-capacity-related costs or readiness-to-serve-related costs.

EQUIVALENT METER-AND-SERVICE COST RATIOS

In determining the ratio of the cost of installing various sizes of meters and related service lines relative to the cost of installing the base size meter, it is important to include all of the costs involved in such installations. This includes the direct cost of the various categories of labor involved in the installation, fringe-benefit-related overheads and other appropriate administrative overheads applicable to the labor costs, all direct materials and supplies costs, and the cost of equipment used in the installation.*

In the cost allocation examples in chapter III.2, the costs of meters and services were combined in the cost allocation procedure. This is an appropriate consideration when it is the responsibility of the utility to install both a portion of the customer service line (generally from the main in the street to the customer's property line) and the meter itself. Accordingly, the example derivation of the cost ratios shown in this appendix and used in chapter III.2 are related to the combined cost of meter-and-service installations for various sizes of connections.

Table B-1 presents an *example* of the costs of meter installations for ⅝-, ¾-, 1-, and 1½-in. meters and the related service lines. These are merely examples and not recommended for use by a specific utility unless they have been verified by the utility. Dividing the total costs of installing the meter-and-service installations of the larger meter sizes by the total cost of the ⅝-in. meter-and-service connection yields the cost ratios shown. The development of these ratios, along with the applicable ratios for larger size meters, is the basis for the tabulation shown in chapter III.2 of this manual.

EQUIVALENT METER CAPACITY RATIOS

The safe operating flow, or capacity, of a particular size of meter is essentially the limiting factor in terms of the demand that can be exerted on the water system through the meter. In establishing a schedule of system development charges based on meter size or assigning a portion of the fixed costs as part of a demand or readiness-to-serve component, the potential demand or capacity requirements placed on the water system by a new customer are generally an accepted basis for determining the level of charge applicable to the

---

* Where actual meter-and-service installation costs are not available due to the absence of detail in property records, current-day installation costs may be used instead.

customer. Accordingly, when the minimum or base system development charge is established for a single-family residential customer with a ⅝-in. meter (as is often the case), the ratio of the safe operating capacity of various sizes of meters, relative to the capacity of a ⅝-in. meter, may be used to determine appropriate charges for the larger meter sizes.

In chapter VII.2 (see Table VII.2-5), the maximum safe operating capacity for meters of various sizes are tabulated, based on AWWA's Standards for Water Meters (C700 series). The ratios of these capacities, relative to that of a ⅝-in. meter, are computed and range from 1.5 for a ¾-in. meter up to 265 for a 12-in. turbine meter. As discussed in chapter VII.2, while capacity ratios for larger meters can be computed, the use of such ratios for larger meters may or may not provide a true indication of the potential demand requirements of the larger meters. Table B-2 displays the safe maximum operating capacity by meter size and meter type based on AWWA's Standards for Water Meters.

It is important to understand and recognize the types of costs that are to be recovered using equivalent meter ratios in order to develop the appropriate meter equivalency factors. As discussed in chapter VII.2, developing equivalent capacity ratios specific to a particular utility and its system characteristics is normally desired, as opposed to using a standardized table of meter equivalencies. For example, a water utility may have significant investment in impounded reservoir source-of-supply facilities (designed on the basis of annual average-day demands), as well as treatment plant, pumping, and transmission facilities (designed on the basis of maximum-day and/or maximum-hour demands). In this instance, the utility would need to recognize both annual usage requirements, as well as peak-demand requirements, for each of its sizes of meters in establishing relevant equivalent capacity ratios appropriate for system development charge determination.

SUMMARY

The selection of equivalent meter ratios is dependent on the purpose for which the ratios are to be used. Care should be exercised in using the correct ratio methodology for the correct purpose. It is normally desirable to develop ratios that are applicable to an individual utility's particular circumstances and facilities. The purpose of this appendix is to clarify the various types of equivalent meter ratios that may be used in rate-making and the general applicability of each of the measures of equivalency. Selection of the appropriate measures for distributing costs should be considered on an individual utility basis.

REFERENCES

AWWA (American Water Works Association). C700-09 *Standard for Cold-Water Meters— Displacement Type, Bronze Main Case*. Denver, Colo.: AWWA.

AWWA (American Water Works Association). C701-12 *Standard for Cold-Water Meters— Turbine Type, for Customer Service*. Denver, Colo.: AWWA.

AWWA (American Water Works Association). C702-10 *Standard for Cold-Water Meters— Compound Type*. Denver, Colo.: AWWA.

AWWA (American Water Works Association). C703-15 *Standard for Cold-Water Meters— Fire-Service Type*. Denver, Colo.: AWWA.

AWWA (American Water Works Association). C704-15 *Standard for Propeller-Type Meters for Waterworks Applications*. Denver, Colo.: AWWA.

Table B-2 Safe maximum operating capacity* by meter type, per current AWWA standards (in gpm)

Meter Size (in.)	C700-09 Displacement Type (bronze main case)	C710-15 Displacement Type (plastic main case)	C708-15 Multijet Type	C712-15 Singlejet Type	C713-15 Fluidic-Oscillator Type	C701-12 Turbine Type, Class I, Vertical-Shaft Type	C701-12 Turbine Type, Class II, In-Line (high-velocity type)	C702-10 Compound Type, Class I	C702-10 Compound Type, Class II	C703-15 Fire-Service, Type I, Proportional Fire-Service Meters w/ Check Valve	C703-15 Fire-Service, Type II, Compound Fire-Service Meter Assembly and Strainer w/ Check Valve	C703-15 Fire-Service, Type III, Turbine Fire-Service Meter and Strainer w/o Check Valve	C704-15 Propeller Type
½	15	15			15								
½ × ¾	15	15			15								
⅝	20	20	20	20	20								
⅝ × ¾	20	20	20	20	20								
¾	30	30	30	30	30	30							
1	50	50	50	50	50	50							
1½	100		100	100	100	100	120						
2	160		160	160	160	160	190	160	160				120
3				320		350	435	320	350	400	350	350	300
4				500		630	750	500	600	700	700	700	600
6				1,000		1,300	1,600	1,000	1,350	1,600	1,600	1,600	1,350
8							2,800	1,600	1,600	2,800	2,800	2,800	1,800
10							4,200			4,400	4,400	4,400	2,400
12							5,300						3,375
14													4,500
16							7,800						5,700
18													6,750
20							12,000						8,250
24													12,000
30													18,000
36													24,000
42													40,000
48													50,000
54													55,000
60													80,000
66													95,000
72													115,000

C700, C710, C708: Operation at this flow rate should not exceed 10% of usage, or 2 hours in a 24-hour period.

C701: *Safe maximum operating capacity* is the maximum flow rate for intermittent service and should not exceed 33% usage (8 h/day).

C704: As shown for use, 10% to 15% of total time meter is operating (also referred to as "intermittent maximum flow").

AWWA (American Water Works Association). C708-15 *Standard for Cold-Water Meters—Multijet Type.* Denver, Colo.: AWWA.

AWWA (American Water Works Association). C710-15 *Standard for Cold-Water Meters—Displacement Type, Plastic Main Case.* Denver, Colo.: AWWA.

AWWA (American Water Works Association). C712-15 *Standard for Cold-Water Meters—Singlejet Type.* Denver, Colo.: AWWA.

AWWA (American Water Works Association). C713-15 *Standard for Cold-Water Meters—Fluidic-Oscillator Type.* Denver, Colo.: AWWA.

This page intentionally blank.

Appendix **C**

Bill Tabulation Methods

The summarization or tabulation of customer bills provides a useful basis for identifying and analyzing customer usage patterns, selecting water-usage rate blocks, and determining utility billing revenue under any rate schedule. Tabulation of customer bills and usage, commonly referred to as a *bill-frequency distribution analysis* or simply *bill tabulation*, used to be a tedious manual task but is now generally accomplished by accessing a utility's customer billing database. Computerization has greatly simplified the process, but preparing an accurate and usable bill tabulation is still a complex task, requiring very careful development of queries and meticulous testing of the completeness and accuracy of the results. Some modern utility billing systems include standard reports that will meet the needs of the rate analyst, but in most cases, unique programs and queries are still required to extract and summarize data in the form required. It is best to begin the bill tabulation at the beginning of any cost-of-service study to create the necessary data and to evaluate the accuracy of the results.

A bill tabulation shows the number of customer bills rendered at various levels of water usage during a specified period of time for each customer class served by the utility. The tabulation of bills for a historical period provides the basis for identifying typical customer-class usage patterns and aids in the development of rates recognizing such patterns. Rate schedules that are intended to be applicable throughout an entire year generally require bill tabulation for a historical 12-month period so that annual usage patterns are properly identified. On the other hand, if a seasonal rate schedule is to be developed, separate bill tabulations would need to be made to coincide with the periods for each part of the seasonal rates to be effective. For instance, if a summer–winter seasonal rate were to be developed with one rate applicable for usage during the 6-month summer period and another for the 6-month winter period, the bill tabulation would need to be made in two parts to coincide with the summer and winter periods as defined. This permits recognition of customer usage patterns and variations in use between seasons. The bill tabulation process can be even further complicated when considering forms of water-budget or other elaborate rate structures. Any structure that relies on or uses metrics based on individual customer characteristics such as persons per household, average winter water use, and so forth, may require significant analytical efforts to calibrate the data and reconcile different rate structures with revenue requirements.

In the following examples, bills are tabulated for one customer class for a continuous 12-month period. Tabulating bills for a continuous 12-month period is strongly recommended to properly account for seasonal variations in customer water-usage patterns. In addition, the selection of the 12-month period should coincide as closely as possible with the utility's fiscal accounting period so that the accuracy of the bill tabulation in generating revenue can be more easily ascertained. The possibility that the period selected for study may represent a year in which water usage was abnormally high or low, due to climatic or other conditions, should be considered when using the bill tabulation for rate-design purposes. If possible, the selection of bills for tabulation should reflect a year in which average conditions prevail.

BILL SUMMARIZATION

The first step in tabulating customer bills is to create a billing system query to reflect existing customer classes and meter sizes within each class. For small utilities, each customer's usage may be tabulated for the 12-month period. However, for larger utilities, a sample tabulation of the residential class, on the order of 10 to 20 percent of the total number of customers in the class, may be adequate to establish usage patterns for that class. However, care should be taken to ensure, to the extent possible, that the selected sample statistically provides a valid and representative sample. It is suggested that 100 percent tabulation be made for other customer classes, because the use per customer in other classes is likely to be much more variable than for the residential class. A less-than-100-percent sample, particularly for large-volume customers, may not provide a representative distribution of water-usage patterns. If a sample of customers is to be made, random sampling procedures should be used.

The bill tabulation process is initiated by selecting the smallest meter size for a particular customer class and tabulating identified individual customer usage onto the summary sheet for that meter size and class. This procedure is continued for each meter size until all customer bills in the class have been summarized. The same process would be repeated for every other customer class.

It is important to summarize bills for each identified customer in all customer classes unless a sample for the class, as previously discussed, has been selected. Bills issued to inactive accounts should be excluded. Bills issued to active customer accounts with zero usage during any billing period should be included as "zero-usage" bills.

While it is unlikely that many utilities would need to use a manual process to prepare a bill tabulation, a brief description of that process may be helpful to an analyst undertaking this process for the first time. To illustrate the bill summarization procedure, hypothetical customer-billing account records and a bill tabulation sheet are shown in Tables C-1 and C-2, respectively.

Table C-1 shows two customer billing accounts, presenting each customer's monthly water use and the amount billed. Both customers are inside-city residential customers with ⅝-in. meters, as indicated on the billing record. Table C-2 shows an example of the type of sheet that was used to tabulate the usage for each monthly bill for the two example customers from Table C-1. The left side of the tabulation sheet provides the various possible levels of customer usage for each billing period in terms of thousands of gallons (1,000 gal).

Beginning with the first customer on a route or billing cycle, for example, customer number 112598 shown in Table C-1, a tick mark was made on the line in Table C-2 that corresponds to the usage billed in a given month. Each tick mark was equivalent to one bill.

Table C-1 Example of customer-account billing records

Customer Account No. 112598   Name: John Smith

Meter Size: ⅝ in.   Address: 123 Main Street

Customer Class: Residential

Jurisdiction: Inside City

Billing Date	Meter Reading, 1,000 gal	Use, 1,000 gal	Amount Due, $	Month Paid	Amount Paid, $
Dec.	12163				
Jan.	12167	4	27.50	Jan.	27.50
Feb.	12172	5	30.50	Feb.	30.50
Mar.	12176	4	27.50	Mar.	27.50
Apr.	12182	6	33.50	Apr.	33.50
May	12189	7	36.50	May	36.50
June	12195	6	33.50	June	33.50
July	12201	6	33.50	July	33.50
Aug.	12207	6	33.50	Aug.	33.50
Sept.	12212	5	30.50	Sep.	30.50
Oct.	12217	5	30.50	Oct.	30.50
Nov.	12221	4	27.50	Nov.	27.50
Dec.	12224	3	24.50	Dec.	24.50

Customer Account No. 117211   Name: Mary Jones

Meter Size: ⅝ in.   Address: 234 Dover Street

Customer Class: Residential

Jurisdiction: Inside City

Billing Date	Meter Reading, 1,000 gal	Use, 1,000 gal	Amount Due, $	Month Paid	Amount Paid, $
Dec.	34367				
Jan.	34371	4	27.50	Jan.	27.50
Feb.	34376	5	30.50	Feb.	30.50
Mar.	34381	5	30.50	Mar.	30.50
Apr.	34387	6	33.50	Apr.	33.50
May	34396	9	42.50	May	42.50
June	34404	8	39.50	June	39.50
July	34411	7	36.50	July	36.50
Aug.	34418	7	36.50	Aug.	36.50
Sept.	34423	5	30.50	Sep.	30.50
Oct.	34429	6	33.50	Oct.	33.50
Nov.	34434	5	30.50	Nov.	30.50
Dec.	34438	4	27.50	Dec.	27.50

For the January billing period, the usage for this customer is indicated to be 4 thousand gallons. Therefore, a tick mark was made on the usage-block line marked "4" on Table C-2, as shown. A tick mark was made for each monthly usage quantity on the appropriate line on Table C-2 for both customers' monthly usage quantities. This procedure would be

Table C-2 Example of a water bill tabulation sheet

Customer Class: Residential

Meter Size: ⅝ in.

Jurisdiction: Inside City

Cycle: 4

Water Usage per Period, 1,000 gal	Tabulation	Total Number of Bills	Total Water Usage, 1,000 gal
0		0	0
1		0	0
2		0	0
3	I	1	3
4	·I I I I I	5	20
5	I I I I I I I	7	35
6	I I I I I I	6	36
7	I I I	3	21
8	I	1	8
9	I	1	9
10		0	0
11		0	0
12		0	0
13		0	0
14		0	0
15		0	0
16		0	0
17		0	0
18		0	0
19		0	0
46		0	0
47		0	0
48		0	0
49		0	0
50		0	0
Total		24	132

repeated for all ⅝-in. residential inside-city accounts in that cycle or route billed during the 12-month period. Similarly, a separate tabulation sheet or sheets for all cycles and for each meter size by customer class would be completed.

Once the bill tabulation is completed for each meter size by class, the number of tick marks or bills is totaled for each usage block and summarized at the bottom of the appropriate column on each sheet. Usage associated with the bills tabulated in each usage block is determined by multiplying the number of bills by the usage amount—shown in the left-hand column for each line. If the two hypothetical customers shown in Table C-1 were the only ⅝-in. residential inside-city customers in that cycle, the total number of bills and usage would be those shown in Table C-2 at the bottom of the two right-hand columns.

After all bills and associated usage have been summarized for each meter size and class, total customer-class usage and bills would be determined by adding the bills and usage for all meter sizes for a given customer class. The selection of the period for which bills are to be summarized to coincide with the utility's fiscal accounting period greatly enhances the ability to check the accuracy of the bill tabulation because cumulative data as to the number of bills, total water sales, and revenue for that period would be readily available. The final check as to the accuracy of the bill tabulation is based on the revenue that the tabulation generates when applied to the existing schedule of rates.

DEVELOPMENT OF CUMULATIVE BILLED USAGE

After tabulating the number of bills and usage for each customer class by meter size, the next step is to determine the cumulative billed water usage by various usage blocks or increments for each customer class and meter size. The procedure includes several steps and is best accomplished by using a computation table similar to the one shown in Table C-3. The data summarized in Table C-3 are for a hypothetical residential customer class (not just the two example customers from Table C-1). Column 1 of Table C-3 shows the usage blocks for which water-usage and bill data are summarized. Selection of usage blocks for summarizing cumulative billing data does not need to set forth all usage blocks used in the bill tabulation sheet described earlier. The usage blocks used in summarizing cumulative billed usage are generally established to include single-unit increments at the lower usage levels to coincide with the use of smaller users and larger increments or groupings of several-unit increments at the higher usage levels. As shown in Table C-3, single-unit increments of usage from 1,000 gallons up to 14,000 gallons are used, and larger increments are used thereafter.

Usage blocks summarized should be selected in part to coincide with the existing rate blocks. This will result in a readily identifiable cumulative level of usage in each rate block against which existing rates may be applied for purposes of checking the accuracy of revenue generated by the bill tabulation.

The number of bills issued for water usage corresponding to the various consumption blocks is shown in column 2 of Table C-3. The number of bills issued for each usage block would be taken directly from bill tabulation sheets similar to the one shown in Table C-2. In this example, total bills represent the summation of bills issued to residential-class customers with ⅝-in. meters. For example, during the 12-month period represented by the bill tabulation, 32,233 bills were issued to the group of customers having a monthly usage of 3,000 gallons. Bills for each usage block are summarized in this manner for each customer class and each meter size individually. Once the number of bills is summarized by usage block, the bills are accumulated in column 3 of Table C-3 by starting with the bills in the largest usage block and adding the next above-usage-block's number of bills to it. As shown in Table C-3, a total of 300,000 bills were issued to residential class customers with ⅝-in. meters. The number of cumulative bills in any particular usage block represents the number of bills issued for the amount of water use shown in that block or more. For instance, at the 3,000 gallon consumption block, 257,698 bills have been issued for usage of 3,000 gallons or more.

Column 4 represents the total use of bills stopping in each usage block and corresponds to the number of bills listed in column 2. These numbers are taken from the far right-hand column of each bill tabulation sheet (an example of which is shown in Table C-2). In the example in Table C-3, 32,233 bills are issued for the 3,000-gallon usage block for a total of 96,699 thousand gallons in total water use.

The value in column 5 for a given usage block represents the cumulative billed usage of all bills with monthly usage less than or equal to the usage represented by the usage

Table C-3   Development of cumulative billed usage for residential ⅝-in. meters

(1)	(2)	(3)	(4)	(5)	(6)	(7)	(8)
Usage Block, 1,000 gal	Number of Bills Ending in Block	Cumulative Bills Through Block	Total Use of Bills Stopping in Block, 1,000 gal	Cumulative Use of Bills Stopping in Block, 1,000 gal	Total Use to This Block of All Bills Passing Through Block, 1,000 gal	Cumulative Billed Usage, 1,000 gal	Cumulative Billed Usage, %
0	6,100	300,000	—	—	—	—	0.0
1	15,200	293,900	15,200	15,200	278,700	293,900	16.4
2	21,002	278,700	42,004	57,204	515,396	572,600	31.9
3	32,233	257,698	96,699	153,903	676,395	830,298	46.3
4	34,201	225,465	136,804	290,707	765,056	1,055,763	58.9
5	54,922	191,264	274,610	565,317	681,710	1,247,027	69.5
6	38,433	136,342	230,598	795,915	587,454	1,383,369	77.1
7	21,836	97,909	152,852	948,767	532,511	1,481,278	82.6
8	14,664	76,073	117,312	1,066,079	491,272	1,557,351	86.8
9	18,227	61,409	164,043	1,230,122	388,638	1,618,760	90.2
10	15,444	43,182	154,440	1,384,562	277,380	1,661,942	92.6
11	10,211	27,738	112,321	1,496,883	192,797	1,689,680	94.2
12	6,121	17,527	73,452	1,570,335	136,872	1,707,207	95.2
13	3,210	11,406	41,730	1,612,065	106,548	1,718,613	95.8
14	422	8,196	5,908	1,617,973	108,836	1,726,809	96.3
15–20	3,454	7,774	56,991	1,674,964	86,400	1,761,364	98.2
21–25	2,105	4,320	48,415	1,723,379	55,375	1,778,754	99.2
26–30	1,291	2,215	35,503	1,758,882	27,720	1,786,602	99.6
31–40	892	924	32,112	1,790,994	1,280	1,792,274	99.9
41–100	32	32	2,880	1,793,874	—	1,793,874	100.0
101+	—	—	—	1,793,874	—	1,793,874	100.0

block. Consequently, the summarization of usage for all usage blocks yields the total use of the customer class for the meter size during the bill tabulation period. In the example, ⅝-in. residential-class customers used 1,793,874 thousand gallons during the 12-month bill tabulation period, as shown in the last line of column 5.

Although the accumulated usage shown in column 5 provides a measure of total customer-class water use, it does not indicate the quantity of water used in a given usage block by bills that exceed that usage level. That is, at the 3,000-gallon usage block, column 5 indicates that a total of 153,903 thousand gallons of water was used by those customers billed for 0, 1, 2, and 3 thousand gallons. This quantity does not include water used by customers who use more than 3 thousand gallons. For rate-design purposes, the total quantity of water used at a particular usage block needs to be determined, including the usage in the block by customers whose usage exceeds the block. Therefore, the next step is to determine the total use in the block of all billed usage passing beyond each block. This quantity may be determined from data in columns 1 and 3 and is summarized in column 6. The values shown in column 6 are calculated for each usage block by multiplying the usage block value in column 1 by the number of cumulative bills through the block corresponding to the next larger usage block, as shown in column 3. For example, the column 6 value for the 21–25 thousand gallon usage block is calculated by multiplying 25 thousand gallons by the number of cumulative bills for the 26–30 thousand gallon block of 2,215 to total 55,375 thousand gallons. The cumulative billed usage of all ⅝-in. residential customers may be developed at this point by adding the values shown in columns 5 and 6 for each usage block. Total cumulative usage for the ⅝-in. residential class is shown in column 7. The cumulative usage figures in column 7 indicate the total usage that would be billed at any given usage block. To determine the usage at interim blocks (e.g., the usage between 3,000 gallons and 10,000 gallons), the cumulative usage corresponding to the smaller block would be subtracted from the cumulative usage of the larger block. In this example, 1,661,942 thousand gallons less 830,298 thousand gallons, or 831,644 thousand gallons, would be the use in a rate block of 4,000–10,000 gallons.

Once the bill tabulation has been completed for all customer classes, the cumulative usage (shown in column 7 of Table C-3) for each existing rate block would be determined. Application of existing rates to the cumulative usage in each rate block as determined from the bill tabulation would result in the indicated "bill tabulation" revenue under existing rates, which is related to existing volume-related charges. Applying existing service charges to the number of bills by meter size and adding the volume-charge revenue produced from the bill tabulation would yield the total bill tabulation revenue under existing rates. This revenue figure can then be compared with the billed revenue recorded by the utility to test the accuracy of the bill tabulation. A correlation of bill tabulation revenue to actual billed revenue of 3 percent or less generally indicates that the bill tabulation is sufficiently accurate for rate-design purposes. Where initial charges in the form of a minimum bill are used, precaution must be taken to avoid multiple counting of minimum usage in computing revenues.

APPLICATION OF BILL TABULATION FOR RATE DESIGN

The bill analysis, once verified for accuracy, provides a useful tool for rate design. The usage pattern of each class of customers, as determined from bill tabulation, is generally considered to remain relatively stable over a period of several years. In designing rates for future study periods, the usage pattern from the bill tabulation may be applied to projected water usage of various classes to determine estimated water usage applicable to each rate block.

For example, if under an increasing block rate approach it becomes necessary to change existing blocks to more equitably recover allocated costs of service from the various customer classes, the bill tabulation provides a means for selecting alternative rate blocks and the associated amount of water usage with the new blocks. To aid in the evaluation and selection of alternative rate blocks, the data in column 8 of Table C-3 presents the percentage of cumulative billed usage for each usage block. These values are determined by dividing the cumulative billed usage for each block in column 7 by the total cumulative usage times 100.

The cumulative billed percentage usage can provide an estimate of the cumulative percentage of future water usage that will occur at a given usage level. For example, if a proposed rate block is chosen at a monthly usage of 3 thousand gallons, Table C-3 indicates that approximately 46 percent of the total water use of customers in this class for this meter size would be expected to be billed in the 0–3 thousand gallon block.

In some instances, it may be more desirable to determine the cumulative billed usage for the combination of all meter sizes in each class. This may be accomplished simply by adding together the cumulative billed usages (similar to those shown in column 7 of Table C-3) determined for each meter size in a class for each respective usage block. To add cumulative billed usages for each meter size, the usage blocks established for each meter size must be exactly the same. The value determined from the summation would represent the cumulative billed usage of all customers in the class and would be used to calculate cumulative billed usage percentages.

It can be useful to examine all customer-class bill tabulation data; the data for each class could be compiled as an aid in the selection of proposed rate blocks for rate design. Trial or alternative rate blocks may be evaluated that effectively separate the majority of the usage for each class into one or more rate blocks using the bill tabulation data (Table C-3 as compiled for each class).

Appendix **D**

Example of Citizens Advisory Committee Guidelines

The Citizens Advisory Committee (CAC) will primarily serve to advise the utility's rate study project team on public concerns and perspectives regarding water rate-making issues. The CAC will operate under the following general guidelines and conditions, subject to consensus revision of rate study participants.

- CAC members will be appointed by the utility's governing board and will be selected to provide representation of a diversity of ratepayer groups. CAC members are asked to solicit the opinions of their constituency and articulate the positions of the members of their respective communities.

- CAC meetings will be open to the public and may include a period for general public comment.

- The CAC is not intended to be a "voting body" on positions related to rate study issues and it is not envisioned that the CAC will adopt positions using majority rule requirements. Rather, members will participate in discussions of rate-making principles with the objective of developing consensus recommendations. The intent is to provide a unified perspective from users, not the results of a majority vote. In the event that consensus may not be achieved on specific issues, both majority and minority opinions will be considered by the project team and reported to the utility's governing board.

- CAC discussions will be conducted to address rate-making options for water rates and related issues. The objective is to elicit a cohesive expression of community values and concerns to the maximum extent practicable. The rate study project team will provide objective information on these rate-making options to the CAC and solicit CAC recommendations. The project team will balance CAC recommendations with its fiduciary and management responsibilities in selecting from available rate-making options. CAC recommendations are nonbinding on either the rate study project team or the utility's governing board. However, all CAC recommendations will be documented and forwarded to the utility's governing board for their review and consideration.

- Project team decisions will be reported to the CAC once determined but will not be subject to re-review during subsequent CAC meetings. Similarly, the CAC will not review and recommend reconsideration of past utility decisions. In particular, CAC activities will not duplicate existing budget practices or processes.

- Project team support of CAC activities will be limited to provision of information necessary for consideration of outstanding rate-making issues and decisions. The project team will provide information that is available from utility records that can be collected and distributed without extensive expenditures of staff time or budget resources.

The CAC will discontinue once the rate study project is completed and water and wastewater rates have been adopted for one year. CAC membership is voluntary and will not be compensated by the utility.

Glossary

accelerated depreciation – Depreciation methods that amortize the cost of an asset at a faster rate than under the straight-line method. The three principle methods of accelerated depreciation are sum of the year's digits, double declining balance, and units of production.

accrual basis – The basis of accounting under which revenues are recorded when earned and expenditures are recorded when they become liabilities for benefits received, notwithstanding that receipt of the revenue or payments of the expenditure may take place, in whole or in part, in another accounting period.

ad valorem tax – A state or local tax based on the assessed value of real or personal property.

availability charge – A limited-use capital-related charge to a property owner between the time when water service is made available to the property and the time when the property connects to the utility's facilities and starts using the service.

base costs – Costs that tend to vary with the total quantity of water used and operation under average load conditions. Costs may include operation and maintenance expenses of supply, treatment, pumping, and transmission and distribution facilities, and capital costs related to plant investment associated with serving customers at a constant or average annual rate of use (100 percent load factor).

base-extra capacity – The method of cost allocation in which the annual costs of service by functional cost category are allocated to the cost components of base, extra capacity, customer, and direct fire protection costs.

bill frequency analysis – A tabulation and summarization of customer bills and usages showing the number of bills rendered at various levels of water usage during a specified period of time. Also referred to as a *bill tab*.

bond covenants – Terms of obligations incurred as conditions of the issuance of bonds.

bonded debt – Indebtedness represented by outstanding bonds.

budget – An estimate of proposed expenditures for a given period or purpose and a statement of the means of financing them.

buy-in method – An approach to determining system development charges based on the value of the existing system's capacity. This method is typically used when the existing system has sufficient capacity to serve new development now and into the future; may also be used in conjunction with the incremental cost method resulting in the combined cost approach.

capacity – The water utility's ability to have a certain quantity or level of resources available to meet the water service needs of its customers. Capacity is the combination of plant- and service-related activities required to provide the amount of service required by the customers. The plant facilities required are a composite of all types of facilities needed to provide service. It represents the ability of the water utility to meet the quantity, quality, peak loads, and other service requirements of the various customers or classes of customers served by the utility.

capital expenditures – Expenditures that result in the acquisition or addition of fixed assets.

capital program – A multiyear plan for capital expenditure spending to meet the regulatory, renewal, replacements, and expansion needs of a water utility. It sets forth each project or other contemplated expenditure in which the water utility is to have a part and specifies the full resources estimated to be available to finance the projected expenditures.

cash basis – The basis of accounting under which revenues are recorded when cash is received and expenditures are recorded when cash is disbursed.

cash-needs revenue requirements – The method of establishing annual revenue requirements giving consideration to the annual budget expenditures for operation and maintenance expenses, debt-service payments, cash-financed capital improvements, reserve fund requirements, and taxes. Debt-service coverage requirements must also be taken into account to establish cash-needs revenue requirements.

combined approach – An approach to determining system development charges based on a blended value of both the existing and expanded system's capacity. This method is typically used where some capacity is available in parts of the existing system (e.g., source of supply), but new or incremental capacity will need to be built in other parts (e.g., treatment plant) to serve new development at some point in the future; a combination of the buy-in and incremental cost approaches.

commodity costs (variable costs) – Costs that tend to vary with the quantity of water produced, including the costs of chemicals, a large part of power costs, and other elements that follow or change almost directly with the amount of water produced. Purchased water costs, if the water is purchased on a unit volume basis without minimum charges or any associated demand charges, may also be considered as commodity costs.

commodity demand method – The method of cost allocation in which the annual cost of service by functional cost category is allocated to the components of commodity, demand, customer, and direct fire protection costs.

connection charge – A charge made by the utility to recover the cost of connecting the customer's service line to the utility's facilities. This charge is often considered as contribution of capital by the customer or other agency applying for service.

construction work in progress (CWIP) – The utility's investment in facilities under construction, but not yet dedicated to service. The inclusion of CWIP in the rate base varies from one regulatory agency to another.

contributions in aid of construction (CIAC) – Any amount of money, services, or property received by a water utility from any person or governmental agency that is provided at no cost to the utility. It represents an addition or transfer to the capital of the utility and is used to offset the acquisition, improvement, or construction costs of the utility's property, facilities, or equipment used to provide utility services to the public. It includes amounts transferred from advances for construction representing any un-refunded balances of expired refund contracts or discounts resulting from termination of refund contracts. Contributions received from governmental agencies and others for relocation of water mains or other plant facilities are also included. All contributions are carried as equity capital in audited balance sheets of publicly owned utilities.

cost allocation – The procedure for classifying or assigning the annual costs of service to appropriate cost components for subsequent distribution to respective customer classes.

cost of capital – A utility's cost of capital is the weighted sum of the costs of component parts of the capital structure (e.g., debt and common equity) weighted by their respective proportions in the capital structure.

cost components – The distinct operational categories of a water utility to which separate cost groupings by utility function are typically allocated or assigned. In the base-extra capacity method of cost allocation, these are the components of base, extra capacity, customer, and direct fire protection costs. In the commodity-demand method, these are the components of commodity, demand, customer, and direct fire protection costs.

cost of debt – Commonly referred to as the *embedded* cost of debt, it is determined by taking the weighted average cost of the embedded debt securities. The cost of each security should include issuance expenses, discounts/premiums, and coupon payments. Under most circumstances, only long-term debt is used in the embedded debt-cost determination.

cost of service – The total annual operation and maintenance expense and capital-related costs incurred in meeting various aspects of providing water utility service. See also *cost-of-service study*.

cost-of-service study – The process of determining the cost of providing water service to each of the defined customer classifications. This includes the functionalization and allocation of water system revenue requirements (the system cost of service) followed by the distribution of costs by customer classification based on the annual usage, peak demands, and customer-related costs for which each class of service is responsible.

curb stop – A shutoff valve attached to a water service line from a water main to a customer's premises, which may be operated by a valve key to start or stop flow in the water supply lines of a building. Also called a *curb cock*.

customer classification – The grouping of customers into homogeneous groups or classes. Typically, water utility customers may be classified as residential, commercial, and industrial for rate-making and other purposes. For specific utilities, there may be a breakdown of these general classes into more specific groups. For example, the industrial class may be subdivided into small industry, large industry, and special. Some water systems have individual customers (large users) with unique water-use characteristics, service requirements, or other factors that set them apart from other general customer classes and thus may require a separate class designation. This may include large hospitals, colleges and universities, military establishments, private and public fire protection, wholesale service districts, irrigation accounts, and other such categories.

customer costs – Costs directly associated with serving customers, irrespective of the amount of water use. Such costs generally include meter reading, billing, accounting and collecting expense, and maintenance and capital costs related to meters and associated services.

debt – An obligation resulting from the borrowing of money or from the purchase of goods and services for the purpose of constructing utility long-lived fixed assets.

debt service – The amounts of money necessary to pay interest and principal requirements for a given series of years.

debt-service coverage ratio – The margin of safety ratio associated with bonded indebtedness reflecting the ratio of the actual or projected net revenue available for debt service to annual debt-service payments. *Net revenue* is generally defined as total recurring operating revenue less recurring operation and maintenance expense. Debt-service coverage is generally expressed as a percentage of current-year debt service, generally in the range of 115 percent to 150 percent, and is a requirement included in the bond indentures associated with revenue bonds.

decreasing block rates – A schedule of rates applicable to blocks of increasing usage in which the usage in each succeeding block is charged at a lower unit rate than in the previous blocks. Each successive block rate is applicable to a greater volume of water delivery than the preceding block(s).

dedicated capacity – The portion of the water utility's total capacity that is set aside, or dedicated, for use by an individual large-use customer or group (class) of customers whose total use is a significant part of the utility's total capacity requirement. Typically, the dedicated capacity and terms of its assignment and responsibilities are set forth in a contractual agreement between the utility and the customer.

demand costs – Costs associated with providing facilities to meet peak demands placed on the system by customers. They include capital-related costs associated with those facilities plus related operation and maintenance expenses.

demand patterns – Profiles and characteristics of the peak-demand requirements of the system, specific customer class or classes, or an individual customer, indicating the frequency, duration, and amount of demand placed on the water production and delivery system.

depreciation – The loss in service value not restored by current maintenance as applied to depreciable plant facilities. Depreciation is incurred in connection with the consumption or prospective retirement of plant facilities in the course of providing service. This depreciation is the result of causes known to be in current operation and against which the utility is not protected by insurance. Among the causes are wear and tear, decay, action of the elements, inadequacy, obsolescence, changes in technology, changes in demand, and requirements of public authorities. The proper level of depreciation expense at any given time should be based on the costs of depreciable plant in service. The funds resulting from depreciation are available for replacements, improvements, expansion of the system, or for repayment of the principal portion of outstanding debt.

depreciation rate – The annual rate at which capital facilities are depreciated, based on the estimated loss in value of the facilities, not restored by current maintenance, that occurs in the property due to wear and tear, decay, inadequacy, and obsolescence. It provides for the recovery of a utility's capital investment over the anticipated useful life of the depreciable assets.

discounted cash-flow (DCF) method – Often used in the rate-making process for estimating the investor-required rate of return on common equity. By definition, the DCF method contends that the market price of a common stock is equal to the cumulative present value of all future cash flows to investors produced by said common stock.

dividend payment – Payment made by an investor-owned water utility to its shareholders based on its earnings.

equity – The net worth of a business consisting of capital stock, capital (or paid in) surplus, earned surplus (or retained earnings), and, occasionally, certain net worth reserves.

equivalent meter-and-service ratio – The ratio of the cost of investment in larger meters and services to those of a base meter size, such as the ⅝-in. meter typically used for residential customers.

essential needs – The quantity of water needed to meet basic human needs, including drinking water for survival, basic hygiene and sanitation purposes, and household needs such as preparing food.

excess-use charges – Charges for usage above preestablished levels, typically used during periods of peak use relative to use during off-peak periods.

expenditures – Amounts paid or incurred for all purposes, including expenses, provision for retirement of debt, and capital outlays.

extra capacity costs – Costs of capital and operation and maintenance associated with meeting rate-of-use requirements in excess of average annual rate-of-use or base-use requirements.

fire protection charges – Charges made to recover the cost of providing both public and private fire protection service to the communities served by the utility. Usually, charges include both the direct capital-related and maintenance costs for fire hydrants and private fire connections, as well as applicable indirect costs for source of supply, treatment, transmission, and distribution of water to the fire protection facilities.

firm service – Dependable service in the amounts and at times as desired by the customer.

flat rate – A periodic stated charge for utility service not based on metered quantity of service. Such a rate is used where service is provided on an unmetered basis.

functional cost category – Costs related to a particular operational function of a utility for which annual operation and maintenance expenses and utility plant investment records are maintained. Generally, specific cost accounting codes are assigned to each functional cost category for purposes of tracking the costs and maintaining generally accepted accounting records. Functional cost categories include those activities related to source of supply, pumping, treatment, transmission and distribution mains, distribution storage, customer meters and services, customer accounting, billing and collections, and general and administrative-related activities.

future capacity – The capacity for service in excess of immediate requirements that is built into a utility in anticipation of increased demands for service resulting from higher uses by existing customers or from growth in the service area.

government-owned water utility – A water utility created by state or other government agency legislative action, with the mandate that the purposes of the utility are public purposes and that its functions are essential governmental proprietary functions. Its primary purpose is to provide its designated service area with potable water in an adequate supply at reasonable costs so that people of the area may promote their health, safety, and welfare. A government-owned water utility may be part of a municipal government operation, a county agency, a regional authority, or take such other form as is appropriate for its service area. Government-owned utilities operate financially to recover their total costs of providing service to their customers and do not have a goal of earning a profit from the provision of such service.

gross receipts tax – Payments made to a government entity based on the gross revenues received by the water utility from its revenues.

increasing block rates – A schedule of rates applicable to blocks of increasing usage in which the usage in each succeeding block is charged at a higher unit rate than in the previous blocks. Each successive block rate may be applicable to a greater volume of water delivery than the preceding block(s).

incremental cost method – An approach to determining system development charges based on the value or cost to expand the existing system's capacity. This method is typically used when the existing system has limited or no capacity to serve new development and new or incremental facilities are needed to serve new development now and into the future; may also be used in conjunction with the buy-in method resulting in the combined cost approach.

indenture – The formal agreement between a group of bondholders, acting through a trustee, and the issuer as to the terms and security for the debt. Ordinarily, it involves the placement of a lien on either the income, property, or both, being acquired from expenditure of the proceeds of the bond issue.

investor-owned water utility – A utility owned by an individual, partnership, corporation, or other qualified entity with the equity provided by shareholders. Regulation may take the form of local or state jurisdiction. Investor-owned utilities operate financially to recover their total cost of providing service to their customers, including the return of a profit or dividend for the benefit of their stockholders.

lifeline rates – Rates applicable to usage up to a specified level that are below the cost of service for the purpose of meeting the social goal of providing essential annual water requirements to qualified customers at a below-cost price.

long run incremental cost approach – The charge or rate for water service equal to the cost per unit of the next capacity increment. This definition is the one most used by water utilities that have adopted some variation of marginal cost pricing.

marginal cost pricing and rates – Charges based on the cost of providing the next unit of production or supply.

minimum bill – A minimum charge to a customer that generally includes a small fixed volume of water delivered to the customer during the applicable period of time.

nonoperating revenues – Includes revenue not usually directly related to the provision of water service; may include tax revenues, gains or losses from the sale of property, rental of nonoperating property, interest income, and other items.

non-revenue water – The sum of "unbilled authorized consumption" (water for firefighting, flushing, etc.) plus "apparent losses" (customer meter inaccuracies, unauthorized consumption, and systematic data handling errors) plus "real losses" (system leakage and storage tank overflows).

off-peak rates – Rates charged for usage during certain designated off-peak periods.

operating revenues – Generally includes the sales of water to general customers and other services directly related to the provision of water; revenue from sales that are usually provided under standard rate schedules or by contractual arrangements.

payment in lieu of taxes (PILOT) – A payment made to a governmental entity by the government-owned utility instead of taxes.

peaking factor – The ratio of the peak rate of demand over a specified period of time (hour, day, etc.) to the average annual rate of demand for a particular customer, customer class, or system. The peaking factor is generally greater than 1.0.

price elasticity of demand – The ratio of the percentage change in use to the percentage change in price. More specifically, price elasticity e_p is calculated as

$$e_p = \frac{\dfrac{\text{Change in Usage}}{\text{Original Usage Level}}}{\dfrac{\text{Change in Price}}{\text{Original Price Level}}}$$

It measures the responsiveness of use to price changes; measures the sensitivity of water use relative to changes in the price of water, after controlling for the influence of other factors that can also alter water demand, such as income and weather.

rate base – The value of a water utility's property used in computing an authorized return under the applicable laws and/or regulatory policies of the agency setting rates for the utility.

rate blocks – Elements of a schedule of charges for specific usages within certain defined volume and/or demand boundaries.

rate-making process – The process of developing and establishing rates and charges. The process is comprised of four phases: (1) determination of revenue requirements; (2) allocation of revenue requirements to appropriate cost components; (3) distribution of the costs of service for each cost component to customer classes; and (4) development and design of a schedule of rates and charges applicable to each class that recovers the allocated cost of service.

rate schedule – A schedule of the rates and charges applicable to the various customer classes and customers.

raw water – Water that is obtained directly from the supply sources, such as wells, reservoirs, rivers, and so on, that has not been treated to potable water standards.

return on rate base – The annual percentage rate of earnings on the rate base.

revenue bond – A bond payable solely from net or gross nontax revenues derived from tolls, charges, or rents paid by users of the facility constructed with the proceeds of the bond issue.

revenue requirements – The total annual operation and maintenance expense and capital-related costs incurred in meeting various aspects of providing water utility service. *Cash-needs* revenue requirements include operation and maintenance expenses, debt-service costs, cash-financed capital improvements, reserve fund requirements, taxes, and consideration of debt-service coverage requirements. *Utility-basis* revenue requirements include operation and maintenance expenses, depreciation expense, taxes, and return on rate base.

seasonal rates – Rates based on the cost-of-service variations with respect to system seasonal requirements. For example, higher rates may be charged during the summer months when a system peak occurs, which requires facilities not needed to meet lower winter loads.

service charge – A fixed charge usually designed to recover customer costs and billed at regular intervals, usually monthly, bimonthly, or quarterly.

service connection – That portion of the service line from the utility's water main to and including the curb stop at or adjacent to the street line or the customer's property line. It includes other valves or fittings that the utility may require at or between the main and the curb stop but does not include the curb box or meter.

standby service – Service provided occasionally under certain defined conditions, such as in the event of failure of the customer's normal water supply system. Fire protection is another form of standby service.

system development charge – A contribution of capital toward existing or planned future backup plant facilities necessary to meet the service needs of new customers to which such fees apply. Three methods used to determine the amount of these charges are the buy-in method, the incremental cost method, and the combined approach, which includes elements of the first two methods. Various terms are used to describe these charges in the industry, but these charges are intended to provide funds to be used to finance all or part of capital improvements necessary to serve new customers.

test year – The annualized period for which costs are to be analyzed and rates established.

treated water – Water that has been obtained from supply sources and treated to produce potable water standards.

uniform volume charge – A single charge per unit of volume for all water used. A single uniform rate can be applicable to all customers of a utility, or a separate uniform rate may be designed for each customer class.

unit cost – The cost of producing a unit of a product or service. An example would be the cost of treating a thousand gallons of potable water for use by the water utility's customers.

unit of service – An element of service for which a cost can be ascertained, such as thousand gallons, hundred cubic feet, million gallons per day, monthly bill, and so on.

unmetered rate – A fixed charge for unmetered service, often simply based on the number of fixtures and water-using devices of the customer.

used and useful – A term applicable to utility plant investment that is includable in the development of the rate base as part of the rate-making process. Plant investment is considered to be used and useful if it is actively used in the provision of service to customers.

user charges – The monthly, bimonthly, or quarterly user charges made to the users of water service through the general water rate structures of the utility for the utility's share of the cost of providing water service. Typically these charges include both a fixed component and a variable or volume-based rate applied to metered water use.

utility-basis revenue requirements – The method of establishing annual revenue requirements giving consideration to annual operation and maintenance expense, depreciation expense, taxes, and return on rate base.

water-budget rates – A form of increasing block rates where the amount of water within the first block or blocks is based on the estimated, efficient water needs of the individual customer. Customers with usage above this efficient usage budget generally pay a higher rate for their "inefficient" or "wasteful" usage.

wheeling – The charge made by a utility for transmission of water of another party through its system.

wholesale service customers – Service in which water is sold to a customer at one or more major points of delivery for resale within the wholesale customer's service area.

working capital – Cash, materials, supplies, and other similar current assets necessary in the operation of the enterprise. It is usually measured by the excess of current assets over the current liabilities, or sometimes as a percentage of annual operation and maintenance expense levels.

This page intentionally blank.

Index

NOTE: *f.* indicates figure; *t.* indicates table

T

targeted volumetric surcharge levels, 201
taxes
  cash-needs approach to payments, 13
  consolidated returns, 38
  deferred, 35–36, 45–46
  depreciation, 34–35
  federal, 34
  flow through, 36–37
  interest synchronization, 37–38
  investment tax credit (ITC), 35
  issues in rate cases, 35–38
  local, 33
  normalization process, 36
  overview, 33
  and revenue requirements, 38
  revenues from, 20
  state, 34
test years, 11–12, 17t.
three-block (and more) rate design, 147
total provision, 35
transfer charges, 265–266
transfer payments, cash-needs approach, 13
transmission and pumping costs, 177, 303
treatment costs, 177, 302–303, 329
treatment facilities, 63
triple bottom line analysis, 177
turn-off/turn-on fees, 262
two-block rate design, 147

U

unbilled revenues, 21–22
uniform rates, 109–113, 112t.
Uniform System of Accounts, 28
unit base cost, 81
unit costs of service, 78–81, 79t.
units of service, 75–77, 77t.–78t.
unmetered water, 304
used and useful standard, 44–46, 276–277
utility-basis approach
  capital-related costs, 42–46
  government-owned utilities, 14–15
  investor-owned utilities, 15
  outside customers, 278t., 279
  overview, 14
utility function, 60–61

V

valuation methodologies
  original cost, 331–332
  rate base (plant investment), 90–91
  replacement cost, 331–332
variable charges
  defined, 149
  vs. fixed charges, 96–97
variable costs, 72
variance procedures, 146–147
volatility, revenue, 149–150, 153–154
volume charges, 225
volumetric surcharges, 198–201

W

wastewater utilities
  and affordability programs, 208
  and price elasticity, 241
  water reuse cost allocation, 182–188, 184t., 186t.–187t.
water allowances, 152–153
water audits, 265
"water budget" concept, 98
water-budget rates, 139–148, 140f., 148t.
water rate structures, 103–108
water reuse
  cost allocation of, 182–188, 184t., 186t.–187t.
  customers, 178–180
  financial planning for, 180–182
  overview, 175–177
  pricing, 188–189
  as a source of supply, 185–187, 187t.
  unique cost characteristics, 177–178
water transmission services, 298
weather
  and evapotranspiration (ET), 145–146
  normalization, 23
  risks, 107
  See also seasonal rates
wheeling services, 298
wholesale services, 75, 286–287, 287t., 297–310
working capital, 45

AWWA Manuals

M1, *Water Rates, Fees, and Charges, #30001*

M2, *Instrumentation and Control, #30002*

M3, *Safety Management for Water Utilities, #30003*

M4, *Water Fluoridation Principles and Practices, #30004*

M5, *Water Utility Management, #30005*

M6, *Water Meters—Selection, Installation, Testing, and Maintenance, #30006*

M7, *Problem Organisms in Water: Identification and Treatment, #30007*

M9, *Concrete Pressure Pipe, #30009*

M11, *Steel Pipe—A Guide for Design and Installation, #30011*

M12, *Simplified Procedures for Water Examination, #30012*

M14, *Backflow Prevention and Cross-Connection Control: Recommended Practices, #30014*

M17, *Fire Hydrants: Installation, Field Testing, and Maintenance, #30017*

M19, *Emergency Planning for Water Utilities, #30019*

M20, *Water Chlorination/Chloramination Practices and Principles, #30020*

M21, *Groundwater, #30021*

M22, *Sizing Water Service Lines and Meters, #30022*

M23, *PVC Pipe—Design and Installation, #30023*

M24, *Planning for the Distribution of Reclaimed Water, #30024*

M25, *Flexible-Membrane Covers and Linings for Potable-Water Reservoirs, #30025*

M27, *External Corrosion Control for Infrastructure Sustainability, #30027*

M28, *Rehabilitation of Water Mains, #30028*

M29, *Water Utility Capital Financing, #30029*

M30, *Precoat Filtration, #30030*

M31, *Distribution System Requirements for Fire Protection, #30031*

M32, *Computer Modeling of Water Distribution Systems, #30032*

M33, *Flowmeters in Water Supply, #30033*

M36, *Water Audits and Loss Control Programs, #30036*

M37, *Operational Control of Coagulation and Filtration Processes, #30037*

M38, *Electrodialysis and Electrodialysis Reversal, #30038*

M41, *Ductile-Iron Pipe and Fittings, #30041*

M42, *Steel Water-Storage Tanks, #30042*

M44, *Distribution Valves: Selection, Installation, Field Testing, and Maintenance, #30044*

M45, *Fiberglass Pipe Design, #30045*

M46, *Reverse Osmosis and Nanofiltration, #30046*

M47, *Capital Project Delivery, #30047*

M48, *Waterborne Pathogens, #30048*

M49, *Butterfly Valves: Torque, Head Loss, and Cavitation Analysis, #30049*

M50, *Water Resources Planning, #30050*

M51, *Air-Release, Air/Vacuum, and Combination Air Valves, #30051*

M52, *Water Conservation Programs—A Planning Manual, #30052*

M53, *Microfiltration and Ultrafiltration Membranes for Drinking Water, #30053*

M54, *Developing Rates for Small Systems, #30054*

M55, *PE Pipe—Design and Installation, #30055*

M56, *Nitrification Prevention and Control in Drinking Water, #30056*

M57, *Algae: Source to Treatment, #30057*

M58, *Internal Corrosion Control in Water Distribution Systems, #30058*

M60, *Drought Preparedness and Response, #30060*

M61, *Desalination of Seawater, #30061*

M63, *Aquifer Storage and Recovery, #30063*

M65, *On-Site Generation of Hypochlorite, #30065*

M66, *Actuators and Controls—Design and Installation, #30066*

This page intentionally blank.